Speech Correction
on the
Contract Plan

PRENTICE-HALL EDUCATION SERIES

E. George Payne, Editor

Speech Correction
on the
Contract Plan

by

RUTH B. MANSER, Ph.D.

Remedial Specialist in Speech, New York University; Formerly Chairman of the Department of Speech, Vassar College

REVISED EDITION

New York
PRENTICE-HALL, INC.
1946

COPYRIGHT, 1935, 1942, BY

PRENTICE-HALL, INC.

70 Fifth Avenue, New York

First Printing.........April, 1935
Second Printing......August, 1935
Third Printing.........June, 1937
Fourth Printing....February, 1940
Fifth Printing.......March, 1941

REVISED EDITION

First Printing..........July, 1942
Second Printing...September, 1944
Third Printing.......March, 1945
Fourth Printing....December, 1945
Fifth Printing ....September, 1946

TO

MY PARENTS

Preface to the Revised Edition

BEFORE revising *Speech Correction on the Contract Plan*, I consulted with many teachers who had used the first edition, and have attempted to follow their suggestions in regard to amplification of the material of the first book and additional contracts and exercises. I am very grateful to these colleagues who have given their advice so freely and hope that they will find this book of greater assistance therefor.

In the chapter on "The Sounds of English" all possible spellings of every sound have been given; this should be helpful to all students, but particularly to the foreigner.

The contracts for "Foreign Accent" have been amplified and more carefully graded, the contracts for "Stammering" have had additional tasks assigned in the section entitled *Test* in order to give the student a diversified experience and more freedom and courage; all the voice contracts have been revised and augmented, and a set of contracts for "Careless Speech" has been added.

Finally, the exercise material has been greatly amplified; not only are there many more sentences stressing difficult sounds, but paragraphs containing these sounds are also provided. Special consideration has been accorded the subject of voice in the inclusion of many exercises designed to strengthen and beautify tone.

I hope that the changes and additions in this revised edition will make *Speech Correction on the Contract Plan* a more helpful book for those who are engaged in the difficult and challenging problem of speech correction.

ACKNOWLEDGMENT

I wish to thank Dr. E. George Payne, Dean of the School of Education of New York University, for his interest in the preparation of this work, and for his encouragement.

It is with pleasure that I express my gratitude to Dr. Letitia Raubicheck, Director of Speech Improvement in the New York

City Schools, for reading the manuscript, for testing the practical value of the contract method in her experimental clinic at New York University, and for her unfailing helpfulness and valuable suggestions.

I should also like to acknowledge my indebtedness to Dr. Dorothy Mulgrave, of the School of Education of New York University, for reading the manuscript and for her many suggestions.

I am grateful to my father for his understanding and encouragement.

Thanks are also due to the editorial department of Prentice-Hall for its unfailing co-operation.

Finally I wish to thank my students, whose enthusiastic reception of the contract method first gave me the confidence to put it in book form, and whose suggestions for changes in the revision have been of great assistance.

RUTH B. MANSER

Editor's Introduction

THE growth of transportation and the development of communication, particularly the radio, have unquestionably placed a premium upon uniformity of expression and have led to a passion for correct enunciation and the elimination of the common defects which were regarded as natural and even unavoidable only a few years ago. Some of these defects are the result of foreign influence; others, such as lisping, are due to a physical condition; and still others are emotional in origin. There is a growing realization throughout the country that corrective measures must be taken if speech is to be efficient.

This realization of the need for speech improvement has made new demands on the writers of textbooks, and the number of new titles recently placed on the market indicates the determination of the specialists in the field to do their part to meet the increasing public demand. The texts, however, have generally been of the conventional type and have not taken full account of the newer developments in the science of education and the accepted principles of learning. After all, learning is an individual matter and is achieved by the learner as a result of his own efforts. The ideal text, therefore, is one that diagnoses the difficulties, defines the methods, and sets the task for the individual for his own improvement.

Speech Correction on the Contract Plan is outstanding in that the contents conform to the psychology of learning by providing definite tasks for the student. He is thus enabled to discover his needs and measure his own progress. The nature of the text guarantees that it will prove to be not only superior to other texts but invaluable for all classes where the correction of speech defects is stressed.

E. GEORGE PAYNE

Foreword

THE systematic correction of the speech defects of adults is a comparatively recent development. The usual speech correction manuals are, therefore, geared to the comprehension and needs of the young child. It is assumed that all exercises will be done in the presence of the teacher and that the assignments will follow the pages of the text.

With adolescent or adult students, however, a different technique is desirable. In the first place, it is essential that responsibility for correction should rest with the student—and that, therefore, he should be encouraged to use his own initiative and to advance as rapidly as possible. The contract plan which forms the second part of this book provides both the stimulation and the procedure for this type of individualized action. By breaking the entire corrective program into small work-units and by providing concrete evidence of progress through the plan of checking items on the general contract sheet, Miss Manser has outlined a progressive technique which will be welcome to teachers of adolescent and adult students.

The practical value of this set-up has been tested both in Miss Manser's own clinics at New York University and also in the demonstration clinic which I conducted there in 1933–34. The definite outline of progressive units made it possible for the teachers-in-training to progress with their students along sound lines. The tests were administered by the director of the clinic, who was enabled to check the achievements of both student and teacher-in-training.

I heartily recommend this modern book to all teachers of speech correction who are working with adolescent or mature students.

LETITIA RAUBICHECK

Contents

CONTENTS

PAGE

The Contract Method

THE contract method for the correction of speech defects is an adaptation of the Dalton contract plan. The purposes of this plan are:

1. To break up a complicated procedure into short, teachable units.

2. To motivate the work by showing the student concretely the steps necessary for correction.

3. To give a clear idea of the work to be covered.

4. To place the responsibility for correction on the student.

A series of these contracts or units, covering all steps necessary to incorporate a correct production as an automatic response, is arranged in order of difficulty. In each series there is a general contract that indicates all the steps necessary for correction, and individual contracts each of which has for its objective the successful performance of one of these steps.

The author has found the contract method to be very effective for the reason that students work more willingly, intelligently, and successfully when a definite objective exists and when they can feel that with the completion of each contract they have progressed one step further toward their goal.

How to Use the Contract Method

To the Teacher

The instructor should first make a careful diagnosis of the student's speech. Then the general contract should be given out, and the plan explained. Contract 1 should be assigned at the same time. It may be wise at first to read over the Procedure, Caution, Practice Material, and Test with the student to make sure that he understands exactly how to go to work. (This step, however, will not be necessary after the first few contracts.) The student should then do the exercises suggested in the Procedure and Practice Material, asking the instructor to give him the Test when he feels competent to fulfill the requirements laid down by the Objective. If the student passes the test, he may begin to work on the following contract; if not, he should be told wherein he has not fulfilled the conditions of the Objective, and should be advised to continue his practice and return later for the Test. In order to prevent the student from becoming discouraged by having to repeat the same contract too many times, extra contracts (1A and 1B, for instance), with the same objective as the original contract but with more detailed procedure and different practice material, have been provided. This extra material makes the student feel that he has advanced further along the road to correction, even though the goal remains the same.

If the student has two or more defects, as is so often the case, it is well to attack one at a time. If one defect happens to be stammering, this should be dealt with first, for it is unwise to hamper the stammerer by making him concentrate on individual sounds.

To the Student

This book is prepared for work in speech correction on the *contract plan*. At the beginning of each contract, you will find a page headed *Contract Sheet*. This sheet contains a list of the steps or contracts that must be carried out in order to overcome the defect concerned. Each contract has five parts: "Objective," "Procedure," "Caution," "Practice Material," and "Test." Ask your teacher to go over the first contract with you in order that you may know how to proceed. Now do the exercises suggested in the sections called "Procedure" and "Practice Material." When you feel that you are competent to fulfill the requirements set up in the "Objective," ask your teacher to give you the test, in the section marked "Test." If, in the opinion of your teacher, you have successfully passed the test, you may ask him to sign his initials and the date at the side of Contract 1, on the general contract sheet. Then proceed to Contract 2.

Aids to Pronunciation

Three different systems of indicating pronunciation have been used in this text: the diacritical markings adapted from

Webster's New International Dictionary, the symbols of the International Phonetic Alphabet, and a key word about whose pronunciation there can be no doubt. It should be noted that in the body of the text the diacritical markings have been italicized in order to make the symbols stand out clearly. (This accounts for the fact that some letters occur in script form in the text and in printed form in the pronunciation key in the Appendix; for instance, *a* [æ] as in *at* is indicated by *ă* in the body of the text and by ă in the key.) A pronunciation key has been provided in the Appendix (page 370) for the benefit of those students who are not familiar with the phonetic symbols. These precautions have been taken in order that there may be no misunderstanding of pronunciation on the part of the student.

PART I

CHAPTER I

The Physiology of the Vocal Mechanism

HAVE you ever stopped to consider how many processes have to be carried out when you utter a single sound? Take, for example, the exclamation "Oh!" Something startles you, and your immediate response is "Oh!" It takes no more than a second to say the word, yet many processes have to be

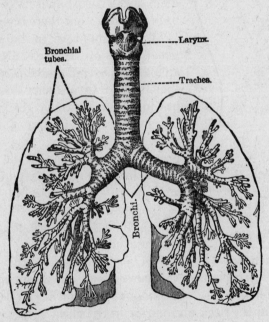

Fig. 1.—Trachea and Connections.*

completed in order to produce that one sound. You may be interested in tracing the various steps that have to be taken in order to make a sound. (See "Breathing process," page 5.) First, however, it will be well for you to become acquainted with certain physiological terms.

---

*From Eddy's *Textbook in General Physiology and Anatomy*, copyright. Used by permission of American Book Company, publishers.

3

On the accompanying diagrams (Figures 1 and 2), locate the following: larynx, trachea, bronchi, lungs, chest cavity, abdominal cavity, diaphragm in inhalation, and diaphragm in exhalation.

The larynx. The larynx, commonly known as the voice box, contains the vocal bands. These vocal bands convert the breath into tone. The larynx is situated at the top of the

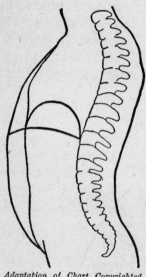

trachea, and is easily located. Place your fingers on the lump known as the Adam's apple. With the fingers placed on that spot, say "Oh." Do you feel the vibration caused by the rapid movement of the vocal bands? Now whisper "Oh." Note that there is no vibration.

When sound is to be made, the vocal bands are approximated, and the air passing over them causes the bands to vibrate. In ordinary breathing, or in whispering, however, the vocal bands are swung apart so that the air may pass through freely. The larynx is protected at the top by the epiglottis, which forms a little trapdoor that is kept open for breathing but that closes in the act of swallowing, in order to prevent food from entering the windpipe and causing choking.

Adaptation of Chart Copyrighted 1930 by Sherman K. Smith, Voice Scientist, New York. Reproduced by permission.

Fig. 2.—The Bellows.

The trachea. The trachea, or windpipe, is the tube that carries the air between the larynx and the bronchi, the two main bronchial tubes. It is about four inches in length, and lies partly in the neck and partly in the chest cavity.

The bronchi. The bronchi are the two tubes into which the trachea divides. The branches of these two main bronchial tubes spread out from the main source like the roots of a tree, and the smallest ones end in the tiny air cells of the lungs. These air cells are known as pulmonary sacs.

The lungs. The lungs are two spongy, slate-colored, vascular organs in which the blood receives the supply of oxygen. They are pear-shaped and larger at the bottom than at the top.

The diaphragm. The human trunk is composed of two cavities: the thorax, or chest cavity, and the abdominal cavity. These are separated by the diaphragm, a dome-shaped membrane, which acts as the floor of the chest cavity and as the roof of the abdominal cavity. In exhalation, you will observe, the diaphragm extends well up into the chest cavity, but in inhalation it is drawn down and flattened out, thus increasing the size of the chest cavity. The abdominal muscles are used to control the movements of the diaphragm; hence, both the abdominal muscles and the diaphragm are very important factors in the breathing process.

Breathing process. Now trace on the diagram in Figure 1 the course of the inhaled air as it proceeds to the lungs. The air is taken in through the nose and mouth. It goes first to the pharynx, or throat, and from there to the larynx. From the larynx it goes to the trachea, or windpipe. From the windpipe it goes to the bronchi; thence, into the smaller and smaller bronchial tubes; and finally, into the pulmonary sacs, or air cells of the lungs. Something has to be done to expand the chest cavity to make room for the air that is rushing in to fill the air cells of the lungs. This is provided for by the expansion of the intercostal and the abdominal muscles and by the flattening out of the diaphragm. (See Figure 2.) This action takes place simultaneously with the intake of the breath. The entire process is known as *inhalation*.

In *exhalation*, the chest cavity is decreased in size by the contraction of the abdominal and the intercostal muscles and by the consequent pushing up of the diaphragm. Hence, the air is forced to go out of the pulmonary sacs, back through the bronchial tubes to the bronchi, then to the trachea, and finally to the larynx. (See Figure 1.) Here the vocal bands come close together, and the air passing over them causes them to vibrate and make tone. This tone is re-enforced, or given resonance, by the walls of the throat, nose, mouth, and head cavities, and is finally shaped into the desired sound by the organs of articulation.

Resonance. The tone produced by the vibration of the vocal bands does not reach the ear until the sound has been strengthened and re-enforced. This re-enforcement of tone is known as *resonance,* or the act of sounding again. The walls of the throat, mouth, nose, and head cavities act as resonators, which increase and beautify tone.

Breathing Exercises

1. Lie flat on the floor or on a bed with the knees flexed. Relax completely. Place one hand on the waistline and one on the abdominal muscles. Breathe naturally. Notice that in inhalation the lower part of the chest cavity and the abdomen expand and that there is very little movement of the upper part of the chest. This is due to the fact that the lungs are much larger at the bottom than at the top.

2. Stand erect. Place your hands as before. Inhale and exhale. Be careful that the lower part of the chest and the abdomen expand and contract, and that there is little activity of the upper chest.

3. Stand erect. Place your hands as before. Inhale; then push the breath out on the sound *oh,* intoning the sound and holding it as long as you can comfortably do so. Be sure to push the tone out steadily, using the abdominal muscles. Inhale again (through both mouth and nose); then send the breath out steadily on the sound *ah.* Inhale and exhale, sending the breath out steadily on the vowels and diphthongs of the following words:

lone	lawn	mat	sign	run
foot	car	see	bid	now
moon	ray	let	word	boy

4. Stand erect. Place one hand on the chest and one on the abdominal muscles. Inhale. As you exhale, push all the air out suddenly on the sound *oh,* thus giving the effect of an explosion. The push with the abdominal muscles should be so forceful that the wall of the upper chest will be lifted up by the sudden impact of the air from below. Do the same with the other sounds given above, practicing on the round and open sounds first, until you are sure of the breathing.

5. Stand erect. Place the hands as in Exercise 4. Inhale and exhale, prolonging the sound *oh* while you count to two mentally, and then exploding the sound. In this case, the sudden push with the abdominal muscles should come at the end of the tone.

6. Stand erect. Place one hand on the abdominal muscles and the other on the waistline. Inhale, and say *one.* Inhale again, and say *one-two,* pushing a little farther in with the abdominal muscles for *two* than for *one.* Inhale, and say *one-two-three,* pushing in still farther with the abdominal muscles for *three* than for *two.* Continue this exercise, counting to five, and as you acquire greater breath control, to ten and fifteen.

7. Read the following lines, taking a new breath whenever the vertical line indicates a pause:

> The rich man's son | inherits lands, |
> And piles of brick, | and stone, | and gold, |
> And he inherits | soft white hands, |
> And tender flesh | that feels the cold, |
> Nor dares | to wear a garment old; |
> A heritage, | it seems to me, |
> One scarce would wish | to hold in fee. |

You will notice that the pauses are natural stopping places for breath, and that the words between the pauses are connected portions of thought, which are called *phrases*. You talk and read in these thought-groups. Hence, you must learn to make the breath fit the phrases, taking a long breath for a long phrase and a short breath for a short phrase. You must also learn to guide and to conserve the outgoing breath; you can do this by pushing the abdominal muscles a little farther in for each succeeding syllable in the phrase, always taking care that you have enough breath for the last syllable in the phrase. The division of thought into phrases and the utterance of each unit on a single breath blast are known as *phrasing*.

Mechanically the above lines should be done as follows. Voice the words and syllables in italics:

> Inhale—push with the abdominal muscles—say *the;* push farther in with the muscles—*rich;* push still farther in—*man's;* push still farther in—*son;* inhale—push—*in;* push farther in—*her;* push still farther in—*its;* push farther in—*lands.*
>
> Inhale—push—*and;* push farther in—*piles;* push farther in—*of;* push still farther in—*brick;* inhale—push—*and;* push farther in—*stone;* inhale—push—*and;* push farther in—*gold* (and so on).

The phrases will probably seem awkwardly short. You should divide the thought into short phrases until you have learned to control your breath; after that, you may proceed to longer phrases. Try to use this method of breathing whenever you read aloud or speak.

Divide the following lines into short phrases, and read as above:

> What doth the poor man's son inherit?
> Stout muscles and a sinewy heart,
> A hardy frame, a hardier spirit;
> King of two hands, he does his part
> In every useful toil and art;
> A heritage, it seems to me,
> A king might wish to hold in fee.

CHAPTER II
Voice Problems

THE most essential characteristic of voice is audibility, and almost equally important is pleasing audibility. There is probably nothing more irritating than to be unable to hear a speaker, whether he is addressing a large audience or speaking informally to a small group. A speaker's first duty toward his listeners is to make them hear without straining their ears; his second duty is to allow them to hear without offending their sensibilities. You have heard speakers—earnest people, too, with a worth-while message—whose loud, strident voices militated against everything they had to say; and you have heard those whose lovely, persuasive voices kept you from realizing that the ideas which they uttered were pretty superficial, until they had stopped speaking and you tried in vain to recall the thread of the argument. It is obvious, then, that any speaker is more persuasive if he has a pleasing voice.

Characteristics of a pleasing voice. What are the characteristics that make a voice pleasing? Perhaps you may discover the answer to this question by thinking negatively—that is, by asking what qualities cause a voice to be unpleasant.

Few people admire a high-pitched voice, because it is usually nerve-racking to listen to for any length of time. Furthermore, such a voice always suggests immaturity, and if the speaker happens to be a man, it makes him appear feminine. On the other hand, a woman's voice so low in pitch that it appears masculine is likewise undesirable. Hence, one characteristic of a pleasing voice is medium pitch—neither too high nor too low. Another unpleasant characteristic is the breathy quality of voice which suggests fear or lack of confidence. Then, there are those unpleasant voices that are due to poor resonance. They include those that are too nasal or too throaty or, worse yet, a combination of the two, which makes the strident nasal

8

voice, and finally the voice that is lacking in nasal resonance. The last kind of voice causes the speaker to sound as if he had a bad cold in his head.

By the process of elimination, then, you may conclude that a pleasing voice must be medium in pitch and have a properly distributed resonance.

Changing the pitch. Training the voice to a higher or lower pitch depends largely on training the ear. It is a good plan to make a mental picture of the desired pitch, and then to compare your own with that. If the pitch seems to be too high or too low, aim to bring it *gradually* to the desired point. A piano is sometimes helpful in accomplishing this, as it is a guide in ear training. A pitch-pipe may likewise be of assistance in cases where a musical instrument is not available.

If your natural pitch is too high, you can lower it in the following way. Find the note on the piano that is the same as your pitch, and sing *oh* on that note. Then, very gradually, sing down the scale from note to note until the desired pitch has been reached. Now, say *oh* in your natural pitch, and proceed as above. When talking, gradually lower your pitch a little each day until it becomes comfortable to use the desired pitch habitually. This process must be carried on *gradually;* otherwise it will cause a strain on the throat that may result in a throaty tone.

Breathiness. A breathy quality of voice gives the impression of nervousness or fear. As a matter of fact, however, it may be due merely to poor breathing. At any rate, even if you are very nervous, you can "fool the public" by using a calm, clear tone. You can acquire this tone if your breathing is well controlled and properly applied to your voice.

The contracts for breathiness (see Part IV of this text) stress the method of breathing suggested in Chapter I. They teach breath control in a single tone, and also in words, sentences, paragraphs, and conversation. The production of a few sounds in a clear tone is given first, and those sounds are immediately incorporated in words and phrases. This practice will help you from the very beginning to use the proper tone in your daily speech. It is important for you to form the habit of listening to your tone and of speaking clearly at all times.

Throatiness. Throatiness[1] is another defect that is the result of poor breathing. A throaty quality of tone exists when there is too much resonance in the throat. This condition occurs when the speaker lacks sufficient breath, or when he does not use what breath he has to support the tone properly. Poor breathing is the chief cause of throatiness; supplementary causes are lack of lip and jaw action, and tension in the throat.

In order to overcome a throaty tone and to acquire a well-balanced resonance, you must learn to control the breath, to exercise the lips and the jaw, and to relax the throat. The breathing exercises suggested in Chapter I should be practiced conscientiously every day, as well as the lip and jaw exercises given in Part III. Relaxation exercises (see Part III) will help both to free the throat from tension and to make the tone more smooth and pleasant. Finally, the practice of energizing the body from the very toes up will aid in removing strain from the throat. The carefully graded contracts for throatiness, found in Part IV, should enable you to use a clear, free tone at all times, whether you are addressing a few people in a small room or a large audience in a big space, even out-of-doors.

Hoarse voice. Hoarse voice may be the result simply of poor breathing or of voice strain, but it is frequently due to sinus infection, deviated septum, chronic laryngitis, or some other physical difficulty that affects the vocal bands. If you are habitually hoarse, you should go at once to a competent nose and throat specialist for a thorough examination, which includes an examination of the larynx. If the specialist thinks it advisable, you may take voice exercises and proceed according to the contracts for throatiness. However, you must use great care in your tone production. Stop to rest the moment you are conscious of any strain. In more serious cases the specialist might advise absolute silence over a period of time. If such advice is given, be sure to follow it as far as possible. Hoarseness is occasionally found to be hysterical; that type will be discussed under "Emotional Disorders." (See Part II, Chapter X.)

---

[1] The terms *throatiness* and *pharyngeal resonance* are used interchangeably. See Part IV: Contracts for "Hoarse Voice and Throatiness."

Nasality. Nasality should not be confused with nasal resonance. Nasality is the result of *too much* nasal resonance. Every normal voice must have a certain amount of nasal resonance. There are three nasal sounds in English: *m* [m], *n* [n], and *ng* [ŋ]. A great deal of beauty of tone may be acquired by giving these sounds their proper resonance. However, if other sounds, particularly the vowels, are spoken with a nasal resonance, the whole tone takes on an unpleasant quality, known as *nasality*. In order to overcome this fault, you must learn to control the soft palate; this acts as a curtain between the throat and the nose and head cavities, and may be raised and lowered at will. (See Figure 3, page 16.) When the soft palate is elevated, most of the tone goes into the mouth; but when the soft palate is lowered, the tone is allowed to go into the nose. Since there are only three nasal sounds in English, the soft palate should be lowered only for those sounds.

Nasality may be of two types: the so-called *lazy* nasality, in which the soft palate is lowered and relaxed; or the *tense* nasality, in which the soft palate is lowered and tightened. The only difference in treatment is that relaxation exercises must be taken for the second type.

The contracts for nasality (see Part IV) teach control of the soft palate for all sounds. They also gradually incorporate those sounds in words, sentences, paragraphs, and conversation.

Denasalization. Denasalization means that there is *too little* nasal resonance. This difficulty may be the result of a catarrhal condition, of chronic sinus infection, or of a polyp in the nasal cavity, but it is most frequently due to excessive adenoid tissue. If you are habitually denasalized, go to a competent nose and throat specialist. If you have excessive adenoid tissue, you should probably have it removed at once. After the tissue has been removed, the vocal organs should be re-educated through exercises designed to increase nasal resonance. It is not enough to clear the passage from the throat to the nose. Unless the tone is trained to go into the nasal and the head cavities, it will continue to lack nasal resonance even though the passage is clear. The contracts for denasalization (see Part IV) will help you, through carefully graded exercises, to gain a properly blended resonance.

PART II

CHAPTER III
Physiology of the Speech Mechanism

LOCATE in Figure 3 the following organs of articulation: the lips, the teeth, the tongue, the upper gum, the hard and soft palates, and the uvula. Now make the sounds ē [i:], ä [ɑ:], ōō [u:]. Look in a mirror, and notice what organs of articulation participate in making these sounds. You will find that the lips are spread in a smiling position for ē [i:], opened in an oval for ä [ɑ:], and rounded for ōō [u:]. You will see that the jaw is scarcely opened at all for ē [i:] and ōō [u:], but that it is wide open for ä [ɑ:]. You will feel that the tongue changes its position for each of these sounds. And if you concentrate your attention on the soft palate, you will find that it is held high throughout. In other words, all the organs of articulation that can move are called into play in making these sounds.

Organs of Articulation

The organs of articulation may be classified as *active* and *passive*. The active organs are the tongue, lips, lower jaw, and soft palate. The passive organs are the teeth, the upper jaw, and the hard palate. The active organs usually work with the passive organs in making a sound: *d* [d] and *t* [t], for instance, are made by placing the pointed tip of tongue on the middle of the upper gum; *y* (j) is formed by raising the middle of the tongue until it nearly touches the hard palate; *f* [f] and *v* [v] are made by bringing the lower lip up against the upper teeth; and the tip of the tongue rests against the back of the lower teeth in making all vowel sounds except the rounded back vowels ōō [u:] and ŏŏ [ʊ]. The passive organs are important, therefore, chiefly because they supply the active organs with a point of impingement in articulation.

Active organs of articulation. The active organs of articulation may make speech clear and beautiful, or cause it to be sluggish and slovenly. Hence, they must be exercised and trained if speech is to be improved. Lips must be made firm and flexible by daily practice of the lip exercises given in Part III (page 69). Training is necessary in order to make the tongue agile enough to articulate such difficult combinations of sounds as *five-fifths, twelfths, fists, thrusts, spirits,* and *statistics.* It will acquire such agility through daily practice of the tongue exercises plus the sentences given for careless speech in Part III,

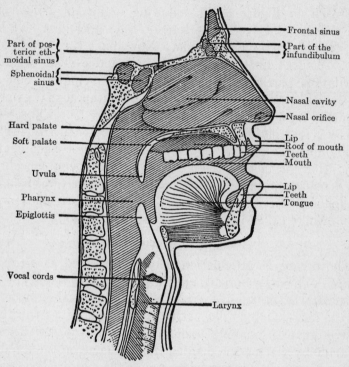

Fig. 3.—Section of the Head and Throat Locating the Organs of Speech, Including the Upper Resonators.*

and the Contracts for Careless Speech in Part IV. The necessity for jaw exercises is great, for if the lower jaw is not relaxed, the tone becomes constricted and throaty and the speech indistinct. Practice in yawning and saying *ah-ah-ah* [ɑ:] with the mouth well opened, and *e* [i:], *ä* [ɑ:], *ōō* [u:] with the position for each sound exaggerated, will help to give control of the jaw.

* By courtesy of Oliver Ditson Company, Inc., from *Resonance in Singing and Speaking,* by Thomas Fillebrown.

The soft palate. The soft palate, which is attached to and is just behind the hard palate, ends in the crocus-shaped muscular tissue known as the *uvula*. The soft palate acts as a curtain to modify the amount of tone that escapes into the nose. If it is elevated, little or no tone is permitted to go into the nose from the throat; but if it is lowered, practically all of the tone goes directly from the throat into the nose. This is what occurs in bad cases of nasality. The soft palate should be lowered only for the nasal sounds *m*[m], *n*[n], and *ng* [ŋ], and should be held high for all other sounds. Control of the soft palate may be gained by yawning, by panting, and by saying the sound *ä* [ɑ:] with the aid of a mirror to make sure that the throat is open and the soft palate held well up. Other exercises for the control of the soft palate will be found in the second contract for nasality (page 336).

CHAPTER IV
The Sounds of English

THE English language, like all other languages, is made up of sounds that flow freely and sounds that, because of some obstacle, are not permitted to flow freely. Those sounds that are unobstructed are called *vowels*, and those that are obstructed are called *consonants*. Take, for instance, the word *eat*. It is made up of the sound *ē* [i:], which flows freely and may be continued as long as the breath lasts, and *t* [t], which stops suddenly because the tip of the tongue touches the upper gum and does not allow the sound to continue. But listen to the word *am*. It is made up of the vowel *ă* [æ], which flows freely and may be continued as long as the breath lasts, and the consonant *m* [m], which also may be continued as long as the breath lasts, but cannot be said to flow freely, as it is forced to go out through the nose because of the closing of the lips and the lowering of the soft palate. Thus, you see that sounds may be obstructed in more than one way.

Sometimes two vowel sounds are combined, and the result is what is called a *diphthong*.

The sounds of English will be discussed through these three classes: vowels, diphthongs, and consonants.

When studying the sounds of English, you must bear in mind that spelling cannot be used as a guide to pronunciation; on the contrary, it is often very misleading, as English spelling is unphonetic. Note the following, which are only a few instances of the differences between spelling and pronunciation:

(1) *So-called "silent" letters:* Although these are not pronounced, they occur in the spelling of words, as the *t* in *often* ['ɒfn̩]; the *g* in *gnat* ['næt] and *gnarl* ['nɑ:l]; the *p* in *psalm* ['sɑ:m] and *pneumonia* [nju'moʈŭnjə]; the *k* in *knife* ['naɪf], *knight* ['naɪt], and *know* ['noʈŭ]; the *h* in *hour* ['aʊə], *heir* ['ɛʒ], *honor* ['ɒnə], and *honest* ['ɒnɪst]; and *l* in *alms* ['ɑ:mz], *palm* ['pɑ:m], and *calm* ['kɑ:m].

18

(2) *Words spelled differently but pronounced alike:* Instances of this are *night—knight*, ['naɪt]; *eight—ate* ['eɪɪt]; *quay—key* ['kiː]; *made—maid* ['meɪɪd]; *bough—bow* ['baʊ]; *team—teem* ['tiːm].

(3) Words spelled alike but pronounced differently: The outstanding example of this is the *ough* in *cough* ['kɔ·f], *bough* ['baʊ], *rough* ['ɪʌf], *hiccough* ['hɪkʌp], *through* ['θɪuː], and *though* ['ðoɪʊ]. Note the six different pronunciations of the same ending.

(4) Different spellings for the same sounds: The sound *ē* [iː], as in *see* ['siː], has seven spellings in addition to the one just mentioned: *e—cede* ['siːd], *ea—each* ['i·tʃ], *i—machine* [məˈʃiːn], *ay—quay* ['kiː], *eo—people* ['piːpəl], *ie—thief* ['θi·f], and *ei—deceive* [dɪˈsiːv]. (See page 21.)

The sound *û* [ɜː], as in *urn* ['ɜːn], has several different spellings: *er—fern* ['fɜːn], *ir—girl* ['gɜːl], *ol—colonel* ['kɜːnəl], *or—word* ['wɜːd], *our—journey* ['dʒɜːnɪɪ], *uer—guerdon* ['gɜːdən], and *yr—myrrh* ['mɜː]. (See page 23.)

The letter *ā* generally indicates the diphthong in the word *ate* ['eɪɪt]. However, the sound is also written *ea—break* ['bɪeɪɪk], *ua—guage* ['geɪɪdʒ], *ai—aid* ['eɪɪd], *ei—freight* ['fɪeɪɪt], *ay—day* ['deɪɪ], and *ey—obey* [oɪˈbeɪɪ]. (See page 28.)

The above mentioned differences between spelling and pronunciation are a very few illustrations of this confusing characteristic of the English language. Note carefully the many spellings given for the various sounds on the following pages. Make it a habit to consult a dictionary whenever you are in doubt about the pronunciation of a word.

VOWELS

In order to make any sound correctly, you must know what each of the active organs of articulation is doing when the sound is made. As there are no nasal vowels in English, the soft palate is held high in making all vowel sounds. Vowel sounds will be studied from the point of view of the position of the tongue, as that is such an important factor in making those sounds. Vowel sounds are made on the front (just behind the tip), middle, or back of the tongue, and they may be high, medium, or low in those positions. For instance, *ē* [iː] is the very highest front vowel—that is, the front of the tongue is held high in making the sound—and *ä* [ɑ:] is the very lowest back vowel. Say *ē* [i:]—*ä* [ɑ:], and feel how the tongue moves from a high front position with the jaw nearly closed to a low back position with the jaw dropped. Now add *ōo* [u:] as in *shoe*, and feel how the back of the tongue rises to a high position and the lips become rounded. Place the tip of the tongue on the back of the lower front teeth in making all vowel sounds except

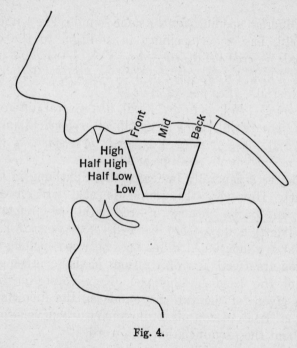

Fig. 4.

the rounded back vowels *ōo* [u:] and *ŏŏ* [ʊ]. It may be helpful to think of the vowels placed on the tongue as shown in Figure 4.

Front Vowels

ē [i:] as in *see*

In order to make the sound *ē* [i:], place the tip of the tongue on the back of the lower front teeth, place the sides of the tongue against the sides of the upper teeth, and hold the front of the tongue high; drop the lower jaw very slightly so that there is

little space between the teeth, and spread the lips. The sound
ē [i:] is called a high, front, tense vowel; if you place your
fingers under both sides of your chin when making the sound,
you will feel the tension of the muscles.

bee	deem	geese	meet	peek	seem
beet	feed	heed	need	reed	tree

Note: The same sound is found in the words *clean,
machine, people, Phoebe, quay, key; field, receive, cedar.*

1. The dream about the machine was so real that it seemed
   not to be a dream.

2. Edith seems to think it will be easy to shell the peas and
   string the beans if we have teamwork at meal time.

ĭ [ɪ] as in *it*

Lower the tongue very slightly from the position for ē [i:],
drop the jaw a very little and relax it, keep the lips spread, and
make the sound ĭ [ɪ]. This is called a high, front, lax vowel.
It is also the first element of the diphthong in the word *here*
['hɪə].

Caution: Do not drop the tongue too far, or the resulting
sound will approximate the ĕ [eⱡ] as in *let*. This mispronunciation is very common in the southern part of the United States
and in New York City.

city	hit	kin	pin	silly	village
dig	ill	lift	sick	timber	wind

Note: This sound is also found in *been, breeches,
busy, build, myth,* and *sieve* and the FIRST syllables of the
words, *England, syrup, pretty,*[1] and *women.*[1]

1. The king lives in a pretty[1] little English village.

2. Minnie[1] received[1] a missive from Miss Smith Tuesday,[1]
   and should have written[1] in reply[1] at once, as it was a
   matter of the greatest[1] importance.

---

[1] In unstressed *prefixes,* such as are found in the words *receive, decry,* and *predict,*
and in unstressed *suffixes,* as in *city, Tuesday, greatest,* and *captain,* the sound is
made a trifle lower in the mouth than it is in *lift* and *mix,* for instance, and is
indicated in *narrow transcription* by the symbol [ɪⱡ]. As this book is concerned
only with *broad transcription* the sound will be indicated by the symbol [ɪ], as
in *mix.*

ĕ [eɪ] as in *let*

Lower the front of the tongue and drop the jaw a little more than for ĭ [ɪ]. Keep the lips spread, and make the sound ĕ [eɪ]. As the position for ĕ [eɪ] is a little more high than low, it is called a half-high, front vowel. The sound is also the first element of the diphthong ā [eɪĭ] as in *say*.

| bevy | fez | lest | men | septic | well |
| ebb | length | member | pen | ten | wreck |

> *Note:* This sound is also found in such words as *heifer, friend, feather, bury, many, said, says, leopard,* and *Thames.*

1. Many members of the crew that had been rescued from the wreck were not well enough to get out of bed.
2. Ted is a very level-headed and dependable helper.

â [ɛ:] as in *there*

Lower the front of the tongue and jaw still more than for ĕ [eɪ]. This gives a sound which is the first element in the diphthong â [ɛɔ̌] as in *there*. This sound is never used in English apart from the diphthong. It is called a half-low, front vowel, as its position is more nearly low than high. (See page 31.)

ă [æ] as in *at*

Lower the front of the tongue and jaw still farther than for [ɛ:], and make the sound ă [æ]. This is called a low, front vowel.

Caution: Pay special attention to this sound, as it is frequently mispronounced. Be careful that you do not add an extra sound and thus make it a diphthong. Be careful that you do not nasalize the sound.

| cat | fancy | hat | man | rap | tack |
| damp | hand | lamp | pant | sand | van |

> *Note:* This sound is also found in the word *plaid.*

1. The man said he would give Nancy a sample of the fancy candy.
2. The cat panted after playing in the damp sand.

à [ɑ]² as in *ask*

Drop the front of the tongue and jaw a little farther than for ă [æ]. This position gives the sound à [ɑ] as in *ask* ['ɑsk], or the so-called intermediate à. It is also the first element of the diphthong ī [ɑĭ].

after	class	fast	past
answer	clasp	grass	raft
ask	dance	last	task

1. It is high time for you to answer the question I asked.

2. I shall call for you to go to the class dance at half past nine.

Mid Vowels

û [ɜ:] as in *term*

Raise the middle of the tongue to a half-high position, drop the jaw to the position for ĕ [eɪ], spread the lips slightly, and make the sound û [ɜ:] as in *bird*. This sound is known as a half-high mid vowel.

Caution: Be sure that the tip of your tongue is placed on the back of your lower front teeth in making this sound. This will prevent the tongue tip from rising and causing the mispronunciation of the sound called an inversion. This mispronunciation is characteristic of midwestern speech. New York City dialect forms diphthongize the sound. This, too, is to be avoided.

berth	err	fern	infer	term	verge
certain	ermine	herd	mercy	verdure	were

Note: The same sound is found in *birth, colonel, earth, guerdon, journey, myrrh, urn,* and *word.*

1. "We were the first
That ever burst
Into that silent sea."

2. The girl received a pearl necklace for her birthday.

---

² This sound is generally used before *ff, ft, ss, st, sp, sk, nt, ns,* and *th voiceless* [θ].

à [ə] as in *about*

Drop the middle of the tongue and the jaw a little from the position for *û* [ɜ:], and make the sound *à* [ə]. This sound is called a half-low mid vowel. It is a neutral vowel and is never used except in unstressed syllables. It is the first sound in *about* and the last in *sofa* and *brother*.

abound	ago	amount	bother	ginger	preacher
account	allow	awake	father	mother	sister

> *Note:* This sound is also found in the *first* syllable of the words *America, companion, confound, correct, Dakota, ferocious, forget, guerilla, occasion, parade,* and *surround;* in the *last* syllable of such words as *cordon, erosion, federation, importance, labor, murmur, problem, sofa, troublesome, unanimous, vowel,* and *western;* in the *first* and *last* syllables of such words as *America, attention, companion, connivance, Dakota, ferocious, guerilla, occasion,* and *survivor;* and in *intermediate, unstressed* syllables, as in *desirable, explicable, incomparable, extemporary, imposition, poverty,* and *sympathetic.*

1. My father will not allow my brother to march in the parade.

2. Jim's temper was aroused when he was accused of copying his sister's problems.

ŭ [ʌ] as in *up*

Drop the middle of the tongue and the jaw to a position a little lower than for *à* [ə], and make the sound *ŭ* [ʌ] as in *up*. This is called a low mid vowel.

abrupt[3]	corrupt[3]	glum	mum	rumble	tumble
bump	dumb	hump	numb	sun	under

> *Note:* The same sound is found in such words as *come, comfort, company, compass, done, frontier, hiccough,* and *rough.*

1. It is troublesome to lose one's gloves or umbrella when running for the subway.

2. If you will come to supper, we shall have some Hot Cross Buns.

---

[3] The first syllable of *abrupt* and *corrupt* has the neutral vowel [ə], while the second syllable has the vowel *ŭ* [ʌ] as in *up*.

Back Vowels

$\overline{oo}$ [u:] as in *moon*

Raise the back of the tongue high, open the mouth slightly, round the lips well, and say $\overline{oo}$ [u:] as in *moon*. This is the highest and roundest of the back vowels, and is known as a high, back, rounded, tense vowel.

Caution: In certain words, such as *roof*, *root*, and *soon*, there is a tendency to use the relaxed, less-rounded sound $\breve{oo}$ [ʊ] as in *book*. This is a dialectal mispronunciation. Avoid it.

boost	loot	noose	raccoon	root	tool
goose	mood	poodle	roof	soon	woo

Note: This sound is also found in such words as *flew,*
flute, plume, rude, true, prune, and *lose.*

1. The goose-girl played her flute and every goose came running for its food.

2. Did you lose the recipe for noodle soup?

$\bar{u}$ [ju:] as in *tune*

This sound is not a vowel, but a digraph, made up of the consonant *y* [j] as in *year* and the vowel $\overline{oo}$ [u:] as in *moon*. However, so many students confuse the sounds [u:] and [ju:] that it may be wise to study them together.

In order to make the sound $\bar{u}$ [ju:] as in *tune*, raise the middle of the tongue until it touches the hard palate very lightly. This will produce the first element *y* [j]. Now move the tongue to the position for $\overline{oo}$ [u:] as described above.[4]

---

[4] There is no confusion in regard to the pronunciation of $\bar{u}$ [ju:] as an initial sound, as in *unite* [ju'naɪt], or when it follows the sounds *b* [b]—*beauty* ['bju·tɪ], *k* [k]—*cube* ['kju:b], *f* [f]—*futile* ['fju·tɪl], *h* [h]—*human* ['hju:mən], *m* [m]—*mute* ['mju·t], *p* [p]—*puny* ['pju:nɪ], or *v* [v]—*view* ['vju:].

After the sounds *t* [t], *d* [d], and *n* [n], however, many speakers are apt to omit the initial element of the digraph, and substitute ['tu:n] for ['tju:n], ['du·k] for ['dju·k], and ['nu:] for ['nju:]. This should be avoided.

After *s* [s], as in *assume* [ə'sju:m], *z* [z] as in *resume* [ɹɪ'ju:m], and *th* [θ] as in *enthusiasm* [in'θju:zɪæzm], the pronunciation $\bar{u}$ [ju:] is *preferred*, but many good speakers suppress the first element, thus substituting [ə'su:m] for [ə'sju:m], and [ɹɪ'zu:m] for [ɹɪ'zju:m].

Remember, however, that, in the best speech, after the sounds l [l] *(except when preceded by another consonant in the same syllable) th* [θ], *d* [d], *t* [t], *n* [n], *s* [s], *and z* [z], *the generally accepted pronunciation of the sound in question is ū* [ju:].

After *l* [l], when preceded by another consonant in the same syllable, as in

| cube | huge | lurid | mute | resume | unite |
| duty | human | lute | puny | tune | usurp |

Note: The same sound is found in such words as
beauty, feud, news, suit, view, Tuesday.

1. It is the duty of the members of the community to unite for human needs.

2. The student was confused by the teacher's views about cube root.

ŏŏ [ʊ] as in *foot*

Lower the back of the tongue very slightly from the position for ōō [uː], relax the jaw and lips, and say ŏŏ [ʊ] as in *foot*. This is known as a high, back, lax vowel.

Caution: Be sure that the lips are rounded when making this sound.

| book | cook | forsook | look | shook | wood |
| brook | crook | good | nook | took | wool |

Note: This sound is also found in such words as *put,*
wolf, and *woman.*

1. I took the cook book so that I could have a good recipe for the pudding.

2. How would you like to sit by the brook and look at this book?

ŏ [oᴛ] as in *obey*

Lower the back of the tongue a little farther than for ŏŏ [ʊ] as in *book*, drop the jaw somewhat, and make the lips less rounded. This position will give you the pure vowel ŏ [oᴛ], which is used in unstressed syllables, as in the word *obey*, and in a stressed syllable when followed by an unstressed syllable beginning with a vowel, as in *poet* or *going*. This vowel is the first element of the diphthong ō [oᴛŭ], as in *old*. It is called a half-high, back, rounded vowel.

| molest | November | obedience | obey | obituary | oblique |
| obliterate | oblivious | omission | omit | opine | opossum |

1. You will not be molested if you obey the rules.

2. His obituary was in the newspaper of November first.

---

plume ['pluːm] and *blue* ['bluː], and after *r* [ɹ] as in *rude* ['ɹuːd], the sound should
be ōō [uː], NOT ū [juː].

ô [ɔ:] as in *all*

Lower the back of the tongue from the position for ŏ [oᴛ], drop the jaw, continue to round the lips, and say ô [ɔ:] as in *all*. This sound, which is a half-low, rounded, back vowel, is also the first element of the diphthong *oi* [ɔĭ] as in *choice*.

Caution: This sound is very frequently mispronounced and requires a good deal of care. In New York City and its environs it is often made too far back in the mouth, and also frequently becomes inverted so that you hear the mispronunciation *sore* ['sɔ:] for *saw* ['sɔ:]. The latter mispronunciation is more frequently called the "intrusive *r*." In midwestern speech, ô [ɔ:] tends to become unrounded and is pronounced like the *ä* [ɑ:] in *father*.

awe	bawl	crawl	jaw	pawn	saw
awl	brawn	draw	lawn	raw	tawdry

> *Note:* This sound is also found in such words as *all, born, bought, caught, orb, quarter, talk, water,* and *wharf.*

1. Saul thought the walls of the hall were falling.
2. I saw Paul and asked him if I might have a drink of water.

ŏ [ɒ] as in *office*

Drop the back of the tongue and jaw still farther than for ô [ɔ:] and relax the jaw. Continue to round the lips and say ŏ as in *office* [ɒ]. This is a low, back, rounded vowel.

Caution: This sound is a difficult one for most Americans, who tend to pronounce it as the *ä* [ɑ:] in *father*. Some New Englanders pronounce it as the ô [ɔ:] in *all*. The accepted pronunciation lies between these two. In the following words, try to acquire the accepted pronunciation by opening the mouth for *ä* [ɑ:] and then rounding the lips a little:

bog	coffee	got	log	not	shot
chocolate	dog	hot	mop	pod	trod

> *Note:* This sound is also found in such words as *what, want,* and *watch.*

1. Do you prefer hot chocolate or hot coffee?
2. John occupied his time by copying an old log-book.

ä [ɑː] as in *father*

Drop the tongue a little farther than for *ŏ* [ɒ], drop the jaw, unround the lips, and say *ä* [ɑː]. This is a low, back, unrounded vowel. It is also the first element of the diphthong *ow* [ɑʊ] as in *house*.

Caution: In New York City and its environs, *ä* [ɑː] tends to be placed too far back and to become rounded. Thus, *father* ['fɑːðə] becomes *fawther* ['fɔːðə]. In New England dialect, it is apt to be placed too far front in the mouth and sound very much like the *à* [a] in *ask* [ask]. In this type of speech, ['fɑːðə] is changed to ['faðə].

| arm | car | farther | market | pardon | tar |
| bark | darn | hark | knarled | sardine | varnish |

Note: This sound is also found in such words as *ah, alms, hearth,* and *sergeant.*

1. The market gardener brings part of his farm products to town in his car.

2. The parson hardened his heart and refused to pardon the boys who played marbles instead of singing psalms.

DIPHTHONGS

A diphthong is a combination of two vowel sounds. Since the first element of a diphthong is always held longer than the second, you should be careful to make the second vowel of the diphthong very short. There are nine diphthongs in English:

ā as in *ate* [eɪɪ]	*ẹ* as in *here* [ɪə]
ī as in *ice* [aɪ]	*â* as in *there—care* [ɛə]
oi as in *choice* [ɔɪ]	*ŏŏr* as in *poor* [ʊə]
ow as in *how* [aʊ]	*ōr* as in *floor* [ɔə]
o as in *old* [oʊ]	

You will notice that three of these diphthongs end in *ĭ* [ɪ], two in *ŏŏ* [ʊ], and four in the neutral vowel *à* [ə].

ā [eɪɪ] as in *ate*

This diphthong is made up of the half-high front vowel *ĕ* [eɪ] followed by the high, front, lax vowel *ĭ* [ɪ]. (For the production of these two sounds, see the preceding section.)

| ate | cane | fade | hate | made | pane |
| bake | date | gale | lane | name | wade |

Note: This diphthong is also found in such words
as *aid, break, day, eight,* and *obey.*

1. The maid was baking cake for the old lady's eightieth
   birthday.

2. Jane feigned sickness in order to have the day free for the
   Yale game.

ī [aɪ̯] as in *ice*

This diphthong is made up of the low, front vowel å [a] followed by the high, front, lax vowel ĭ [ɪ]. (See pages 21–23.)

Caution: In making the diphthong ī [aɪ̯], be careful that the
first element is made on the front of the tongue and not on
the back. If the sound is made on the back of the tongue, the
pronunciation becomes [ɑɪ̯], as the ä [ɑː] in *father* has been
substituted for the correct sound. This is a very usual dialect
form in New York City and its environs.

bicycle	cite	file	ice	might	pint
bite	dine	libel	item	nine	whine

Note: This diphthong is also found in such words
as the following: *aisle, aye* (meaning *yes*), *buy, choir,*
cry, eye, geyser, guile, height, and *vie.*

1. The child whined because she couldn't buy a pint of ice
   cream.

2. The hikers tried to climb the mountain in the icy blast.

oi [ɔɪ̯] as in *choice*

The diphthong is made up of the half-low, rounded back
vowel ô [ɔː] and the high, front, lax vowel ĭ [ɪ̆]. (See the preceding section.)

Caution: In the local dialect of New York City and its
environs, this sound sometimes resembles the sound of û [ɜː]
as in *purse.* In order to avoid this mispronunciation, be sure
to round the lips when making the sound.

boil	coil	foil	join	poison	sirloin
choice	doily	groin	loiter	soil	toil

Note: This sound is also found in the words *boy*
and *royal.*

1. The woman toiled to iron the doilies and was annoyed
   when they became soiled.

2. The boy's plan to poison the oil was quickly foiled.

ow [aŭ] as in *how*

This diphthong is made up of the low, back vowel *ä* [ɑ:], and the high, back, rounded vowel *ŏŏ* [ŭ]. (See the preceding section.)

Caution: In the speech of New York City and its environs, there is a strong tendency to place the initial sound too far forward in the mouth, thus substituting the *à* [a] as in *ask* for the correct sound. Thus, *town* is pronounced ['taŭn] instead of ['taŭn]. This mispronunciation should be avoided.

around	cloud	found	house	loud	noun
bound	doubt	gout	jounce	mouth	pronounce

> *Note:* This sound is also found in such words as *cow, now,* and *scowl.*

1. The house was found to be on the outskirts of the town.

2. Pronounce all round sounds with rounded lips.

ō [oᴛŭ] as in *old*

This diphthong is made up of the half-high, back vowel *ŏ* [oᴛ] and the high, back vowel *ŏŏ* [ŭ]. (See the preceding section.)

bold	doting	mote	ocean	potion	sold
cold	folk	gnome	odor	rote	zone

> *Note:* This diphthong is also found in such words as the following: *beau, brooch, foe, grow, oh, owe, roam, shoulder,* and *yeoman.*

1. The pony roamed along the open road near the ocean.

2. The lotion was scented with the odor of sweet clover.

ę [ɪɜ] as in *here*

This diphthong is made up of the high, front, lax vowel *ĭ* [ĭ] followed by the neutral vowel [ə].

dear	fear	hear	rear	tear
ear	gear	near	sear	weary

> *Note:* This diphthong is also found in the words *cheer, mere, pier,* and *weird.*

1. The hero was cheered as the boat neared the pier.

2. The peer feared that the car was too highly geared.

â [ɛ̌ə] as in *there*

This diphthong is made up of the half-low front vowel [ɛ:] followed by the neutral vowel [ə].

beware	dare	glare	mare	rare	spare
care	fare	hare	pare	snare	wares

> *Note:* This diphthong is also found in such words
> as *air, fairy, heir, malaria, Mary, parent, there, their,*
> *various, vary,* and *where.*

1. Mary's parents had fair hair.
2. Sarah despaired of procuring that pair of rare vases.

ŏor [ʊ̌ə] as in *poor*

This diphthong is made up of the high, back vowel *ŏŏ* [ʊ] followed by the neutral vowel [ə]. Note its various spellings:

boor	moor	poor	tour
doer	plural	sure	your

1. The poor man toured the moors.
2. A doer of kind deeds is sure to be a true friend.

ōr [ɔ̌ə] as in *floor*

This diphthong is made up of the half-low, back vowel *ô* [ɔ:] followed by the neutral vowel [ə].

> *Note:* The pure vowel *ô* [ɔ:] is frequently sub-
> stituted for the diphthong *ōr* [ɔ̌ə] in acceptable Ameri-
> can speech.

bore	core	implore	more	shore	wore
chore	galore	lore	pore	tore	yore

This diphthong is also found in such words as *door, nor,* *pour,* and *soar.*

1. Dora implored Flora to allow her to go to the shore.
2. The explosion tore the door from its hinges and threw it on the floor.

CONSONANTS

A consonant is an obstructed flow of voice or breath. This obstruction may occur in different ways. If the sound is stopped abruptly in mid-channel, it is called a *plosive; b* [b], *p* [p], *t* [t], *d* [d], *g* [g] and *k* [k] are plosives.   If the sound may be prolonged as long as the breath lasts, it is called a *continuant*.   If the continuant flows through a narrow space so that the breath or voice passing through that space causes friction, the sound is called a *fricative; f* [f], *v* [v] *th* voiced [ð], *th* voiceless [θ], *wh* [ʍ] and *h* [h] are fricatives, and *s* [s], *z* [z], *sh* [ʃ], and *zh* [ʒ] are *sibilant fricatives*.   If the pressure of the organs of articulation forces the sound out through the nasal passage instead of through the mouth, the sound is called a *nasal continuant; m* [m], *n* [n], and *ng* [ŋ] are nasal continuants.   If the continuant flows so freely that it seems like a vowel, it is called a vowel-like consonant or a *semi-vowel; w* [w] and *y* [j] are semi-vowels.   If the continuant is so formed that the sound flows off the sides of the tongue, it is called a *lateral; l* [l] is a lateral.

As you listen to the sounds given above, you will discover that consonants may be voiced or voiceless.   If the vocal bands vibrate in making a sound that is obstructed, it is said to be a voiced consonant.   If the vocal bands do not vibrate, it is a voiceless consonant.   If your ear will not help you to discover whether a sound is voiced or voiceless, place your fingers on the larynx, and note whether you can feel a vibration while you are making the sound in question.   If you feel a vibration, the consonant is voiced; if you feel none, it is voiceless.[5]

The voiceless plosives *p* [p], *t* [t], and *k* [k] are aspirated (followed by a slight puff of breath) when followed by a vowel or when they are final in a phrase.   This is indicated in *narrow* transcription by a small *h* [h] after the letter.   The word *pipe*, in which the aspirated *p* [p] occurs twice, would be written as follows: [ˈpʰaɪpʰ].   When these consonants precede another consonant, however, there is no puff of breath.   This is indicated in narrow transcription with a small line after the letter, as follows: *pray* [ˈpɹˌeɪˈ], *cry* [ˈkɹˌɹaɪˈ].   This book contains only broad transcription; hence, those modifiers are not used.

You will find, too, that consonants may be obstructed in various places, as well as in various ways.   If you press your

---

[5] When a consonant is voiced, the vowel or diphthong preceding it is lengthened. This is indicated in phonetic script in the following manner: if a vowel is lengthened, two dots are placed after it : *ē* [i:] as in *bead* [ˈbiːd]; if a diphthong is lengthened, one dot follows each element of the diphthong: *ī* [aˑɪˑ] as in *ride*—[ɹaˑɪˑd].   This rule is very important for the foreigner.

lips together and stop the sound suddenly, you will make the sound *b* [b] or *p* [p], according to whether the sound is voiced or voiceless. If you let the upper teeth rest gently on the lower lip, you will make the sound *f* [f] or *v* [v]. Through experimentation, you will find that consonants may be formed by the lips, by the upper teeth and lower lip, by the teeth and tongue, by the front of the tongue and gum or hard palate, by the middle of the tongue and hard palate, and by the back of the tongue and soft palate.

Note: It will be noticed that very frequently two consonants are made in exactly the same way, but that one is voiced and the other voiceless. These are companion sounds, or *cognates,* and will be treated together. If an unvoiced sound is substituted for its voiced cognate, or if a voiced sound is used instead of its unvoiced cognate, the resulting mispronunciation is known as a *cognate substitution.*

Lip Consonants

b [b] as in *bib; p* [p] as in *pipe*

Press the lips together gently, and then separate them suddenly by the force of the breath. The resulting sound will be the voiced plosive *b* [b] or the voiceless plosive *p* [p].

be	peep	imbibe	pipe	ribbon	pippin
bib	pip	web	pep	pebble	pepper
Bob	pop	stable	staple	dabbled	dappled
rub	sup	Bible	piper	robber	copper

1. Put the pipe and the pebbles behind the copper pepper pot.
2. Betty lost her hair ribbon when she was blowing bubbles beside the babbling brook.

m [m] as in *mum*

Close the lips gently, lower the soft palate, and let voiced air come out through the nose. The resulting sound will be the voiced nasal continuant *m* [m].

seem	them	comb	mimic	murmur	marmalade
hymn	thumb	mime	memory	mummer	mama

1. "The murmuring pines and the hemlocks."
2. I seem to remember that the mummers sang hymns as well as carols at Christmas time.

w [w] as in *wear; wh* [ʍ] as in *where*

Round the lips and let voiced air flow through them; the resulting sound is the voiced semi-vowel *w* [w].

Place the lips in the same position, and send a stream of air out through them; the resulting sound will be the voiceless fricative continuant *wh* [ʍ].

we	wheat	watt	what	wile	while
witch	which	wight	white	wail	whale
wen	when	wine	whine	wear	where

1. Which shall we plant, winter wheat or buckwheat?

2. Winifred wore a white sweater when we went to Winstead on our wheels.

Teeth-Lip Consonants

f [f] as in *fine; v* [v] as in *vine*

Let the upper teeth rest gently on the lower lip. If voiced air is allowed to flow through the very small space between the teeth and the lip, the resulting sound will be the voiced fricative *v* [v]. If breath alone flows through this space, the resulting sound will be the voiceless fricative *f* [f].

veal	feel	fever	reefer	alive	life
vine	fine	favor	safer	glove	rough
vane	feign	rover	sofa	five	fife

Note: The sound *f* [f] is also indicated by *ph* as in *phase* and *phonetic.*

1. Following are four famous forecasting factors.

2. "Unheedful vows may heedfully be broken."

Teeth-Tongue Consonants

th voiced [ð] as in *this; th* voiceless [θ] as in *thin*

Let the upper teeth rest gently on the front of the tongue. If a stream of voiced air is allowed to flow through the narrow space between the teeth and the tongue, the voiced fricative *th* [ð] as in *that* is the resulting sound. If a stream of breath

THE SOUNDS OF ENGLISH

flows through the space, the resulting sound is the voiceless fricative *th* [θ] as in *think*.

θ	ð	θ	ð	θ	ð
thistle	this	breath	breathe	loath	loathe
thigh	thy	teeth	teethe	bath	bathe
thane	they	sooth	soothe	wreath	wreathe

Caution: Do not confuse *th* voiced [ð] with *d* [d], or *th* voiceless [θ] with *t* [t].

1. The victorious youths were wreathed in garlands.
2. I never thought that you would do this thing to Theodore.

Front-of-Tongue Consonants

d [d] as in *did;* *t* [t] as in *tight*

Place the tip of the tongue, pointed, on the middle of the upper gum and then take it away suddenly; the resulting sound will be the voiced plosive *d* [d] or the voiceless plosive *t* [t].

deem	team	dare	tear	bidder	bitter
dad	tat	fade	fate	ladder	latter
dart	tart	ride	right	siding	citing

1. It was a perfectly maddening catastrophe.
2. Sadie dared to go right down to the door in her faded dress to greet the riders.

n [n] as in *nun*

Place the tip of the tongue on the upper gum, and lower the soft palate; the resulting sound is the voiced, nasal continuant *n* [n].

neat	none	been	sign	cleaner	banner
net	nose	then	feign	dinner	sunny
nap	name	soon	noun	tenor	tiny

Note: The letter *n* is sometimes preceded by *g* or *k*. These occur in the spelling but are not pronounced. (See "Silent Letters," page 18.) Examples are *gnat, gnarled, knife, knit*.

1. Name the nine men who signed the amendment.
2. It is a boon to have a moonlight night for the President's dinner.

l [l] as in *lull*

Flatten the front of the tongue against the upper gum, and let the sound flow from both sides of the tongue. The resulting sound will be the front-gum, lateral consonant *l* [l]. This sound is usually voiced, but it becomes partially unvoiced when it follows a voiceless consonant.

Caution: Be sure that this sound is made well forward in the mouth. If the tongue is allowed to relax and drop back, the resulting sound is a blurred, dialectal sound known as a "dark *l.*"

leal	lull	ballad	lily	clay
lilt	lisle	delicate	lollipop	play
loll	Lowell	follow	willy-nilly	sleigh

1. The little girl lay on the lawn eating lollipops.
2. "A life that leads to melodious days."

r [ɹ] as in *red*

Point the front of the tongue upward and curl it very slightly back toward the soft palate. If the tongue is held in this position, the resulting sound is the voiced fricative *r* [ɹ].

Note: The consonant *r* [ɹ], like *l* [l], is usually voiced but becomes partially unvoiced when it follows a voiceless consonant.

reel	rat	rather	berry	hurry
rid	run	ride	cherry	merry
ready	rule	round	ferry	very

Note: The letter *r* is sometimes preceded by the letter *w.* This occurs in the spelling but not in the pronunciation. Examples are *wren, write, wreck.* (See note under *n,* page 35.)

1. Rita and Rose had a very merry time gathering red currants and raspberries.
2. Ralph wrote a rather hurried letter about the newsreel.

Sibilant Fricatives

s [s] as in *sing; z* [z] as in *zinc*

Bring the teeth together so that the edges of the upper and lower front teeth just meet; hold the tongue immediately in back of the top of the upper teeth *but do not let the tongue touch the teeth.* On the other hand, do not hold it too far back—a pencil point's width is about a good distance. Make a tiny groove down the middle of the tongue. If you send a stream of voiced air gently through this groove, the result will be the voiced fricative *z* [z]. If a stream of breath is sent gently through the groove, the resulting sound will be the voiceless sibilant fricative *s* [s].

see	zeal	race	raise
sipper	zipper	pace	bays
sown	zone	fussy	buzzer
soon	zoom	prices	prizes

1. Zounds! I hear strange sounds.
2. The lazy lass will miss her supper if she lies too long by the side of the sea.

sh [ʃ] as in *sure; zh* [ʒ] as in *pleasure*

Draw the tongue a little farther back from the position for *s* [s] and *z* [z], widen the channel, and relax the tongue. The resulting voiced sibilant fricative will be the sound *zh* [ʒ] as in *pleasure*. The resulting unvoiced sibilant fricative will be the sound *sh* [ʃ] as in *sure*.

sheen	shut	fish	pressure	pleasure	garage
shin	show	fresh	meshes	lesion	azure
shed	shine	lash	garish	fusion	measure

> *Note:* The sound *sh* [ʃ] is also found in *sure, sugar, issue, chandelier, conscience, anxious, mission,* and *special.* Note also the different spellings used to indicate the sound *zh* [ʒ] in the words in the last two columns.

1. I'm sure the pleasure is all mine.
2. The garage was burned to ashes.

ch [tʃ] as in *church; j* [dʒ] as in *judge*

These sounds are digraphs, made by joining the voiceless plosive *t* [t] to the voiceless sibilant fricative *sh* [ʃ] to make *ch* [tʃ] as in *church*, and by joining the voiced plosive *d* [d] to the voiced sibilant fricative *zh* [ʒ] to make the sound *j* [dʒ] as in *judge*.

Jane	chain	jar	char	region	reaching
jeer	cheer	June	chew	trudging	crutches
rejoice	choice	jot	chop	urge	church

Note: The sound *j* [dʒ] is also found in *region*, *magic*, *vengeance*, and *soldier*. The sound *ch* [tʃ] is also found in *catch*, *fortune*, *nature*, *question*, *righteous*, and *satchel*.

1. Jane was trudging along home crushing a bunch of birch blossoms in her hand.
2. The judge urged the children to go to church.

Note: Foreigners should be particularly careful not to substitute one of these sounds for the other.

Mid-Tongue Palate Sounds

y [j] as in *yes*

Raise the middle of the tongue until it presses lightly against the palate. The resulting sound will be the vowel-like consonant *y* [j] as in *yes*. This sound *y* [j] is inserted before *ōo* [u:] in words like *Tuesday, new* and *duke*.[6]

ye	year	young	yolk	yonder	tube	tunic	tutor
yet	yearn	youth	yea	yard	music	due	duty[6]

1. Were you in your back yard yesterday?
2. There was a hue and cry last year when the young duke was lost over yonder.

Back-Tongue Palate Consonants

g [g] as in *girl; k* [k] as in *kick*

Raise the back of the tongue until it touches the soft palate, and then release it suddenly. The resulting sounds will be the voiced plosive *g* [g] and the voiceless plosive *k* [k].

key	geese	back	bag	bicker	bigger
kettle	get	lack	lag	lucky	luggage
king	giggle	rack	rag	knuckle	nugget

Note: The sound [k] is also found in such words as *cat, curtain, question, quick,* and *luck.*

1. The girl beckoned to the beggar and gave him some coffee and cake.
2. The sack was so packed with coal that it sagged in the center.

---

[6] Note the insertion of the consonant *y* [j] before the vowel *ōo* [u:] in *tube, music, tunic, due, tutor,* and *duty*. See pages 25–26.

ng [ŋ] as in *song*

Press the back of the tongue gently but firmly against the lowered soft palate, and allow the sound to go out through the nose. The resulting sound will be the voiced nasal continuant *ng* [ŋ] as in *song*. Learn the symbol [ŋ] for the so-called soft sound of *ng*.

Caution: This is a difficult sound for the foreigner. Not only is he faced with the production of an unfamiliar sound, but he must learn when to say *ng* [ŋ] as in *song*, when to say *ng-g* [ŋg] as in *finger*, and when to say *nj* [ndʒ] as in *hinge*. The following rules govern the pronunciation of these sounds:

1. A root word ending in *ng*[7] has the pronunciation [ŋ].

bring	fling	sing	rung
clang	gang	thong	wrong

2. A root word ending in *ng* and adding a suffix retains the pronunciation [ŋ] as in *song*.

bringing	longing	singer	swinging
hanger	ringer	songster	youngster

Exceptions: The comparative and superlative degrees of the adjectives *young, long,* and *strong,* and the words *diphthongal, elongate, elongation, prolongate,* and *prolongation* have the pronunciation [ŋ] plus [g] making [ŋg].

longer	stronger	younger	diphthongal
longest	strongest	youngest	elongation

3. A root word that has *ng* within it has the pronunciation [ŋ] plus [g] making [ŋg].

England	dangling	hunger	linger
English	finger	language	mangle

Exceptions: The common nouns *gingham* and *tungsten,* and many proper nouns, such as *Bingham* and *Washington* have the pronunciation [ŋ].

---

[7] Note that the words *tongue* ['tʌŋ], *meringue* [mə'ræŋ], and *harangue* [hə'ræŋ] follow this rule; *ng* [ŋ] is the last SOUND, as the *ue* is silent in each case. See "Silent Letters," page 18.

4. Words ending in *nge* have the pronunciation *nj* [ndʒ] as in *hinge*.

fringe	plunge	revenge	strange
hinge	range	singe	tinge

1. The singer sang a song.

2. The foreign student is studying in America in order to learn the English language.

The Aspirate

A puff of breath produces the aspirate *h*. Sometimes the position of *h* appears to be in the front of the mouth, sometimes in the middle, and sometimes in the back, depending upon the position of the vowel that follows it.

Note the different positions of the aspirate in the following words:

heat   harm   whom   Hugo

1. The heat of the room was so great as to be harmful to anyone who might be in it.

2. He has clean hands and a pure heart.

CHAPTER V

Strong and Weak Forms

ONE of the most mystifying idiosyncrasies of the English language from the foreigner's point of view is the fact that a word is not always pronounced in the same way. It is often difficult to convince Americans themselves that this is true. They admit contractions such as *can't* for *cannot* and *didn't* for *did not*, but they are unwilling to believe that contractions are only one way in which forms change. Of course, all words do not change their forms. Unimportant words, however, such as prepositions, connectives, definite and indefinite articles, pronouns, and auxiliary verbs, make use of two or more forms, according to whether they are stressed or unstressed. This change of form from the one found in the dictionary is known as *weakening* the form. The strong form of the word is used when the word is stressed, and the weakened form is used when it is unstressed. A few illustrations will demonstrate this principle.

John: I'm going to the ball game. [aɪm 'goʊɪŋ tə ðə 'bɔːl 'geɪm]
Mary: O no, you're not. ['oʊ 'noʊ 'jʊə 'nɒt]
John: Yes, I *am* going. ['jes aɪ 'æm 'goʊɪŋ]

Note that when John makes a simple, unchallenged statement, he uses the contraction, or weak form, "I'm" [aɪm]; but as soon as Mary attempts to interfere with his plans, he asserts himself by using the strong form "I am" [aɪ'æm].

Mary: I saw John going to the store.
Mary: [aɪ 'sɔː 'dʒɒn 'goʊɪŋ tə ðə 'stɔə]
Ted: Was he going *to* the store or coming *from* there?
Ted: [wəz hɪ goʊɪŋ 'tuː ðə 'stɔː(ɪ) ɔː kʌmɪŋ 'fɪɒm ðɛə?]

As a general rule, a preposition is used in the weak form because it is unimportant. This is the case in Mary's statement. However, in Ted's question the words *to* and *from* are brought into prominence, hence the strong forms are used.

Words that are strong, when used alone, are usually weakened when combined with other words. For instance, you say:

John is a tall man [mæn],

using the strong form as indicated, but you also say:

John is a gentleman, policeman, motorman [mən]

In the latter instances, *man* is joined to other words, and hence becomes weakened.

The change from a strong to a weak form is usually brought about by changing a vowel. The vowel most frequently used when making this change is the neutral [ə]. For instance [ðæt] is weakened to [ðət], [ˈbʌt] is weakened to [bət] and the strong form of the indefinite article *a* [eɪ̆] is always changed to the neutral [ə] in both talking and reading. Other vowels occasionally used for this purpose are ĭ [ɪ] and o͝o [ʊ]. Before a consonant, for example, the definite article *the* [ði:] is weakened to [ðə], as in *the sea* [ðə ˈsi:]; but before a vowel, it becomes [ðɪ], as in *the ocean* [ðɪ ˈoɾŭ̆ʃən]. Before a consonant, the strong form of the preposition *to* [tu:] is weakened to [tə], as in *to go* [tə ˈgoɾŭ̆]; but before a vowel it is better to use the weak form [tʊ], as when saying *to own* [tʊ ˈoɾŭ̆n]. Another method of weakening a form is to make use of contractions. Auxiliary verbs such as *shall*, *can*, and *am* are usually shortened in this manner in informal speech. Thus, *I shall* [ˈaɪ̆ ˈʃæl] becomes *I'll* [ˈaɪ̆l], *I am* [ˈaɪ̆ ˈæm] becomes *I'm* [ˈaɪ̆m], and *cannot* [ˈkænɒt] is shortened to *can't* [ˈkɑnt].

The proper application of the principle of strong and weak forms is essential to good English speech. The subordination of less important ideas by the use of weakened forms in unimportant words lends emphasis to the ideas that should stand out. The weakened form makes, also, for more rhythmical and fluent speech. The use of nothing but strong forms, on the other hand, detracts from the thought and spoils the rhythm of speech. It is likewise an indication of foreign influence or the too-careful speech of the pedant.

The question often arises as to whether or not the use of weak forms is slovenly. Teachers are particularly disturbed for fear their students will criticize them if they use weak forms. The answer is that not only is it not slovenly to use the weakened forms in their proper place, but it is absolutely necessary to use them in order to speak acceptable, idiomatic English.

Practice reading some of the sentences and paragraphs given in the exercise material in Part III, using the weakened forms when they are necessary to the meaning and rhythm of the sentence.

A Short List of Words That Have Two or More Forms

PREPOSITIONS

	Strong Form	Weak Forms
of	['ɒv]	[əv]
to	['tu:]	[tʊ]*a*, [tə]*b*
from	['fɹɒm]	[fɹəm]
at	['æt]	[ət]

AUXILIARY VERBS

	Strong Form	Weak Forms
am	['æm]	[m]
was	['wɒz]	[wəz]
would	['wʊd]	[wəd]
had	['hæd]	[həd]
is	['iz]	[z]
shall	['ʃæl]	[ʃəl], [ʃl], [l]

CONNECTIVES

	Strong Form	Weak Forms
and	['ænd]	[ənd] [nd]
but	['bʌt]	[bət]
or	['ɔ:]	[ə] [ə]
than	['ðæn]	[ðən]
nor	['nɔ:]	[nə] [nə]

PRONOUNS

	Strong Form	Weak Forms
he	['hi:]	[hi] [hɪ]
me	['mi:]	[mi] [mɪ]
you	['ju:]	[jʊ]
your	['juɚ]	[jʊ]
us	['ʌs]	[əs]
them	['ðeɪm]	[ðəm]

ARTICLES

	Strong Form	Weak Forms
the	['ði:]	[ðɪ]*a* [ðə]*b*
a	['eɪ]	[ə]
an	['æn]	[ən]

a Before a vowel.
b Before a consonant.

CHAPTER VI

Intonation

IF you have ever been surrounded by foreigners in the subway, or the bus, or any public place, and have become interested in listening to them speak English, you will have noticed that the German speaks it in one tune, the Italian in another, the Russian in another. In other words, people of different nationalities speak English to the tune or speech melody of their mother tongue. This tune, or melody of speech, is known as *intonation*. Each language has its characteristic intonation, which must, of course, be acquired before that language is entirely mastered.

How may correct intonation be learned? Suppose, for example, that an American wishes to learn to speak Italian. He can go to Italy, engage a native teacher, live with a family that speaks good Italian, and learn the speech melody through imitation. A more scientific and more accessible method, however, was evolved by a German scholar, Professor Hermann Klinghardt.

Professor Klinghardt worked out a system by means of which you can learn the intonation of any language. The principle is very simple: a horizontal line, known as a *measuring line*, is used to indicate the normal pitch of the voice; a heavy dot ● indicates a stressed syllable, while a light dot ‧ marks an unstressed syllable; a dot is used for every syllable; a dot with an up-glide ♪ denotes a rising inflection, while one with a down-glide ⌐ indicates a falling inflection. Thus, the correct intonation for the statement, "This is a nice day," should be mapped out as follows:

There are, of course, individual differences in the speaking of a language, as no two persons speak exactly alike, but certain main tendencies govern the intonation of each language.

There are three main tendencies that characterize English intonation:

1. A complete thought ends with a falling inflection or down-glide. A question that begins with a question word, such as *who, which, where, when,* or *what,* also ends with a falling inflection.

Examples:

I shall go.

Where will you go?

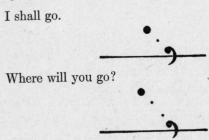

Note: Foreigners should be particularly careful about the use of the falling inflection, as they generally tend to use the rising inflection.

2. An unfinished thought and a question that does not begin with a question word should be spoken with a rising inflection, or up-glide.

Examples:

Once upon a time.

Will you go?

3. The first stressed syllable in an intonation group, or phrase, is higher in pitch than any other syllable in the group.

Hence, the heavy dot indicating this syllable should be placed well above the measuring line. Any unstressed syllables that precede the first stressed syllable are placed in a line just above the measuring line.

Example:

    It is a nice morning.

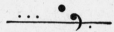

An unstressed syllable following the last stressed syllable is placed just below the measuring line.

Example:

    He is coming Tuesday.

These illustrations show that unstressed syllables in these positions are spoken in a pitch as low as or lower than the normal pitch of the voice.

Sometimes there are two or more possible variations of the same statement to bring out different meanings. For example, the statement, "I *like* Mary so much," would be said as follows:

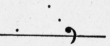

If, however, you wish to compare Mary with someone else, you would say, "I like *Mary* so much."

Read the following phrases, and indicate the intonation:

1. In the meantime.
2. I like candy.
3. Are you ready?
4. Good afternoon.
5. What a nice day!
6. Is it you?
7. What time is it?
8. It was a fine meeting.
9. On the other hand.
10. Come on home.

CHAPTER VII
Speech Problems

SPEECH problems include all deviations from accepted speech, in degrees varying from a mild form of regional dialect to a bad case of stammering. The question then arises: Are all speech problems necessarily speech defects? Is the girl who raves about the *priddy lil kiddy,* when she is speaking of a small cat and not a small child, suffering from a speech defect? She certainly must be accused of careless speech, at any rate. Has the boy who has reached the age of sixteen still speaking of a red rose as a *wed wose* a speech defect? It may be a difficult fact for him to accept, but his speech has some of the characteristics of prolonged infantilism. What about foreign accent? If a German has a good command of his own language, but speaks English with a decided accent, should he be said to have a speech defect? What about stammering? Stammering is a personality problem, as the stammerer is perfectly able to say the words that trouble him if only he thinks he can, yet almost anyone would consider it a speech defect.

It is needless to say that different authorities have differing views about what constitutes a speech defect. There is little use in carrying such a discussion further here. It may be said arbitrarily that any deviation from normal accepted speech, serious enough to prevent a person from taking his place satisfactorily in society, must be considered to constitute a speech defect.

Speech defects may be divided into three classes:

1. Functional defects, or those which are not due to a physical handicap, but merely to a misuse of the speech mechanism. Among these are defective phonation, lisping (in which the mispronunciation of the sibilant sound occurs even though there is perfect occlusion), careless speech, and foreign accent.

2. Organic defects, or those due to a physical handicap, such as cleft palate, tongue-tie, and malocclusion of the teeth. These defects include lisping and cleft-palate speech.

3. Emotional disorders, which include hysterical aphonia, cluttering, and stammering.

The question of whether or not the above defects are remediable may very naturally occur to you. Functional defects should be entirely remediable; in many cases organic and emotional disorders are remediable, and nearly every case is greatly helped by remedial work. Some defects are more serious and more difficult to overcome than others, but the substitution of a correct production for an incorrect one and its incorporation in daily speech are tedious at best. The great factor in speech correction is co-operation. If you really wish to improve your speech, if you desire it so earnestly that you are willing to spend hours on drills and ear-training exercises, to keep working conscientiously every day for a long period of time if necessary, to attempt to use the correct sounds all the time and not merely in the classroom—if you are willing to do all of these things, your chances of overcoming any defect are very good. You will, of course, need careful guidance, but in the last analysis you have to do the work yourself; no one can do it for you.

Certain exercises are helpful in the correction of all defects. Just as breath control is essential for voice improvement, control of the tongue and lips and jaw is absolutely necessary in speech improvement. The setting-up exercises that should precede every practice period will be found on pages 67–71.

Ear-training is another important factor in the correction of all speech defects. If you have difficulty in hearing certain sounds, you should have an audiometer test to make sure that your hearing is adequate. If it should be discovered that you have a marked hearing disability, you should go at once to a competent ear specialist. If, however, your hearing is adequate, you may find that, like many other people with excellent hearing, you are not conscious of mispronouncing a sound because you do not know what the correct pronunciation is. If you can become conscious of the correct sound and your deviation therefrom, you will be well on the way to correction. Ear-training is of immeasurable help in this respect. A list of ear-training exercises will be found on pages 71–73.

CHAPTER VIII
Functional Defects

Defective phonation. Defective phonation may be defined as the incorrect production of sounds. It usually consists of consonant substitutions; for instance, the substitution of *t* [t] for *k* [k] (*tandy* for *candy*), *v* [v] and *f* [f] for *th* voiced [ð] and voiceless [θ] (*vis fing* for *this thing*), and *w* [w] for *r* [ɹ] (*wed wose* for *red rose*). Sometimes, however, all sounds are so curiously formed as to be very difficult and at times almost impossible to understand. These substitutions and incorrectly formed sounds are generally found in the speech of childhood. However, as a considerable number of people carry the bad speech habits formed in early youth into their adult life, defective phonation is a problem that frequently has to be dealt with on the high-school and college levels. It is obvious that much of this difficulty might be avoided if parents could be persuaded not to encourage baby talk. Unfortunately, too many misguided relatives think it is "cute" and therefore encourage the child to go on speaking in that way. They should be reminded firmly that what seems attractive at two or three years of age becomes distressing at eighteen or twenty; that everybody does not outgrow baby talk; and, finally, that it is much easier to form a bad habit than to break one.

The evidences of defective phonation which are likely to persist into adult life are the substitution of *w* [w] for *r* [ɹ], especially after another consonant (*bweak* for *break*), the mispronunciation of *l* [l], and one type of the lingual protrusion lisp, which consists of the substitution of *th* voiced [ð] and voiceless [θ] for *z* [z] and *s* [s].

If you have difficulty in making any of these sounds, ask the teacher to pronounce them correctly and incorrectly for you, and listen carefully to the difference between the two pronunciations. If you can hear a difference, try to imitate the correct pronunciation, saying, for instance, *r-red-r-rose*.

49

If, however, you have difficulty in imitating the correct sound, turn to the chapter on "The Sounds of English" (Part II, Chapter IV), and find out just what to do with each of the organs of articulation in order to make the particular sound correctly. After you have learned to make the particular sound in isolation, try it in words, and then in phrases and sentences. For the correction of the various mispronunciations mentioned in this section, see the contracts for defective phonation given in Part IV. In correcting any sound, listen to your own speech carefully to be sure that you do not slip back into the incorrect pronunciation in informal conversation. After you have once learned to make a sound correctly, never allow yourself to make it incorrectly. This, as you will realize, requires constant watchfulness.

Careless speech. Careless speech usually consists of poor enunciation, but it may include incorrect pronunciations, such as *reconize* for *recognize* and *apern* for *apron*. The careless speaker usually substitutes *d* [d] for *t* [t], or omits it altogether, except at the beginning of a word, and shows a lamentable tendency to omit final and middle *d* [d]. The phrase *in the middle of the room* becomes *in the mil a the room* or *in de mil a de room*, and *a pretty kitty* is changed to *a pri kiddy*. Other consonants are omitted, too; *of* becomes *a*, *fifths* becomes *fiths*, *with* becomes *wid* or *wit*, *this* is changed to *dis*, and *didn't* and *couldn't* become something like *din* and *cun*. Equally common in this type of speech is the substitution of *n* [n] for *ng* [ŋ] in words such as *coming* and *going*.

If you discover that your speech is careless and slovenly, you will, of course, be eager to clear it up. Practicing the contracts for "Careless Speech," given in Part IV, the sentences especially designed to overcome careless speech, the exercises for articulation, as well as those given for *d* [d] and *t* [t], *b* [b] and *p* [p], *f* [f] and *v* [v] and *g* [g] and *k* [k] in Part III, will help you to speak clearly when reading aloud. Questions based on the exercises may be used as a basis for conversation. Classroom conversation is an important factor in overcoming careless speech, as it will help you to bear in mind that you must speak clearly all the time, and that careful speech should not be confined to reading and doing exercises.

Foreign accent. Foreign accent refers to those deviations from accepted English usage in the pronunciation of vowels and consonants, in stress and intonation, that characterize the foreigner's use of English. If you wish to overcome a foreign accent, it will be wise for you to approach the study of the language phonetically. The contracts for foreign accent in Part IV are based on the phonetic method. A few sounds are taught at a time, and these sounds are combined at once in syllables, words, phrases, sentences, and conversation. They are presented in this way in order that you may have the knowledge, and the courage as well, to begin to speak English at once. Later contracts take up the principles of strong and weak forms and of intonation, both of which are so necessary for the correct use of English.

Certain characteristics are found in the English of nearly all foreigners. Most people who speak English as a second language, and people who hear another language or English spoken with a foreign accent almost continually, have the following deviations from accepted English: they make the sounds *d* [d] and *t* [t] on the teeth instead of on the upper gum (this is known as *dentalization*), or they may make the sounds *d* [d] and *t* [t] with the front of the tongue against the hard palate (this is called *palatalization*); they unvoice their final consonants and make other cognate substitutions[1]; they substitute *ng-g* [ŋg] or *ng-k* [ŋk] for *ng* [ŋ]; they substitute *d* [d] and *t* [t] for *th* voiced [ð] and voiceless [θ]; they lengthen vowels before voiceless consonants and shorten them before voiced consonants; they use strong forms where weak forms are necessary; and they frequently mistake the syllable that should be stressed. It may be helpful to list according to nationality the characteristics frequently found in the speech of foreigners.

Germans usually make the following substitutions:

w [w] for *v* [v] as in *vain*.
ōō [u:] for *ŏŏ* [ʊ] as in *book*.
t [t] for *th* [θ] as in *thumb*.
d [d] for *th* [ð] as in *this*.
z [z] for *s* [s] as in *say*.
s [s] for *z* [z] as in *reason*.

---

[1] See the note on cognate substitutions, page 33.

p [p] for *b* [b] as in *buy*.
f [f] for *v* [v] as in *of*.
ch [tʃ] for *j* [dʒ] as in *judge*.
j [dʒ] for *ch* [tʃ] as in *church*.
r trilled [r] for *r* untrilled [ɹ] as in *red*.

In addition, Germans generally use the dental *d* [d] and *t* [t], and sometimes use *ng-g* [ŋg] for *ng* [ŋ] as in *singing*. They also use strong forms when weak ones are required.

The English of people who speak Yiddish as a first language has many of the characteristic substitutions found in the German's use of English; in addition, in New York City and its environs, it contains many of the vulgarisms of New York City speech, such as placing *ī* [aɪ] and *aw* [ɔ:] too far back in the mouth, and substituting *oi* [ɔɪ] for *û* [ɜ:] as in *third*. The following substitutions are also made:

ng-g [ŋg] or *ng-k* [ŋk] for *ng* [ŋ] as in *sing* or *singer*.
ng [ŋ] for *ng-g* [ŋg] as in *finger*.
dental or palatal *d* [d] and *t* [t] for *d* [d] and *t* [t] made on the upper gum as in *debt*.
ĕ [eᴛ] for *ă* [æ] as in *cat*, or *à* [ɑ] as in *ask*.
s [s] for *z* [z] as in *because*.

Italians frequently make the following substitutions:

ē [i:] for *ĭ* [ɪ] as in *hit*.
ĭ [ɪ] for *ē* [i·] as in *heat*.
ō [oᴛŭ] for *ô* [ɔ·] as in *caught*.
ōō [u:] for *ŏŏ* [ʊ] as in *book*.
à [ɑ] as in *ask* for *ă* [æ] as in *bad*.
t [t] for *th* [θ] as in *thin*.
d [d] for *th* [ð] as in *this*.
ng-g [ŋg] for *ng* [ŋ] as in *singing*.
trilled *r* [r] for untrilled *r* [ɹ] as in *red*.
dental *d* [d] and *t* [t] for *d* [d] and *t* [t] made on the upper gum as in *debt*.

In addition, they unvoice their final consonants and make other cognate substitutions. They also use strong forms instead of weak ones.

Spaniards frequently make the following substitutions:

ē [i:] for *ĭ* [ɪ] as in *hit*.
ĭ [ɪ] for *ē* [i·] as in *heat*.
ô [ɔ:] for *ō* [oᴛŭ] as in *go*.

ō [oтŭ] for ŏ [ɔ·] as in *caught.*
à [ɑ] as in *ask* for ă [æ] as in *bad.*
d [d] for *th* [ð] as in *this.*
t [t] for *th* [θ] as in *thin.*
ng [ŋ] for *n* [n] usually following ĭ [ɪ] as in *tin.*
trilled *r* [r] for untrilled *r* [ɹ] as in *red.*

In addition, they insert the sound *i* [ɪ] before the sibilant, dentalize *d* [d] and *t* [t], and use strong forms instead of weak.

People from the Near East frequently make the following substitutions:

ĕ [eт] for ā [eтĭ] as in *take.*
ē [i:] for ĭ [ɪ] as in *sit.*
ĭ [ɪ] for ē [i·] as in *east.*
à [ə] for ŏ [ɔ:] as in *small.*
ŏ [ɔ:] for ō [oтŭ] as in *though.*
ĕ [eт] for ă [æ] as in *chapel.*
ŏŏ [ʊ] for ōō [u·] as in *group.*
ƒ [f] for *v* [v] as in *of.*
ng-k [ŋk] for *ng* [ŋ] as in *going.*
trilled *r* [r] for untrilled *r* [ɹ] as in *red.*

In addition, they dentalize or palatalize *d* [d] and *t* [t], unvoice their final consonants, and substitute strong forms for weak.

Slavs usually make the following substitutions:

ŏ [ɔ:] for ō [oтŭ] as in *go.*
ŏŏ [ʊ] for ōō [u:] as in *cool.*
ĕ [eт] for ă [æ] as in *mat.*
w [w] for *v* [v] as in *vain.*
s [s] for *z* [z] as in *because.*
b [b] for *p* [p] as in *cap.*
p [p] for *b* [b] as in *cab.*
t [t] for *d* [d] as in *red.*
ng-g [ŋg] for *ng* [ŋ] as in *coming.*

In addition, they unvoice their final consonants, dentalize or palatalize *d* [d] and *t* [t], and use strong forms for weak.

Inorganic lisping. "Lisping may be defined as any habitual mispronunciation of the sibilant sounds."[2] The sibilants are *s* [s], *z* [z], *sh* [ʃ], *zh* [ʒ], *ch* [tʃ], and *j* [dʒ]. There are three general types of lisps: the lingual protrusion, the lateral emission, and

---

[2] Raubicheck, Davis, Carll, *Voice and Speech Problems*, Revised Edition, Prentice-Hall, Inc., 1939.

the nasal emission. Any of these defects may be functional, organic, or emotional. If you have perfect occlusion—that is, if your teeth come together properly so that there should be no difficulty in forming the sibilant sounds—and you lisp in spite of this, you have what is known as a functional defect. You may have imitated someone who lisped, or you may have formed the habit at the time of second dentition, when the desire of the tongue to investigate the space left vacant by the loss of the front baby teeth starts so many children on the road to lisping.

The lingual protrusion lisp is very easily recognized. It may consist of the substitution of the voiceless *th* [θ] for *s* [s] and of the voiced *th* [ð] for *z* [z] which occurs because the tongue protrudes beyond the upper front teeth in making the sibilant sounds. However, any mispronunciation of *s* [s] or *z* [z] that results from placing the tongue so far forward that it *touches* the teeth, gums, or hard palate is called a *lingual protrusion lisp*. In order to correct this defect, you must, of course, know exactly what to do with the organs of articulation in order to make the sounds correctly (see page 36); you will also have to control the tongue carefully. The following exercises will help you to see and hear the difference between correct and incorrect sounds:[3]

thä [θɑ:]	sä [sɑ:]	thä [θɑ:]	sä [sɑ:]	thä [θɑ:]	sä-sä-sä- [sɑ:]
thē [θi:]	sē [si:]	thē [θi:]	sē [si:]	thē [θi:]	sē-sē-sē [si:]
thä [ðɑ:]	zä [zɑ:]	thä [ðɑ:]	zä [zɑ:]	thä [ðɑ:]	zä-zä-zä- [zɑ:]
thā [ðeтɪ]	zā [zeтɪ]	thā [ðeтɪ]	zā [zeтɪ]	thā [ðeтɪ]	zā-zā-zā [zeтɪ]

After you have learned to make the sound properly (and this is a very small part of the task), practice using it as an initial, middle, and final sound in words, then incorporate it in sentences and conversation. The carefully graded contracts for lisping in Part IV will be the best guide as to what steps to take in overcoming this defect.

The lateral emission lisp occurs when the tongue tip is curled back so that the sound comes out of the sides of the mouth. The remedy is to relax the front of the tongue and bring it forward; then proceed as in the lingual protrusion lisp. The

---

[3] These exercises may be extended to include all vowels and diphthongs.

exercise below may be more helpful as a setting-up exercise in this type of lisp than the one given above. The contracts for lisping in Part IV should, of course, be followed.

	t t t	sssssssssssssssss
to see	to see	to see [si:]
to say	to say	to say [seɪ]

The nasal emission is like the lateral emission, except that the tongue is curled so far back that the sound is emitted from the nose. The correction of this defect calls for control of the soft palate so that the sound may be forced to come out of the mouth. Practice yawning and doing the other exercises designed to give control of the soft palate; these exercises are found in contract 2 of the contracts for nasality. Then proceed with the contracts for lisping.

CHAPTER IX

Organic Defects

Malocclusive lisping. Malocclusion means that the teeth do not occlude, or meet properly, or, in other words, that there is not a perfect bite. A person may be overshot, in which case his upper jaw will protrude beyond his lower jaw, so that in closing the jaws a space is left between the upper and lower front teeth; on the other hand he may be undershot, and again there will be an open space between the upper and lower teeth, but this time the lower jaw will protrude. Both of these malformations naturally cause a lisp because the open space permits the sibilant sound to rush out too vigorously; moreover, the tongue is almost bound to protrude into the space between the teeth. Another type of malformation is known as the open bite; in such a case the teeth meet in the back, but due to some obstruction they are unable to meet in the front; again, the upper front teeth may come to a point or be widely separated; the teeth may be out of alignment, or merely very crooked. If you suffer from any of these difficulties, you should consult an orthodontist. Little can be done toward correcting a lisp, however, while the orthodontia is in progress. It is much better to wait until the work has been completed and then re-educate the organs of articulation to function properly in a new environment. The contracts for lisping that are given in Part IV will be helpful here. If the orthodontist decides that nothing can be done to help the condition, you will have to depend upon constant ear training to improve the sound. Do not be discouraged, as it frequently happens that a person with malocclusion is able to acquire a very acceptable sibilant sound.

Tongue-tie. In cases of tongue-tie, the fraenum, the muscular tissue that joins the tongue to the middle line of the floor of the mouth, is too short. If it is only a little too short, it may be stretched by tongue exercises such as those given in Part III (see page 68). If, however, it is very short, a competent surgeon should be consulted. It is a very simple operation to have the fraenum slightly clipped, and thus lengthened. The sounds mispronounced because of this difficulty are the sibilants and the consonants that require the tongue to be raised, particularly those made by placing the tip or front of the tongue on the upper gum. After the fraenum has been stretched or cut, the tongue must be trained to reach up to the upper gum for the sounds *t* [t], *d* [d], *n* [n], and *l* [l], and to take the correct position for the sibilants. If you have had this difficulty, you will have to learn the proper position of the organs of articulation for the above-mentioned sounds and practice saying the sounds correctly. You will also have to learn to control the tongue. The following exercise will help in strengthening the muscles and giving control of the movements of the tongue: open the mouth as for *ä* [ɑ:] and hold the jaw firmly in that position; then at the count of 1 raise the tongue to the upper gum, and at the count of 2 lower it. Do this a number of times, keeping the jaw open during the entire exercise. After you have practiced this exercise, try making the sounds given above in isolation, and then use them in syllables, as in the following:[1]

dā	dā	dā		[deɪ̆]
tā	tā	tā		[teɪ̆]
lā	lā	lā		[leɪ̆]
nā	nā	nā		[neɪ̆]
dā	tā	lā	nā	lā [deɪ̆ teɪ̆ leɪ̆ neɪ̆ leɪ̆]
ăd	ăd	ăd		[æd]
ăt	ăt	ăt		[æt]
ăl	ăl	ăl		[æl]
ăn	ăn	ăn		[æn]
tăd	tăd	tăd		[tæd]

After you have learned to make the sounds correctly in syllables, try to use them correctly in words, phrases, sentences, paragraphs and, finally, in conversation. The use of conversation is particularly important, as you must learn to make the sounds properly when you are thinking about something else. The sentences given under *n* [n], *l* [l], *d* [d], and *t* [t] in Part III

---

[1] These exercises may be extended to include all vowels and diphthongs.

will give you good practice in using these sounds; they may also be used as a basis for practice in conversation. For the correction of the sibilants, proceed as with any other case of lisping.

Cleft palate. In cases of cleft palate, the cleft, or cut, may be in the lip (in which case it is known as a hare lip), the hard palate, the soft palate, or merely the uvula, or it may extend from the lip through both palates. A competent surgeon who has specialized in cleft palates should be consulted at the earliest possible moment in cases of this sort. After the surgeon has done all he can to alleviate the difficulty, the organs of articulation must be re-educated to meet the new situation. The sounds most affected by this difficulty are g [g], k [k], the sibilant sounds, and all the vowels. The latter are distorted because of their extreme nasal quality. All of the speech is nasal, however, because, due to the cleft in the palate, there is nothing to prevent the sound from going into the nasal passage. An expert surgeon believes that it is safe to begin exercising the palate a month after the operation has taken place. This, of course, must be done very cautiously under the guidance of an expert. Exercises to aid in overcoming the nasality consist in yawning, panting, and then endeavoring to raise and lower the soft palate without either of these devices. The contracts for nasality may be used at the instructor's discretion. The sounds g [g] and k [k], which are ordinarily made by the back of the tongue and the soft palate, may be brought forward toward the hard palate. The following exercises may be used to train the tongue to come forward on these sounds:[2]

kā	kā	kā	[keꜱɪ]
gā	gā	gā	[geꜱɪ]
ăk	ăk	ăk	[æk]
ăg	ăg	ăg	[æg]
găk	găk	găk	[gæk]
kăg	kăg	kăg	[kæg]

The exercises given for g [g] and k [k] in Part III may be used for practice in using these sounds in words and sentences, and may be employed as a basis for conversation as well. The sibilants should be corrected according to the contracts for lisping.

---

[2] These exercises may be extended to include all vowel sounds.

CHAPTER X
Emotional Disorders

Neurotic lisping. In the discussion of inorganic lisping in Chapter VI, the statement was made that if a person with a perfect occlusion lisped, he might be said to have a functional defect. There is one other possibility that has to be taken into consideration; that is, that the person might be suffering from a neurotic lisp. If, after careful training, an inorganic lisp fails to show any improvement, the probability is that the lisp is neurotic. In such a case the person consciously or unconsciously desires to lisp and hence continues to do so. The reason for this desire must be discovered and dealt with if a cure is to be accomplished. This type of lisper will insist that he has every desire to overcome the defect and may think he is perfectly honest when he says it. The fact remains, however, that if he is intelligent and properly taught, he will overcome a lisp for which there is no physical reason. As in all other emotional disorders, each lisper is an individual problem. Suffice it to say that lisping is an infantile characteristic, and any student who wishes to enjoy the respect of his or her fellows in an adult civilization will strive to overcome this childish mannerism at the earliest possible moment.

Hysterical aphonia. Hysterical aphonia refers to an inorganic absence of voice. The person suffering from this difficulty is perfectly capable of speaking in a clear tone if he thinks he can. He may begin speaking clearly and then, losing confidence, suddenly have no voice at all. He may be able to read aloud in a clear tone and still be apparently unable to speak aloud; or he may be able to speak in a clear tone and unable to read except in a whisper. The following rules may be helpful to the person suffering from this difficulty:[1]

---

[1] Hysterical hoarseness may be treated in the same way.

1. Build up your physical condition through long hours of undisturbed sleep, proper food, fresh air, and exercise.

2. Avoid excitement, friction, and overwork, if possible.

3. Practice breathing and voice exercises every day, as they will help you to control your voice and speak in a clear tone.

4. Practice reading aloud by yourself; this will give you the confidence to read and speak to others in a clear tone.

5. Always speak slowly and smoothly.

6. Say to yourself, "I *can* and *will* speak in a clear tone."

Cluttering. The term cluttering refers to very rapid, indistinct speech, in which the person frequently repeats the same syllable several times before he can go on to the next one. The clutterer, unlike the stammerer, is not afraid to speak; he jumbles and repeats sounds through haste and excitement. The following rules may be of assistance to the clutterer:

1. If you are troubled with this difficulty, remember that the key to the situation is to speak *slowly*.

2. If you find yourself talking rapidly and repeating syllables, stop and begin over again, trying to speak slowly and smoothly.

3. Learn to breathe properly, to speak and read in thought groups, and to articulate distinctly.

4. Practice in reading aloud, conversation, and speaking to a group will also be helpful.

5. Always remember that you can speak well if you are careful to speak slowly and distinctly.

Stammering. Stammering, the apparent inability to pronounce a sound, because of laryngeal cramp, lip cramp, or some other source of tension, is a common speech problem.

The stammerer can pronounce all sounds under certain favorable conditions. These conditions vary with individual cases. Nearly all stammerers can sing without any difficulty, and most of them can whisper—probably because neither of these is actually talking. One boy, by his own account, can go for long periods of time without stammering when speaking to his friends, but he begins to stammer painfully when confronted with a question in the classroom. Another answers questions and carries on discussions in a classroom with a reasonable degree of ease, but stammers when talking to his family and friends.   Still another can talk with friends and take part in a play with no speech difficulty, but, to his great embarrassment, stammers when asked to read aloud from a printed page.   And so it goes; each stammerer is an individual problem.

The stammerer usually suffers from emotional strain. This may be the result of his reaction to a bad illness or fright. It may also be caused by a feeling of insecurity due to conditions at home or in school.   If the cause of the emotional strain can be discovered and removed, the stammerer may be cured without a single speech exercise.   Jim, for instance, had become emotionally upset because he could not compete successfully in any respect with his brother Frank, who was five years his senior.   It was pointed out to him that there was no good reason why he should attempt to compete with Frank, who had five years' advantage over him.   He was also made to realize that in studies and sports he did as well as, if not better than, boys his own age.   As a result, his ego was built up and his speech improved.   If, however, the cause of the emotional strain from which the stammerer suffers is irremediable, if there is serious and protracted illness at home, or if there is a clash of personalities in the family group, he will have to adjust himself to the situation and build up enough strength within himself to prevent an emotional reaction.   If the cause of the emotional strain cannot be discovered, the stammerer must attempt to change his pattern of living so that there is less opportunity for strain.   If he is bumptious, he must try to become more subdued; if, on the contrary, he is too retiring, he must learn to take his place in the group.

The teacher plays a very important part in helping the stammerer to adjust himself more happily.   The teacher must be sympathetic, as well as wise and firm.   In *The Spoken Word* for November, 1933, Dr. Letitia Raubicheck has listed the following ways in which the teacher may help the stammerer:

1. Give him a non-speaking job in the classroom. . . . Help him to do this job well and praise him when he does.

2. Allow the stammerer to sit as near you as he can without being conspicuous. Encourage him to reply briefly but regularly, especially in subjects in which he is proficient.

3. Measure his knowledge of the subject by his written work, but allow him to respond orally, by single-word answers, if necessary, so that he has a feeling of solidarity with the group.

4. Insist kindly, but firmly, that he meet all non-speaking assignments as well as his abilities will permit. The stammerer is apt to excuse himself from all obligations because of his disability. His written work should be as neat, as complete, and as promptly produced, as that of the rest of the class.

5. Enlist the coöperation of the class to help him by keeping quiet when he speaks, and by encouraging him by praise when he has succeeded in speaking well.

6. Win the confidence of the stammerer, and help him, as one friend helps another. to find happiness and security in his classroom circle.

In the same article, Dr. Raubicheck adds a list of "Dont's" for teachers:

1. Don't ignore the stammerer. Give him a chance to take part in all the class activities.

2. Don't create an atmosphere of tension by rapid fire staccato speech, loud and peremptory commands, military discipline.

3. If you must have rapid oral drills, exclude the stammerer, but do not make this exclusion obvious.

4. Don't pamper the stammerer, or in any way make him conscious of any difference between him and his classmates.

5. Don't punish the stammerer for speech faults. Encourage him.

6. Don't ridicule him, and don't let anyone else do it.[2]

The coöperation of the stammerer's family is another important factor. Relatives and friends who do not understand the situation are unfortunately apt to scold, ridicule, punish, or pamper the stammerer. Once they know how harmful such attitudes may be, they are, of course, very eager to do their part in making the stammerer's home life as serene, secure, normal, and healthful as possible.

---

[2] Raubicheck, Letitia, "The Stuttering Child," in *The Spoken Word* for November, 1933.

It is very important that the stammerer's health should be built up. He needs more rest than other people, and he should not take on so much work or so many activities that he cannot get plenty of rest. He should also take plenty of outdoor exercise. He should eat good, wholesome food, including fruits, green, leafy vegetables, and milk. It is an obvious fact that as a person's physical condition improves, he becomes less nervous.

The stammerer can do much for himself psychologically if he will think in a constructive manner—in what Mabel Farrington Gifford, in her book, *Correcting Nervous Speech Disorders*, calls "a constructive use of the imagination." If, instead of setting up a fear of certain speech sounds, the stammerer will set up an image of free-flowing speech; if instead of thinking of himself as tense and nervous, he will picture himself as calm and poised; if, instead of fearing to meet people, he can visualize himself as successful in a social situation, he will gradually become less nervous and tense, and his speech will improve correspondingly.

Tom, for instance, apparently could not start to speak outside the family group without going through all sorts of bodily contortions. He was an intelligent and imaginative lad, and his teacher helped him out of his tenseness and fear through the use of his imagination. With the help of his mother, who was most coöperative, the teacher planned situations which could actually occur, and inspired him to imagine himself meeting those situations successfully. One of these was to go to a store and ask for one or two articles—a difficult feat for a boy who feared to speak before strangers. After rehearsing the situation, always seeing himself speaking freely and confidently when giving the order, Tom was requested by his mother to go to the store to ask for these articles. He accomplished the errand with sufficient success to encourage him to go on with further experiments. These were made a trifle harder each time, and, after a long period of training, Tom was able to speak to strangers without fear. This desired result was not accomplished through the psychological approach alone, but it proved to be a valuable aid. Relaxation and speech exercises were carried out conscientiously. These speech exercises were not practiced merely as phonetic drills but were designed to improve the student's general speech pattern. When he realized that this had improved, he was better able to carry out the psychological experiment; that is, because he knew his speech was better, it was easier for him to think of himself as successful in a given speech situation; on the other hand, the beneficial effects of constructive suggestion, plus the speech exercises, helped to improve the speech pattern. The speech exercises and the psychological approach worked *together* toward the desired end. Hence both were important.

Miss Gifford says that many people have been helped out of their difficulties by applying the principle of the "constructive use of the imagination." She continues: "If we would dispel a fear of appearing before people, we must establish what we would like to feel and keep on repeating it, thus building up the expectancy of meeting our audience, whether that be one person or a large number, with confidence and poise. It is possible to change old associations with regard to situations by rehearsing new associations."[3]

Relaxation is an important factor in overcoming stammering. The student should do the relaxation exercises suggested on page 67 night and morning and, if possible, several other times during the day. Every clinic period should, of course, be started with relaxation exercises.

Speech exercises, reading, and conversation are valuable aids to the stammerer because they help him to improve his speech pattern and give him confidence. The contracts in Part IV which are designed for stammerers are intended to give the student courage in speaking. They accomplish this end by first proving to him that he can make all the sounds of the language, and then by indicating that if he can do it once, he can do it all the time. The carefully-graded exercises, ranging in difficulty from ability to say a word, to the ability to read a phrase, sentence, paragraph, or short story, and the suggestions about carrying out assignments which require greater and greater poise, prove to the stammerer that by going slowly and by acting calmly, he can meet any speech situation.

---

[3] Gifford, Mabel Farrington, *Correcting Nervous Speech Disorders*, New York, Prentice-Hall, Inc., 1939.

PART III

Exercises

Relaxation Exercises
Tongue Exercises
Lip and Jaw Exercises
Exercises for the Control of the Palate
Voice Exercises
Ear-Training Exercises
Exercises for the Correction of Careless Speech
Exercises for Vowels
Exercises for Diphthongs
Exercises for Consonants
Exercises for Sibilants
Exercises for the Correction of Cognate Substitutions
Further Exercises for Difficult Sounds
Exercises for Articulation
Exercises for Volume and Energy of Tone
Exercises for Round, Free Tone

EXERCISES

Relaxation Exercises

1. Lie down on the bed, flat on your back, and tell yourself that the bed is holding you. Let yourself go completely; relax your whole body even to the smallest finger and toe. Rest, *rest, REST!*

2. Lie on the floor with your knees flexed. Think of nothing. Again rest, *rest, REST!*

3. Stand or sit. Make believe your head is a cannon ball and rotate it in the following fashion: drop it forward on your chest, push it over the right shoulder, let it drop down in the back, and then let it come over the left shoulder by its own weight. Do this several times in each direction.

4. Let the jaw drop, and say *ah* as you do the preceding exercise.

5. Sit in a comfortable position. Think of the head as a hollow shell containing nothing—relax the muscles of the face—let go at the base of the brain and the back of the neck—let the shoulders sag—let go of the upper arms—the forearms—the hands—the fingers—relax all down the spine—at the waist-line—let the abdominal muscles sag—relax the hips—the thighs—the legs—the feet, even to the toes. Now feel that every part of your body from your head to your toes is resting against a strong support. In imagination, listen to quiet soothing music, or visualize a scene which has made you feel quiet and calm, or think of some lines of poetry which symbolize a relaxed state of being, as:

"Now fades the glimmering landscape on the sight
And all the air a solemn stillness holds."

Let these lines flow slowly through your inward ear. Remain in this relaxed state for a few minutes.

6. Stand upright. Energize the whole body; feel the energy from the toes to the top of the head. Raise the arms over the head, stretch the fingers, pull with the fingers. Then bend from the waist, letting yourself go completely limp, as if you were a rag doll. Return slowly to an upright position. Repeat several times.

7. Stand upright. Bend from the waist as before. Relax completely, and let the arms sway from side to side like an elephant's trunk. Walk forward, swaying from side to side until you tumble in a heap on the floor. Be sure that you are completely relaxed when you fall.

Tongue Exercises

Note: For all tongue exercises, be sure to open the mouth so that there is a distance of two fingers' space between the teeth.

1. At the count of 1, run the tongue out and point it. At the count of 2, draw it back in the mouth. Repeat several times.

2. At the count of 1, run the tongue down toward the chin and point it. At the count of 2, draw it back in the mouth. Repeat several times.

3. At the count of 1, run the tongue up toward the nose and point it. At the count of 2, draw it back in the mouth. Repeat several times.

4. At the count of 1, place the tongue at the right-hand corner of the mouth and point it. At the count of 2, draw it back in the mouth. Repeat several times.

5. At the count of 1, place the tongue at the left-hand corner of the mouth and point it. At the count of 2, draw it back in the mouth. Repeat several times.

6. Open the mouth. At the count of 1, curl the tongue back toward the soft palate. At the count of 2, drop it back to the floor of the mouth. Repeat several times.

7. At the count of 1, put the tip of the tongue on the back of the lower teeth, and bite down gently with the upper teeth. (This is known as bulging the tongue.) At the count of 2, let the tongue go back to its natural position. At the count of 1, put the tip of the tongue on the back of the upper teeth and press up with the lower teeth. Alternate these two exercises, slowly at first, and then rapidly.

8. At the count of 1, run the tongue out and groove it. At the count of 2, let it go back in the mouth. Now groove the tongue and blow through the groove as you draw the tongue gently back in the mouth. Repeat several times.

9. Place the tip of the tongue at the right-hand corner of the mouth, and rotate the tongue up across the upper lip, around and down across the lower lip, and back in the mouth. Start at the left-hand corner and rotate up, around, down, and back in the mouth. Start at either corner and rotate down, across the lower lip, around and up across the upper lip. Repeat these exercises several times, remembering to keep a sweeping motion of the tongue around the lips and to cover as wide a surface as possible.

10. Hold the mouth open as if you were going to say *ah*. At the count of 1, raise the tongue to the upper gum; at the count of 2, lower the tongue to the floor of the mouth. Do this an increasing number of times; keep the mouth open throughout the entire exercise. *Remember* that this is a *tongue* exercise; if the mouth is not sufficiently open, the tongue will not get enough exercise.

Lip and Jaw Exercises

1. At the count of 1, pout the lips. At the count of 2, relax them.

2. At the count of 1, spread the lips. At the count of 2, relax them.

3. At the count of 1, lift the right-hand side of the upper lip. At the count of 2, relax it.

4. At the count of 1, lift the left-hand side of the upper lip At the count of 2, relax it.

5. At the count of 1, thrust the under lip forward. At the count of 2, relax it.

6. Spread the lips and say *e* [i:]; round the lips and say *ōō* [u:]; repeat this at least twenty times, going slowly at first and gradually increasing the speed.

7. Spread the lips and say *ē* [i:]; open the mouth wide and say *ä* [ɑ:]; round the lips and say *ōō* [u:]. Repeat as above.

8. Say the diphthongs *ow* [aʊ] and *oi* [ɔɪ], exaggerating the positions of the lips and jaw. Repeat as above.

9. Say *ē* [i:], *ä* [ɑ:], *ōō* [u:], *ow* [aʊ], *oi* [ɔɪ]. Repeat as above.

10. Repeat the sound *p* [p] several times in rapid succession, as follows: *pppppp.*

11. Say *pip-pap; tip-tap; snip-snap.* Repeat ten times.

12. Repeat the sound *b* [b] several times in rapid succession: *bbbbbbbbbbbbbbbb.*

13. Say *tib-tab; dib-dab; sib-sab; bibble-bobble, bibble-bobble, bibble-bobble.* Repeat ten times.

14. Say *bā* [beʀɪ] *bē* [bi:] *bä* [bɑ:] *bō* [boʀʊ] *bōō* [bu:]. Repeat ten times.

15. Say *pā* [peʀɪ] *pē* [pi:] *pä* [pɑ:] *pō* [poʀʊ] *pōō* [pu:]. Repeat ten times.

Exercises for the Control of the Soft Palate

Note: See Contract 2 under "Nasality."

1. Yawn: open the mouth wide, and feel the back of the throat open as well.

2. Yawn: keep the mouth closed, attempt to suppress the yawn, then open the mouth wide and yawn deeply.

3. Pant like a dog; feel the air in the back of the throat.

4. Open the mouth wide and say *ä* [ɑ:]; feel the soft palate rise. Repeat ten times.

5. Lower the soft palate and say *m* [m]. Hold while you count ten mentally. Repeat ten times.

6. Say *m* [m] (with the soft palate down), then *ä* [ɑ:] (with the soft palate up). Repeat fifteen times.

Voice Exercises

> *Note:* Before engaging in voice exercises, do the relaxation exercises given above. Then yawn; if the throat becomes tense during the exercise period, stop and yawn. Yawning is an excellent relaxation exercise for the throat.

1. Inhale and exhale, prolonging the tone on the following sounds:

ō [oᴛʊ] as in *low*
ŏŏ [ʊ] as in *foot*
ōō [u:] as in *soon*
ô [ɔ:] as in *hall*
ä [ɑ:] as in *father*
ā [eᴛĭ] as in *day*
ă [æ] as in *cat*
ē [i:] as in *tea*
ĕ [eᴛ] as in *met*

ī [aĭ] as in *mine*
ĭ [ɪ] as in *fit*
û [ɜ:] as in *word*
(*er* as in *berth*,
ir as in *birth*,
ur as in *burn*)
ŭ [ʌ] as in *come*
ow [aʊ] as in *how*
oi [ɔĭ] as in *noise*

2. Inhale and explode the tone suddenly on the above sounds.

3. Inhale; exhale, holding the sound for a short time and exploding it quickly at the end. In other words, stress the end of the tone.

4. Strive to increase your breath span by doing the following exercises:

Inhale—exhale saying *1*.
Inhale—exhale saying *1-2*.
Inhale—exhale saying *1-2-3*.

Continue in this manner until you can count to *ten* on one breath.

Proceed in the same manner with the following:

ah [ɑ:]
ah-ā [ɑ: eᴛĭ]
ah-ā-ē [ɑ: eᴛĭ i:]
ah-ā-ē-aw [ɑ: eᴛĭ i: ɔ:]
ah-ā-ē-aw-ō- [ɑ: eᴛĭ i: ɔ: oᴛʊ]
ah-ā-ē-aw-ō-ōō [ɑ: eᴛĭ i: ɔ: oᴛʊ u:]

Proceed in the same manner with the following:

ō [oтŭ]
ō—ah [oтŭ ɑ:]
ō—ah—aw [oтŭ ɑ: ɔ:]
ō—ah—aw—ow [oтŭ ɑ: ɔ: aŭ]
o—ah—aw—ow—oi [oтŭ ɑ: ɔ: aŭ ɔɪ]
ō—ah—aw—ow—oi—oō [oтŭ ɑ:·ɔ: aŭ ɔɪ u:]

5. Read the following lines, taking great care that you have enough breath for each phrase—especially for the end of the phrase.

An Austrian army, awfully arrayed,
Boldly, by battery, besieged Belgrade.
Cossack commanders cannonading come,
Dealing destruction's devastating doom.
Every endeavor engineers essay,
For fame, for fortune, fighting furious fray.
Generals 'gainst generals grapple, grasping good,
How honors heaven heroic hardihood!
Infuriate, indiscriminate, in ill,
Kindred kill kinsmen, kinsmen kindred kill.
Labor low levels loftiest, longest lines;
Men march mid mounds, mid moles, mid murderous mines.
Now noisy, noxious, noticed nought,
Of outward obstacles opposing aught,
Poor patriots, partly purchased, partly "pressed,"
Quite quaking, quickly quarter, quarter quest.
Reason returns, religious right redounds,
Suwarrow stops such sanguinary sounds.
Truce to thee, Turkey, triumph to thy train!
Unjust, unwise, unmerciful Ukraine!
Vanish vain victory, vanish victory vain!
Why wish we warfare?   Wherefore welcome were
Xerxes, Ximines, Xanthus, Xaviere?
Yield, ye youths! Ye yoemen yield your yell!
Zeno's, Zapater's, Zoroaster's zeal,
And all attracting arms against acts appeal.

Ear-Training Exercises

1. Make a list of five words for each of the following sounds: (a) ă [æ] as in *man;* (b) ē [i:] as in *seem.*[1]

2. From the words given below, make two lists of two columns each, as follows:

---

[1] This exercise may be extended to deal with all vowels and diphthongs.

(a) In the first column put the words that begin with a voiced sound, and in the second put those that begin with a voiceless sound.

(b) In the first column put the words that end with a voiced sound, and in the second put those that end with a voiceless sound.

love	dot	this	chum	because
think	bat	water	seize	cease
dogs	rough	jerk	thumb	twice
cats	which	tab	lamb	hat

3. Read the following columns of words horizontally; tell which word or words have the same vowel sound or diphthong as the first word:

ice	niece	lit	tight	is	aye (*yes*)
cap	aunt	father	ran	last	all
lay	eight	rat	class	sample	take
book	moon	put	spoon	spot	choose
there	here	sere	fair	cheer	rear
mean	bet	smear	fare	machine	clique
poor	floor	hour	sower	sure	door
heard	fear	beard	berth	tear	curl

4. What *sound* (not what letter) do the names on each of the following horizontal lines have in common?

Coleridge	Pope	Goldsmith	Rossetti	Holmes
Whittier	Shelley	Milton	Robinson	Dickens
Wordsworth	Churchill	Burns	Erskine	Herbert
Blake	Hale	Payne	Gay	Shakespeare
Bryant	Wilde	Dryden	Byron	Prior

5. What is the most predominant sound in each of the following lines?

"Alone, alone, all, all, alone."
"After life's fitful fever, he sleeps well."
"An Austrian army awfully arrayed."
"And the rain, it raineth every day."

6. What are the *two* predominant sounds in each of the following lines?

"Yield, ye youths, ye yoemen, yield your yell."
"Peter, Peter, pumpkin-eater."
"Kindred kill kinsmen."
"Said Simple Simon to the pieman."
"The furrow followed free."

7. Name the vowel sound in each of the following words:

mean	foot	tongue	cough	bath
earth	strength	mute	through	grass
moon	tent	rough	plot	laugh

8. List the following words in two columns; in the first column put the words that contain a vowel sound, and in the second put those that contain a diphthong:

light	may	length	loaf	grasp	tough
all	bite	came	sick	plow	sought

9. Which word or words on the following horizontal lines rhyme with the first word?

might	pine	freight	kite	file	kind
plea	meek	dream	sleep	flee	drain
sieve	leave	retrieve	give	lift	receive
comb	tomb	foam	bomb	come	home
rough	bough	stuff	cough	cuff	rush
mope	moan	smoke	rope	mole	mode

Exercises for the Correction of Careless Speech

1. "Sometimes his tinkling waters slipt
Down through a frost-leaved forest crypt."

2. "All night by the white stars' frosty gleams,
He groined his arches and matched his beams."

3. "Polly, put the kettle on, we'll all take tea."

4. "Slender and clear were his crystal spars,
As the lashes of light that trim the stars."

5. "The forest cracked, the waters curled,
The cattle huddled on the lea."

6. "In Xanadu did Kubla Khan
A stately pleasure dome decree."

7. "With mirth and laughter let old wrinkles come."

8. "What thou see'st when thou dost wake,
Do it for thy true love's sake."

9. "Once more unto the breach, dear friends, once more,
Or close the wall up with our English dead."

10. "Hold hard the breath, and bend up every spirit
To his full height."

11. "Double, double, toil and trouble,
Fire burn and caldron bubble."

12. "Here are sweet peas on tiptoe for a flight."

13. "This fellow pecks up wit, as pigeons peas,
And utters it again when God doth please."

14. "My good blade carves the casques of men,
My tough lance thrusteth sure."

15. "My strength is as the strength of ten."

16. "Are these the breed of wits so wondered at?"

17. "Necessity will make us all forsworn,
Three thousand times within this three years' space."

18. "She heard the singing, she heard the clatter,
But, oh, the feast was no such matter."

19. "Splashing and paddling with hoofs of a goat,
And breaking the golden lilies afloat
With the dragon fly on the river."

20. "But the tender grace of a day that is dead
Will never come back to me."

21. "Swiftly, swiftly flew the ship,
Yet she sailed softly too,
Sweetly, sweetly blew the breeze,
On me alone it blew."

22. "That orbed maiden with white fire laden,
Whom mortals call the moon,
Glides glimmering o'er my fleece-like floor
By midnight breezes strewn."

23. "I remember the black wharves and the ships
And the sea-tides tossing free."

24. "My spirit beats her mortal bars,
As down dark tides the glory slides
And, starlike, mingles with the stars."

25. "The thick, black cloud was cleft."

26. "Last night she slept not, nor tonight she shall not."

27. "Blow! Swiftly, blow, thou keel-compelling gale!"

28. "How far that little candle throws its beams,
So shines a good deed in a naughty world."

29. "Strike—till the last armed foe expires!"

30. "Your betters have endured me say my mind,
And if you cannot, best you stop your ears."

Exercises for Vowels

$\bar{e}$ [i:] as in *seem*

eagle	even	geese	pea	believe	naïve
equal	ease	heed	queen	careen	physique
eel	bee	keep	read	convene	receive
each	cede	lean	senior	discreet	serene
east	deem	meat	team	gaberdine	tureen
eat	feed	neat	zebra	machine	vaccine

Note: See $\bar{e}$ [i:], page 21.

1. Jean is sewing seams on the electric machine.

2. There were three seniors on the team.

3. Please keep the house clean and neat.

4. Please shell the peas, feed the geese, and keep away from the bee-hive.

5. The teacher permitted the senior to read the latest book about Mary Queen of Scots.

6. The teams of horses were eating their dinner in the east pasture.

7. I believe that there is a bean soup in the tureen.

8. "All that we see or seem
Is but a dream within a dream."

9. "For the moon never beams without bringing me dreams
Of the beautiful Annabel Lee."

10. "Take heed lest by your heat you burn yourselves."

11. "Chill as a down-east breeze should be."

12. "Where I will heal me of my grievous wound."

13. "In one scene no more than three should speak."

14. "The sword within the scabbard keep,
And let mankind agree."

15. "Little lamb, who made thee?
Dost thou know who made thee?
Gave thee life and bid thee feed
By the stream and o'er the mead?"

$\breve{i}$ [ɪ] as in *it*

if	bit	jib	rinse	belief	equality
ill	cinder	kindle	sill	defect	liberty
immune	finish	lilt	tint	receive	yesterday
innate	guilt	niche	will	rehearse	Tuesday
issue	hill	pitch	zinc	serene	Saturday

Note: The first syllable of the words *belief, defect, deprive, receive, rehearse, serene,* and the last syllable of all the words in the last column contain the sound ĭ [ɪ]. See footnote 1, page 21.

1. *The Master Builder* is a play by Henrik Ibsen.

2. Kitty finished knitting a pair of mittens yesterday before she went to the city.

3. I should like to see you on Saturday, if you are going to be at liberty.

4. The pretty little village is situated near the river.

5. Will you please stop at the sixth floor?

6. The French Revolution had for its slogan, "Liberty, Equality, Fraternity."

7. The linnet was singing in the cherry tree.

8. The Christmas tree was trimmed with gifts and tinsel.

9. Will you please rinse the handkerchiefs and put them in the sun to dry?

10. The nurse will put zinc ointment on the sore finger.

11. Jim's brother and sister visited him Sunday.

12. They are going to rebuild the cottage on the side of the hill.

13. The beautiful city of Washington is situated in the District of Columbia.

14. The little boy was deprived of his dinner Thursday, as a punishment for running away.

15. The ichthyosaurus was a prehistoric reptile that had some of the characteristics of the fish.

ĕ [eτ] as in *let*

ebb	ensign	bed	met	beset	pretend
edit	enter	den	nest	confess	protest
efficacy	epic	fed	pen	contend	respect
egg	equity	get	sent	defend	September
edge	escalator	hen	tend	descend	suspend
elbow	etch	jet	west	invest	tremendous
elevate	excavate	lend	yet	November	unbend

Note: See ĕ [eτ], page 22.

1. The west was red from the sunset glow.

2. The maid hung the etching over the bed in the guest room.

3. It is less pleasant to ride on an escalator than on an elevator.

4. Jenny fed the hens and then went in to get supper.

5. Ted set up the bed in the tent.

6. If you will lend me ten dollars until tomorrow, I will send you a check.

7. Ezra found ten eggs in the hen's stolen nest.

8. The test was given on the eleventh of September.

9. The ensign entered the room with a pen in his hand.

10. The eccentric men pretended that they were going to descend into the excavation.

11. The poet read an epic poem by request.

12. This is a memento of a trip to the west.

13. The red dress was trimmed with jet.

14. The doctor contended that the medicine was not fresh.

15. Helen and Betty were learning French by the phonetic method.

ă [æ] as in *at*

abolition	apt	ban	mantle	collaborate
action	aristocrat	candy	natural	detached
add	arrogant	dad	pansy	evaluate
affable	aster	fancy	rattle	examine
aggravate	atom	gallery	sand	intangible
alimony	average	hand	tack	preamble
amicable	axiom	jamb	van	procrastinate
antic	azure	land	yam	unravel

Note: See ă [æ], page 22.

1. Indianapolis is the capital of Indiana.

2. The tacks rattled around in the tin can.

3. The actions of affable people can sometimes be aggravating and antagonizing.

4. The average person is apt to become weary after a morning in an art gallery.

5. The man made an impassioned plea for a "back to the land" movement.

6. Sally was reprimanded for unravelling the sweater.

7. The traveler landed at San Francisco Saturday.

8. There were asters and pansies on the mantle in the parlor.

9. The man was ill after a luncheon of sandwiches, bananas, and canned yams.

10. The average man is apt to procrastinate.

11. The examination was scheduled for Saturday the twentieth of January.

12. Frances bought tan candles for the mantle in the living room.

13. The actor ran frantically toward the gallery.

14. The family carried a great deal of baggage when travelling.

15. The man ran madly in order to catch the early train.

16. "By any reasonable plan,
I'll make you happy if I can."

17. "He hath brought many captives home to Rome,
Whose ransoms did the general coffers fill:
Did this in Caesar seem ambitious?"

18. 　　　　　　　"O! how wretched
Is that poor man that hangs on princes' favors!"

19. "Why should a man, whose blood is warm within,
Sit like his grandsire cut in alabaster?"

20. "Slave, I have set my life upon a cast,
And I will stand the hazard of the die."

ȧ [ɑ] as in *ask*

after	fast	mask
answer	glance	mast
can't	glass	past
class	grass	rasping
clasp	lance	rascal
dance	last	trance

Note: See footnote 2, page 23; also see note under ä [ɑ:], page 28.

ä [ɑ:] as in *father*

are	bark	farm	park
arduous	carp	garden	part
ark	charm	heart	psalm
alms	chart	jar	tar
arm	darn	lard	varnish
art	dart	market	yard

1. The beggar asked my father for alms.

2. He asked me if I intended to go to art class.

3. The grass in the yard is fast becoming green.

4. The rasping voice of the commander made a jarring note in the class.

5. The barking dogs darted around the farm.

6. The country was up in arms about the farm bill.

7. Rather more than half the road was coated with tar.

8. I can't answer your question until after class.

9. The boat with the tall mast was going fast when it passed the launch.

10. The arduous task is finished at last.

11. A farm cart cannot go as fast or as far in a day as a motor car.

12. She glanced at her reflection as they danced past the looking-glass.

13. Father said his arms were tired from varnishing the floor of the farm house.

14. You cannot see half the charm of "Far Acres" from a motor car.

15. "My good blade carves the casques of men,
My tough lance thrusteth sure."

16. "O you hard hearts, you cruel men of Rome!"

17. "In arguing too, the parson owned his skill,
For e'en though vanquished, he could argue still."

18. "Poets that lasting marble seek,
Must come in Latin or in Greek."

19. "Hark, hark! The lark at heaven's gate sings."

20. "Art is long and Time is fleeting,
And our hearts, though stout and brave,
Still, like muffled drums, are beating
Funeral marches to the grave."

û [ɜ:] as in *berth* (*ir* as in *birth, or* as in *word, ur* as in *fur*)

Note: See *û* [ɜ:], page 23.

err	burn	learn	adjourn	invert	perfume
irk	dearth	nerve	assert	rehearse	pergola
earl	girl	spurn	concern	return	pertinence
earn	hurt	virtue	converse	revert	sermon
earth	journey	word	disperse	unfurl	servile

1. The earl returned from the journey because of a nervous breakdown.

2. Thirteen girls were hurt when the theater burned to the ground.

3. Irving earned his living by doing irksome tasks.

4. Earl's birthday is the thirteenth of December.

5. There was a great deal of murmuring during the rehearsal.

6. The chairman asserted that the meeting would adjourn to the adjoining room.

7. The scent of perfume permeated the pergola.

8. The girl was badly hurt when the oil burner exploded.

9. If we would control others, we must first learn to control ourselves.

10. Promptness is often said to be a servile virtue.

11. The murderer returned to the scene of the crime.

12. The earl visited the oil wells early in the morning.

13. "Early to bed and early to rise
Makes man healthy, wealthy and wise."

14. "We were the first
That ever burst
Into that silent sea."

15. "A verse may find him who a sermon flies,
And turn delight into a sacrifice."

16. "Here naught but winds can hurtful murmurs scatter."

17. "Purple the sails, and so perfumed
That the winds were lovesick with them."

18. "Errors, like straws, upon the surface flow;
He who would search for pearls must dive below."

19. "Purple-curtained, fringed with gold."

20. "About each rustic porch the humming bird
Tried with light bill, that scarce a petal stirred,
The Old World flowers to virgin soil transferred."

ŭ [ʌ] as in *up*

ugly	but	glum	none	bundle	become
unction	cut	gull	pun	gutter	befuddle
up	done	hunt	sun	humble	defunct
us	drum	jut	ton	muddle	refund
utter	fun	much	won	putter	unsullied

Note: See ŭ [ʌ], page 24.

1. Mary's chum was coming up to the house to help her get supper.

2. The boy was stung on the thumb by a bumblebee.

3. On Thanksgiving day we ate turkey, onions, plum pudding, and pumpkin pie.

4. Running and jumping are too strenuous for some people.

5. Autumn comes between summer and winter.

6. The sea gulls were hunting for fish along the shore.

7. The store refunded the money for the damaged gloves.

8. The mother cuddled the little one as she bundled her up in warm clothes.

9. The ugly duckling may become a lovely swan.

10. How much money did you make on the luncheon?

11. The children had great fun drumming on their new drums.

12. He had cut the string, and the parcel had become undone.

13. Mother was puttering about the garden in the hot sun.

14. "We are such stuff as dreams are made of."

15. "Peace brooded over all.   No trumpet stung
The air to madness, and no steeple flung
Alarums down from bells at midnight rung."

$\overline{oo}$ [u:] as in *soon*[2]

boon	June	soon	broom
coop	loot	too	crucial
doom	moon	tool	droop
fool	noon	voodoo	glue
goose	pool	woo	stoop
hoop	rune	zoo	truce

Note: See $\overline{oo}$ [u:], page 25.

u [ʊ] as in *put* ($\breve{oo}$ as in *foot*)[2]

bull	nook	forsook
could	puss	fulsome
full	rook	hoodwink
good	soot	outlook
hood	took	unhook
look	wood	undertook

Note: See $\breve{oo}$ [ʊ], page 26.

---

[2] If you are in doubt about the pronunciation of any of these words, consult a dictionary.

1. The moon shone over the roof of the next house and into the bedroom.

2. The outlook from this window is better by moonlight than at high noon.

3. Jim foolishly took the wood in too soon.

4. Look at that bull chasing the goose.

5. Will you please glue the handle on the broom so that I may have it to sweep the soot out of the room?

6. There were antique silver spoons in the crook's loot.

7. They made a truce at the crucial moment.

8. The rose bushes drooped before the gardener pruned them.

9. The children enjoyed rolling hoop after being cooped up all day.

10. The fool undertook to hoodwink the troubadour.

11. The water in the pool was too cool today.

12. Did you lose your good silver soup spoons?

13. Who is using the tools in the workroom?

14. "Health that mocks the doctor's rules,
Knowledge never learned of schools."

15. "And sometimes through the mirror blue
The knights came riding two and two."

$\bar{u}$ [ju:] as in *music*

cute	nude	abuse	induce	beautiful	supreme
duke	puny	assume	institute	culinary	tuberculosis
feud	suit	attitude	latitude	dutiful	Tuesday
huge	student	confuse	renew	newspaper	tulip
mute	tutor	deduce	resume	studious	tumult

Note: See footnote 4, page 25.

1. Does the tutor ride in the tube or the subway?

2. Tuesday's paper announced the suicide of the Duke of Ammond.

3. Tulips and daffodils are beautiful spring flowers.

4. In the midst of the tumult incident to the feud, Susan assumed she was on neutral ground.

5. It was impossible to induce Uriah Heep to assume a less humble attitude.

6. The student abused his health and contracted tuberculosis.

7. The pupil's attitude did not suit the studious tutor.

8. Beulah refused to attend the institute because the tuition was too high.

9. It is easy to confuse the tunes of these two songs.

10. Susan bought a new suit when she was in New York Tuesday.

11. Some students consider it a nuisance to have to study latitude and longitude.

12. The duke went to New Hampshire to renew old acquaintances.

13. The musicians assumed that the audience knew the tune.

14. "What's the new news at the new court?"

15. "If music be the food of love, play on."

ô [ɔ:] as in *awe*

all	horn	raw	already	haughty	brawl
ball	law	sought	balsam	laundry	broad
call	morn	tall	dawdle	mausoleum	crawl
fought	naught	vaunt	fawning	saunter	fraud
Gaul	pawn	wall	gaudy	water	wrought

Note: See ô [ɔ:], page 27.

1. The boys were already calling their base ball teams together.

2. The police were able to maintain law and order.

3. The crowds were mourning, the morning after the battle was fought.

4. The tall man vaulted over the garden wall.

5. The hall was trimmed with cedar and balsam.

6. The children shouted and the horns blew raucously.

7. The jaunty Thane of Cawdor vaunted himself and sought to be king.

8. The naughty children were too talkative in school.

9. That laundryman was a fraud and has gone away.

10. The town was surrounded by balsam trees and water.

11. The haughty matron sauntered along in a gaudy dress.

12. The lawyer paused to look at the drawing in the window.

13. Relax the lower jaw and yawn.

14. The battle was fought at dawn.

15. Laura asked Paul to go to the well and draw a bucket of water.

16. The architect was drawing a plan of the tall building.

17. The law of supply and demand is all-important in business dealings.

18. "Nor fame I slight, nor for her favors call,
She comes unlooked for, if she comes at all."

19. "We do not what we ought;
What we ought not, we do;
And lean upon the thought
That Chance will bring us through."

20. "Heap high the farmer's wintry hoard!
Heap high the golden corn!
No richer gift has Autumn poured
From out her lavish horn."

ŏ [ɒ] as in *coffee*

bomb	jot	rot	bottle	jolly	quarrel
cot	lot	sod	coddle	lottery	rotten
dot	mop	tot	domino	model	sorry
fob	nod	trod	fondle	noddle	trotting
God	pod	wad	goblet	office	volley
hot	quod	what	hot	otter	waddle

Note: See ŏ [ɒ], page 27.

1. I want hot chocolate and not hot coffee.

2. He nodded to the stenographer to jot down the main points of the contract.

3. The jolly fairy waved her wand and stopped the clock.

4. The bottle and goblet came from Holland.

5. John won a watch fob in the lottery.

6. The ducks waddled along beside the trotting donkey.

7. The old man plodded sorrowfully through the clods of earth in the hot sun.

8. Doctors prescribe cod liver oil to prevent colds.

9. There were a lot of mops and brushes for sale in the window.

10. She wore a white dotted swiss dress and red socks and shoes.

11. What are you doing to the sod in this plot?

12. The fop wore a domino to the masquerade.

13. Tom's mother served "hot dogs" and coffee at the Halloween party.

14. What time do you expect to go to the office tomorrow?

15. John told Robert that he was sorry about the broken ship-model.

16. "And the rockets' red glare,
The bombs bursting in air."

17. "Others shall sing the song;
Others shall right the wrong."

18. "A foolish consistency is the hobgoblin of little minds, adored by little statesmen and philosophers and divines."

19. "'Tis sweet to hear the watch-dog's honest bark."

20. "Once upon a midnight dreary, while I pondered weak and
weary,
Over many a quaint and curious volume of forgotten lore,
While I nodded, nearly napping, suddenly there came a
tapping,
As of someone gently rapping, rapping at my chamber door."

Exercises for Diphthongs

ī [aɪ] as in *ice*

ice	bicycle	jibe	rind	divide	recite
idea	dine	kind	sign	divine	repine
isle	fight	line	time	imbibe	resign
I'm	finally	mine	vine	incline	unguided
ire	guile	nine	white	precise	unkind
I've	height	pint	wind	preside	untried

Note: See ī [aɪ], page 29.

1. Nine members of the hiking club climbed the high mountain Friday.

2. We dined at the "Sign of the Pine Tree" in fine style.

3. It is unwise to be behind the times.

4. We will have pineapple pie and ice cream for dessert.

5. The life-guard threw a life-line to the tired swimmer.

6. "The amber midnight smiles in dreams of dawn."

7. "Lives of great men all remind us
We can make our lives sublime,
And departing, leave behind us
Footprints on the sands of time."

8. "On either side the river lie
Long fields of barley and of rye."

9. "Be not the first by whom the new is tried,
Nor yet the last to lay the old aside."

10. "O Tiber! Father Tiber!
To whom the Romans pray,
A Roman's life, a Roman's arms
Take thou in charge this day."

11. "Life is not so short but that there is always time enough for courtesy."

12. "The summer skies are darkly blue,
The days are still and bright,
And evening trails her robes of gold
Through the dim halls of night."

13. "Here's a sigh to those who love me,
And a smile to those who hate;
And, whatever sky's above me,
Here's a heart for any fate."

14. "He who fights and runs away,
May live to fight another day;
But he who is in battle slain,
Can never rise and fight again."

15. "I know a bank where the wild thyme blows,
Where ox-lips and the nodding violet grows."

16. "Some praise at morning what they blame at night,
But always think the last opinion right."

17. "Autumn's sighing,
Moaning, dying;
Clouds are flying
On like steeds."

18. "Love never fails to master what he finds,
But works a different way in different minds,
The fool enlightens, and the wise, he blinds."

19. "She walks in beauty, like the night
Of cloudless climes and starry skies;
And all that's best of dark and light
Meet in her aspect and her eyes."

20. "Lying, robed in snowy white
That loosely flew to left and right—
The leaves upon her falling light—
Thro' the noises of the night
She floated down to Camelot."

ā [eɪ̆] as in *say*

aid	bay	jade	rate	blame	grape
ale	cane	kale	sane	brain	plate
aim	dale	lane	tame	drain	pray
ape	fade	mate	vain	drape	sleigh
ace	gain	name	wait	frame	trail
eight	hale	pain	Yale	grain	train

Note: See ā [eɪ̆], page 28.

1. The policeman came to the aid of the eight skaters who had fallen in the lake.

2. They waited in vain for the late train.

3. The man was hale and hearty on his eightieth birthday.

4. There was a bunch of beautiful Tokay grapes on the plate in the middle of the table.

5. The old man left his cane on the eight o'clock train.

6. They draped the picture frames with holly and bayberry for Christmas.

7. The Dartmouth team was in training for the game with Yale.

8. Did you play the ace of spades?

9. The ripe grain lay rotting in the rain.

10. The extra-fare train was late, so we got a rebate on our tickets.

11. Did you gain anything by placing your name on the waiting list?

12. "Fame is the fragrance of heroic deeds."

13. "All day the darkness and the cold
Upon my heart have lain,
Like shadows on a wintry sky,
Like frost upon the pane."

14. "Now fades the glimmering landscape on the sight."

15. "Here's to the brave upon the wave,
The gallant English tar."

oi [ɔɪ̆] as in *boy*

oil	moist	doily	adjoin	disloyal	purloin
boil	noise	loiter	anoint	embroider	rejoice
coin	poise	noisy	appoint	embroil	unalloyed
foil	soil	pointer	avoid	enjoin	uncoil
join	toil	royal	destroy	enjoy	unspoiled

Note: See *oi* [ɔɪ̆], page 29.

1. The noisy boys were in the adjoining room.
2. The beggar loitered on the corner asking for coins.
3. The girl toiled at embroidering a doily.
4. They played the game according to Hoyle.
5. The royal prince was unspoiled by the adulation of the crowd.
6. The soil was moist after the rain.
7. The boys rejoiced over the purloined apples.
8. The meeting adjourned to the adjoining room.
9. Many people joined the group in the cloister.
10. Mary spoiled the fish by boiling it instead of broiling it.
11. The employer rejoiced because his men were loyal.
12. The boy's lack of poise spoiled the effect of his speech.
13. The boy was allowed to take his choice of all the coins in the purse.
14. His head was anointed with oil.
15. Mary avoided her disloyal friends.

ō [oᴛŭ] as in *go*

ode	bone	moan	bovine	arose	barrow
oaf	code	knoll	coaster	behold	borrow
oak	dole	pole	doleful	control	elbow
old	fold	roast	postman	devote	fellow
omen	goal	soul	Roman	propose	piano
own	hold	vote	sober	remote	pillow
oat	jolt	yoke	toasted	suppose	studio
ozone	load	zone	yodel	unfold	window

Note: See ō [oᴛŭ], page 30.

1. The lone wolf came loping along the lonely road.
2. The crowd paused to salute the grave of the Unknown Soldier.
3. "He sold his horses, sold his hawks and hounds."
4. "Roll on, thou deep and dark blue ocean, roll."
5. "The lowing herd winds slowly o'er the lea."
6. "O you hard hearts, you cruel men of Rome!"
7. "His broad clear brow in sunlight glowed;
   On burnished hooves his war-horse trode;
   From underneath his helmet flowed
   His coal-black curls as on he rode,
   As he rode down to Camelot."

8. "'How they'll greet us!'—and all in a moment his roan
   Rolled neck and croup over, lay dead as a stone."

9. "With bolted doors and window-shutters closed,
   The habitants of Atri slept or dozed."

10. "The sun, above the mountain's head,
    A freshening lustre mellow
    Through all the long green fields has spread,
    His first sweet evening yellow."

11. "Perhaps the plaintive numbers flow
    For old, unhappy, far-off things,
    And battles long ago."

12. "For what are men better than sheep or goats
    That nourish a blind life within the brain,
    If, knowing God, they lift not hands of prayer
    Both for themselves and those that call them friend?"

13. "Yet a few days, and thee
    The all-beholding sun shall see no more
    In all his course; nor yet in the cold ground,
    Where thy pale form was laid, with many tears,
    Nor in the embrace of ocean, shall exist
    Thy image."

14. "Mother of ships whose might
    England, my England,
    In the fierce old Sea's delight
    England, my own,

    .   .   .

    There's menace of the Word
    In the song of your bugles blown, England—
    Out of heaven on your bugles blown!"

ow [aʊ] as in *how*

our	pout	brow	grouch	allow	chowder
cowl	round	brown	ground	confound	doubtful
down	sound	crowd	proud	pronounce	mountain
fowl	town	crown	prowl	renown	powder
mouse	vow	drought	trout	resound	rowdy
now	wound	drown	trounce	surround	vowel

Note: See *ow* [aʊ], page 30.

1. I found a beautiful gown at Townsend's dress shop.

2. The counsel he gave was wise and sound.

3. The country mouse followed the town mouse into the pantry.

4. The sound of loud voices is unpleasant indoors or out.

5. The profound man was confounded by the amount of information his opponent had about the subject.

6. Can you pronounce all the vowel sounds correctly?

7. It is doubtful whether our party will attempt to climb the mountain tomorrow.

8. The grounds about the house were covered with a light powder of snow.

9. Now the Crown Prince has become a person of high renown.

10. Please go down town and buy a pound of tea.

11. The teacher frowned at the howling sounds the rowdies were making outside the classroom windows.

12. Someone was prowling around the house soundlessly.

13. The town was crowded because of the antics of the clown.

14. He scowled and acted as if he were proud to be so grouchy.

15. "Down she came and found a boat
Beneath the willow left afloat.
And round about the prow she wrote,
The Lady of Shalott."

16. "No other voice nor sound was there,
No drum, no sentry's pace;
The mist-like banners clasped the air,
As clouds with clouds embrace."

17.   "I stood on the bridge at midnight
As the clocks were striking the hour,
   And the moon rose over the city
Behind the dark church tower."

18. "He who ascends to mountain tops shall find
The loftiest peaks most wrapped in clouds and snow."

19. "The mariners shout,
The ships swing about,
The yards are all hoisted,
The sails flutter out."

20. "Often I think of that beautiful town
That is seated by the sea;
The pleasant streets of that dear old town,
And my youth comes back to me."

ŏŏr [ʊɚ] as in *poor*   â [ɛɚ] as in *there*   ōr [ɔɚ] as in *floor*

boor	bare	pair	door
jury	care	rare	floor
moor	dare	share	four
poor	fare	tear	pour
sure	hair	various	roar
tour	lair	wear	shore

ę [ɪɚ] as in *here*

bier	gear	peer
cheer	hear	rear
clear	jeer	sere
dear	leer	tear
drear	mere	year
fear	near	we're

Note: See â [ɛɚ], page 31; ę [ɪɚ], page 30; ōr [ɔɚ], page 31; ŏŏr [ʊɚ], page 31.

1. Mary cheered the shivering child with a new coat and a pair of mittens.

2. Poor Sarah wears out four pairs of shoes a year.

3. I hope to hear a concert in the near future.

4. They are tearing out the rear of the store.

5. I am sure Mary is nearly ready to go.

6. She poured soapy water on her hair, which she washed carefully.

7. I fear poor Aunt Clara will be unable to hear the roaring of the waves on the shore.

8. The hunters cheered the hounds as they dared to follow the fox to its lair.

9. The wayfarers shared the pure water from a spring near by.

10. Autumn is a dreary time of year.

11. "The skies they were ashen and sober;
The leaves they were crisped and sere—
The leaves they were withering and sere;
It was night in the lonesome October
Of my most immemorial year."

12. "And moving through a mirror clear
That hangs before her all the year,
Shadows of the world appear."

13. "Great plenty, much formality, small cheer,
And everybody out of their own sphere."

14. "The ice was here
The ice was there
The ice was all around."

15. "What is so rare as a day in June?"

16. "Then he said, 'Good night!' and with muffled oar
Silently rowed to the Charlestown shore."

17. "I shot an arrow into the air,
It fell to earth, I knew not where."

18. "And stairways worn, and crazy doors,
And creaking and uneven floors."

19. "And all the old gods, the austere
Oppressors in their strength,
Stand aghast and white with fear
At the ominous sounds they hear."

20. "So through the night rode Paul Revere;
And so through the night went his cry of alarm
To every Middlesex village and farm,—
A cry of defiance and not of fear,
A voice in the darkness, a knock at the door,
And a word that shall echo forevermore!"

Exercises for Consonants
b [b] as in *bib; p* [p] as in *pipe*

bee	pea	boat	poke	babble	rapping
bib	pip	ball	Paul	bauble	pauper
bed	pet	bond	pond	bubble	supple
ban	pan	bar	par	cable	capable
burr	purr	by	pie	noble	toper
bun	pun	bay	pay	ribald	ripple
boon	pool	bound	pound	sobbing	sopping
bull	pull	boy	point	turbulent	turpentine

1. The Pied Piper played his pipe and compelled the children to leave their play.

2. Some people prefer pumpkin pie, while others prefer plum pudding.

3. The apparently peaceful dog bit the baker's boy badly.

4. It is hard to believe that prices can be so reasonable.

5. Peter planted peas and beans and barley in the spring.

6. The children were blowing soap bubbles in the billiard room.

7. Ping-pong is often played on board ship.

8. It is a bad habit to gobble your breakfast.

9. The children happened to be taking a nap when the bell in the neighboring steeple was rung.

10. Patricia drew a map of Spain on the windowpane.

11. The boy grappled with the robber bare-handed and thrashed him with a horsewhip.

12. The boys pitched pebbles in the brook and made ripples in the water.

13. Man was not supposed to be a beast of burden.

14. "Bent like a laboring oar . . . bent but not broken."

15. "Yellow and black and pale and hectic red,
Pestilence-stricken multitudes."

16. "His prayer he saith, this patient holy man,
Then takes his lamp and rises from his knees."

17. "'Pipe a song about a lamb,'
So I piped with merry cheer.
'Piper, pipe that song again,'
So I piped; he wept to hear."

18. "With beaded bubbles winking at the brim."

19. "O for boyhood's painless play."

20. "Blessings on thee, little man,
Barefoot boy with cheek of tan."

m [m] as in *mum*

me	molest	beam	beaming	stammer
men	morn	film	coming	taming
mat	mob	elm	dimmer	grumble
mask	mar	germ	humming	humble
murmur	mere	hum	mummer	rumble
muff	moor	doom	numbing	symbol
moon	mound	home	roomy	thimble

1. The man's face wore an impenetrable mask.

2. The mummers came to Mary's home on Christmas Eve.

3. Robin Hood's messenger met the Merry Men under the massive elm.

4. The bumblebees and humming birds were murmuring melodiously.

5. You must memorize this poem in twenty minutes.

6. Marion sat meditating by the Mediterranean.

7. Tom grumbled because he had to come home when he wanted to see the new film at the movies.

8. Moses was known as the meekest man.

9. My mother made a warm muff for Mary out of my mink coat.

10. The explosion of the bomb on the moor sounded like the coming of doom.

11. "Simple Simon met a pieman."

12. "Little Miss Muffet
Sat on a tuffet."

13. "How sweet the moonlight sleeps upon this bank!
Here will we sit, and let the sounds of music
Creep in our ears."

14. "The murmurous haunt of flies on summer eves."

15. "Most musical, most melancholy."

16. "Muttering and murmuring in his ear."

17. "The murmuring pines and the hemlocks."

18. "Eternal smiles his emptiness betray,
As shallow streams run dimpling all the way."

19. "Through caverns measureless to man."

20. "All went merry as a marriage bell."

w [w] as in *will;* wh [ʍ] as in *which*

weal	wheel	wen	when	wight	white
wig	Whig	wear	where	wine	whine
wit	whit	wagon	whang	wile	while
wince	whence	were	whirr	way	whey
weather	whether	woe	whoa	wail	whale
wet	whet	watt	what	wittier	Whittier

1. Did you look in the paper to see whether the weather forecast for Wednesday was fair?

2. The woebegone boy shouted "whoa" to the running and whinnying horse.

3. Jonah wailed at his fate when he was swallowed by the whale.

4. Is the man in the white wig a Whig or a Tory?

5. Where do you expect to wear the wine-colored wrap?

6. "Wait a while," said the wily White Queen.

7. Which one of these caves is called "the witches' cauldron"?

8. "Welcome all wonders in one night."

9. "Poor world," said I, "what wilt thou do?"

10. "Quips, and Cranks, and wanton Wiles,
    Nods, and Becks, and wreathed Smiles."

11. "He must not float upon his watery bier
    Unwept, and welter to the parching wind,
    Without the mead of some melodious tear."

12. "Saw the vision of the world, and all the wonder that would be."

13. "He trudged along, unknowing what he sought,
    And whistled as he went, for want of thought."

14. "'How now, wit, whither wander you?'"

15. "Now tell us all about the war,
    And what they fought each other for."

16. "Water, water, everywhere."

th [ð] as in *this*

this	that	clothe	bother	hither
them	thus	lithe	brother	mother
their	though	scythe	father	northerly
there	thy	tithe	fathom	rather
than	they	writhe	further	southern

th [θ] as in *thing*

thin	thump	thong	theater	earth
thank	thermometer	theta	death	heath
third	thaw	thrice	doth	myth

Read the following pairs of columns horizontally and vertically:

theme	these	throne	though	ether	either
thick	this	thrive	thy	sheath	sheathe
thread	them	bath	bathe	sooth	soothe
thumb	thus	breath	breathe	width	with

1. There have been many good things at the theater this season.

2. Our thermometer registered zero today for the fifth time this season.

3. Arthur lives at Three thirty-three North Thirteenth Street.

4. Have you enough cloth to make clothes for both children?

5. This car throttles down to three miles an hour.

6. Theodore entered the theological seminary Thursday.

7. Would you rather live in the north or south?

8. My brother likes arithmetic, but I loathe it.

9. There was a thick fog followed by a heavy thaw on Thursday.

10. His thesis was three hundred and thirteen pages in length.

11. There is something that looks like a thimble in the thicket.

12. Those girls talked of this and that all through the night.

13. Arthur thought he ought to visit Theodore although he was loath to do so.

14. I think there is only a third-rate company at the theater this evening.

15. "Full fathom five thy father lies."

16. "He that ever hopes to thrive,
Must begin by thirty-five."

17. "Thoughts that breathe, and words that burn."

18. "First of this thing, and of that thing, and of the other thing, think."

19. "And in thy right hand lead with thee
The mountain nymph, sweet Liberty;
And if I give thee honor due,
Mirth, admit me of thy crew."

20. "Though the mills of God grind slowly,
Yet they grind exceeding small."

21. "A whisper and then a silence:
Yet I know by their merry eyes
They are plotting and planning together
To take me by surprise."

22. "From them I learn whatever lies
Beneath each changing zone.
And see, when looking with their eyes,
Better than with mine own."

23. "Language is the picture and counterpart of thought."

24. "Yet I doubt not through the ages one increasing purpose runs,
And the thoughts of men are widened with the process of the suns."

25. "One of those little places that have run
Half up the hill beneath a blazing sun,
And then sat down to rest, as if to say,
'I climb no farther upward, come what may.'"

26. "All night long their nets they threw."

f [f] as in *fife; v* [v] as in *vine*

fee	veal	fife	five	reefer	fever
fairy	various	half	halves	stiffer	river
fan	van	leaf	leave	deafen	Heaven
fast	vast	knife	knives	taffy	ravenous
fall	vault	proof	prove	suffer	cover
feign	vain	strife	strive	roofer	mover
fowl	vowel	wife	wives	rifle	rival

1. The famished family was given a good meal of veal and vegetables.

2. The butcher has fine fancy fowl for sale today.

3. Please inform Frances and Vera that I want to see them at once without fail.

4. That boy in the reefer jacket seems to have a high fever.

5. There is an old saying that we have either feast or famine.

6. "The fair breeze blew,
The white foam flew,
The furrow followed free."

7. "Pride and ambition here,
Only in far-fetched metaphors appear."

8. "Among the long black rafters,
The wavering shadows lay,
And the current that came from the ocean.
Seemed to lift and bear them away."

9. "Variety's the very spice of life,
That gives it all its flavor."

10. "Fame is the fragrance of heroic deeds,
Of flowers of chivalry and not of weeds."

11. "Full fathom five thy father lies."

12. "Vanity of vanities, saith the preacher, all is vanity."

13. "Did universal charity prevail, earth would be heaven and hell a fable."

14. "We here highly resolve that these dead shall not have died in vain."

15. "Four score and seven years ago our fathers brought forth on this continent, a new nation, conceived in Liberty, and dedicated to the proposition that all men are created equal."

16. "We are met on a great battlefield of that war. We have come to dedicate a portion of that field, as a final resting place for those who here gave their lives that that nation might live."

d [d] as in *did; t* [t] as in *tot*

deem	team	bid	bit	bidden	bitten
dead	Ted	and	ant	bedding	better
dare	tear	bud	but	saddle	satin
damp	tamper	code	coat	burden	certain
dirt	turn	sawed	sought	sudden	button
done	ton	hard	heart	boding	boating
doled	told	hide	height	coddle	bottle
dawn	torn	raid	rate	carding	carting
dot	tot	spade	spate	bounding	bounty
dart	tart	trade	trait	siding	citing

1. Tom wouldn't go to the party.

2. The bad boy hadn't any excuse for doing such an unkind deed.

3. The letter was written in a strange style of handwriting.

4. Mary couldn't see the value of studying Latin.

5. The driver shouldn't have turned the corner against a red light.

6. Teddy asked his partner to pardon him for treading on her toes.

7. The master of the riding school was writing to a friend in Littleton.

8. The bad little boys were holding a snowball battle in the middle of the street.

9. The broken bottle punctured the tires of the little car and caused an accident.

10. Tim told Tom not to tease the poodle unless he wanted to be bitten.

11. Uncle Don's story of the battle seemed endless to Betty, but completely satisfactory to Teddy.

12. The streets of the little city were flooded with bright lights.

13. Tom evidently intended to go on a long trip, because he carried a lot of luggage.

14. Ted's family had settled permanently in a mid-western city.

15. Betty was a kindly little person who treated everyone pleasantly.

16. The clever partners confidently expected to win the game of Contract Bridge.

17. "Time and tide wait for no man."

18. "Double, double, toil and trouble,
    Fire burn and cauldron bubble."

19. "The dropping of the daylight in the west."

20. "Till the dappled dawn doth rise."

21. "In what distant deeps or skies
    Burnt the fire of thine eyes?"

22. "The day is done and the darkness
    Falls from the wings of night."

23. "Come and trip it as you go
    On the light fantastic toe."

24. "Towers and battlements it sees
    Bosomed high in tufted trees."

25. "Doth God exact day-labor, light denied?"

26. "The night is dark, the stinging sleet,
    Swept by the bitter gusts of air,
    Drives whistling down the lonely street,
    And glazes on the pavement bare."

27. "The moon shines white and silent
    On the mist, which, like a tide
    Of some enchanted ocean,
    O'er the wide marsh doth glide,
    Spreading its ghost-like billows
    Silently far and wide."

28. "The mighty pyramids of stone
    That wedge-like cleave the desert airs,
    When nearer seen and better known,
    Are but gigantic flights of stairs."

29. "The drawbridge dropped with a surly clang,
    And through the dark arch a charger sprang."

30. "It now was dew-fall; very still
    The night lay on the lonely hill,
    Down which our homeward steps we bent,
    And, silent, through great silence went,
    Save that the tireless crickets played
    Their long monotonous serenade."

n [n] as in *name*

knee	knot	seen	lone	bonny	nonage
knit	nine	in	gone	contemplate	pony
net	name	then	lawn	dinner	rainy
gnat	noun	cairn	rain	funny	shiny
nurse	noise	an	vine	gunning	sunny
nut	near	can't	own	honey	tiny
noon	Noah	earn	town	incongruous	tonnage
known	newer	sun	coin	linen	vanish
gnaw	nude	moon	tune	money	whinny

Note: See *n* [n], page 35.

1. The sun shines by day and the moon by night.

2. Anita knits industriously morning, noon, and night.

3. Does this town maintain its own electric light plant?

4. Nan can't earn enough money to buy all the new novels.

5. Nelly's new linen dress is clean and neat.

6. Nora lives at the corner of Ninetieth Street and Ninth Avenue.

7. Nonresident students often travel late at night and early in the morning.

8. John was suspended for non-performance of duty and non-payment of fees.

9. The tiny gnats settled in the vines outside the window.

10. Vachel Lindsay wrote a poem called "The Congo."

11. John's ideas were frequently incongruous.

12. The two friends engaged in conversation far into the night.

13. The knights were confident of victory in the impending conflict.

14. "Necessity is the mother of invention."

15. "So many hours must I contemplate."

16. "A little nonsense now and then,
Is relished by the wisest men."

17. "The wild November comes at last
Beneath a veil of rain."

18. "Now the hungry lion roars,
And the wolf behowls the moon,
Whilst the heavy plowman snores,
All with weary task fordone."

19. "The nightingale, if she should sing by day,
When every goose is cackling, would be thought
No better a musician than the wren.
How many things by season seasoned are
To their right phase, and true perfection."

20. "Be noble! And the nobleness that lies
In other men, sleeping, but never dead,
Will rise in majesty to meet thine own;
Then wilt thou see it gleam in many eyes,
Then will pure light around thy path be shed,
And thou wilt nevermore be sad and lone."

l [l] as in *lull*

lea	lurk	eel	pull	billiard	annually
lit	lull	ill	awl	dullard	casually
let	loon	ell	isle	lily	particularly
lair	loan	earl	ale	million	peculiarly
land	lane	hull	old	pillion	regularly
last	loud	pool	oil	William	secularly

1. The little lake was full of lily-pads.
2. Leslie was allowed to go to the ball game.
3. Lillian lived near a lighthouse on Long Island.
4. The English language is not easily learned by adults.
5. All children like lollipops and licorice sticks.
6. The Alps are lofty mountains located in Switzerland.
7. "Life is short and art is long."
8. "And love to live in dimple sleek."
9. "Lulled by the coil of his crystalline streams."
10. "And full-grown lambs loud bleat from hilly bourn."
11. "When Liberty is gone,
    Life grows insipid and loses its flavor."
12. "I wield the flail of the lashing hail,
    And whiten the green plains under."
13. "It was now dew-fall; very still
    The night lay on the lonely hill."
14. "The bell tolls late, the moping owl flies round,
    Fear marks the flight, and magnifies the sound."
15. "And young and old come forth to play
    On a sunshine holiday,
    Till the livelong daylight fail."
16. "And leaping down the ridges lightly, plunged
    Among the bulrush beds, and clutched the sword,
    And strongly wheeled and threw it."
17. "And as the boat-head wound along
    The willowy hills and fields among,
    They heard her singing her last song,
    The Lady of Shalott."
18. "Life's but a walking shadow; a poor player,
    That struts and frets his hour upon the stage,
    And then is heard no more: it is a tale

Told by an idiot, full of sound and fury,
Signifying nothing."

r [ɹ] as in red

real	wrote	bride	pride	herring
rich	raw	brush	shrub	lorry
wrench	rot	cradle	tread	merry
rare	rather	crust	carry	narrow
rat	rate	dream	cherry	parrot
raft	rind	drudge	dairy	rarify
run	round	fringe	ferry	tarry
rule	roil	grit	fairy	very
room	rear	grudge	garret	weary

1. The bride wrote to Mary to thank her for the wedding present.

2. Would you rather hurry to catch the train, or run the risk of losing it?

3. Rita's new dress is trimmed with red fringe.

4. Mary and Harry spent the rainy day in the garret reading fairy stories.

5. The children rode merrily on the merry-go-round.

6. The parrot had red and green plumage.

7. The white rabbit ate the raw carrot ravenously.

8. Harriet drove furiously along the rough and narrow road.

9. The roundest and reddest cherries were found at the top of the tree.

10. The dairy maid had pretty, round, rosy cheeks.

11. The rich man rambled around the rocks searching for red raspberries.

12. These Christmas presents are a rare treat for the poor children.

13. "The flying rumors gathered as they rolled."

14. "Nor rural sights alone, but rural sounds
Exhilarate the spirit, and restore
The tone of languid nature."

15. "And see the rivers how they run
Through woods and meads, in shade and sun."

16. "Far up the blue sky a fair rainbow unrolled."

17. "Superior worth your rank requires:
For that, mankind reveres your sires."

18. "The quarrel is a very pretty quarrel as it stands."

19. "And, spite of pride, in erring reason's spite,
One thing is clear: 'Whatever is, is right.'"

20. "Approach thou like the rugged Russian bear,
The armed rhinoceros, or the Hyrcan tiger."

y [j] as in *yes*

yield	yearn	yawn	year
yeast	young	yard	you're
yet	youth	yarn	yellow
yank	yolk	yea	yoemen

1. Yesterday Eunice wore a yellow dress and yellow shoes.

2. You will have to use plenty of yeast to make the bread rise.

3. What kind of yarn are you going to use for your sweater?

4. You must have used at least six egg yolks for this cake.

5. There is a beautiful view from Glacier Point in Yosemite Valley.

6. This young man is going to go to Yale next year.

7. Is that yacht a yawl?

8. I am not yet ready to go to New York.

9. This field will yield many yams.

10. I received your Yuletide greeting yesterday.

11. Do you see that beautiful yew tree over yonder?

12. "And you, good yeomen, whose limbs were made in England,
Show us here the mettle of your pasture."

13. "Years following years steal something every day,
At last they steal us from ourselves away."

14. "Let your speech be 'Yea, yea, and nay, nay.'"

15. "Yield, ye youths, ye yoemen, yield your yell."

g [g] as in *gig; k* [k] as in *kick*

geese	keen	goal	coal	wriggle	wrinkle
guest	quest	gone	con	beggar	beckon
gamut	camp	guard	cart	lugging	lucky
girl	curl	game	came	sugar	looking
gun	cunning	guile	quiet	logging	locking
goose	cruise	gouge	couch	gargling	skylarking
good	could	gore	core	tiger	likely

Note: See *k* [k], page 38.

1. There were candy canes, cookies, and cornucopias of popcorn on the Christmas tree.

2. To the schoolboy, school days seem to creep slowly by, but vacations always go quickly.

3. The beggar considered himself lucky when he came upon the six coins in the bag.

4. The girl was searching for a kit to take on the Canadian cruise.

5. Gertrude's quiet guest had a keen wit and a good sense of humor.

6. I am curious to see whether the curtains were packed well, or whether they were wrinkled.

7. Clara cleaned the house until it was spick and span from attic to cellar.

8. The cart was crammed with chickens and turkeys and geese.

9. The carpenter decided to put casement windows in the casino, but the architect objected on account of the cost.

10. "Petty laws breed great crimes."

11. "The bare black cliff clanged round him."

12. "Distinction is the consequence, never the object, of a great mind."

13. "A politician must often talk and act before he has thought and read. He may be very ill-informed respecting a question: all his notions about it may be vague and inaccurate; but speak he must."

14. "The King was in the counting-house, counting up his money."

15. "The maid was in the garden hanging up clothes."

16. "A good talker, even more than a good orator, implies a good audience."

17. "The brain may devise laws for the blood; but a hot temper leaps o'er a cold decree: such a hare is madness, the youth, to skip o'er the meshes of good counsel, the cripple."

18. "A clear fire, a clean hearth, and the rigor of the game."

19. "Conceit causes more conversation than wit."

20. "That is a good book which is opened with expectation and closed with profit."

ng [ŋ] as in *song*   *ng-g* [ŋg] as in *finger*

bring	young	anger	languid
clang	hanger	anguish	linger
drink	singer	bangle	longer
fang	wringer	bungle	longest
gong	banging	dinghy	mangle
hung	clinging	diphthongal	mingle
link	doing	England	single
mink	finding	English	stronger
rung	hanging	finger	strongest
song	longing	hangar	wrangle
tang	ringing	hunger	younger
wing	singing	language	youngest

Note: See *ng* [ŋ], page 39.

1. Mary was nursing a sore finger.

2. The wrestler had strong arms.

3. Is John coming out to play hockey?

4. The bell ringer was tolling a bell.

5. The blind singer sang a popular song.

6. The girls were going out on Long Island for the holiday.

7. Is the elevator going up or coming down?

8. The dress was hanging on the line on a coat-hanger.

9. A gang of younger boys broke up the meeting.

10. The clanging of the gong was a signal for a fire-drill.

11. Fishing and hunting and trespassing are forbidden in these grounds.

12. Tom is frowning over his lessons, but Mary is singing at her work.

13. Jim is doing a fine piece of work as managing editor of the *Newport Gong.*

14. Lucy looked longingly at the beautiful fringe trimming on Sarah's dress.[3]

15. The children are running and shouting and leaping in their joy at the coming of the holiday season.

16. The learning of the English language is a long, hard process for those speaking a foreign tongue.

---

[3] *nge* as in *fringe* is pronounced *nj* [ndʒ].   See page 40.

17. The freshmen were entertaining all the other students by an informal sing-song.

18. The aeroplane was coming up the field toward the hangar.

19. Be sure to hang all your dresses and coats on hangers.

20. Grace Bingham has a new lining in her mink coat.

21. There was a crowd of people looking up at the many dirigibles which were circling about the sky.

22. The English Singers sang all the lovely old carols at Christmas.

23. Those silly girls were banging on the piano and giggling over nothing.

24. Long, long ago, there was a king of England by the name of John.

25. The dog was jumping up and claiming attention from his master.

26. Passing over these theories, we come to the actual facts of the case.

27. We are spending all our spare time reading aloud.

28. At last the longed-for moment came, and all the children began running out of doors.

29. We have every chance of passing our examinations since we have been doing our work faithfully from day to day.

30. Nothing is ever accomplished by nagging at people.

31. The visitors were waiting in the hall before going upstairs.

32. The dogs were lying on the ground panting in the heat.

33. Sarah was sitting at her desk writing a long letter.

34. Tom is riding up the street in his cart, which is called *Young America*.

35. If Mary makes that decision, she is siding against her friends.

36. I won't go camping as I don't enjoy putting up with all kinds of inconvenience.

37. In the olden days in England, the barking of the dogs indicated that the beggars were descending upon the town in great numbers.

38. "I am a man
More sinned against, than sinning."

39. "The task he undertakes
Is numbering sands, and drinking oceans dry."

40. "And the muscles of his brawny arms,
Are strong as iron bands."

41. "An ancient saying is no heresy,
Hanging and wiving go by destiny."

42. "Songs are but sweet and skilful words,
That tinkle unto certain chords,
And are but born to die."

43. "To the swinging and ringing
Of the bells, bells, bells.

. . .

To the rhyming and the chiming of the bells."

44. "Oh! these were hours when thrilling joy repaid
A long, long course of darkness, doubts, and fears."

45. "There was a rustling that seemed like a bustling
Of many crowds jostling and pitching and hustling;
Small feet were pattering, wooden shoes clattering,
Little hands clapping, and little tongues chattering."

h [h] as in *high*

he	hut	half	hew	high-handed	inhale
hit	who	hay	huge	hobbyhorse	inherit
hen	hood	high	Hugo	hogshead	inhibit
hair	hotel	how	humid	horehound	inhospitable
had	haul	hoist	humility	horsehair	manhood
heard	hot	hold	humor	hothouse	womanhood

Note: See *h* [h], page 40.

1. Harry studied his history lesson for half an hour.

2. The hotel was very hot in the humid weather.

3. We heard you had a half-holiday because of the heat.

4. Whose car went up the hill at such high speed?

5. Did you go to Hanover when you were in New Hampshire?

6. Herbert treated the matter in a high-handed fashion.

7. Rip Van Winkle was a henpecked husband.

8. The farm hands attended the harvest-home festival at Hard-castle.

9. Hubert was a hard-hearted and inhospitable herdsman.

10. Henry was a hidebound but high-minded historian.

11. I should hestitate to say that the heiress was not honest.[4]

12. Hetty fell from her horse and was hurried to the hospital.

---

[4] See "Silent Letters," page 18.

13. "Hence, home, you idle creatures, get you home,
Is this a holiday?"

14. "But heaven hath a hand in these events."

15. "O holy Hope! and high Humility!
High as the heavens above."

Exercises for the Sibilants

s [s] (*initial*) as in *say*

seed	set	some	sew	sardine	safe
seat	sand	supper	soak	psalm	sour
sin	sat	soon	sower	side	soil
sit	serve	sooth	sob	sight	seer
said	serf	soot	sop	save	suit

1. The farmer sowed the seed.

2. Susan and her family lived in Seattle.

3. Mary sat down by the side of the road.

4. Katherine sang a solo on Sunday.

5. The fortune-teller predicted that Sarah would soon take a trip to the South.

6. Tom gave the sick woman a seat in the subway.

7. We will celebrate the Fourth of July in a safe and sane manner.

8. Fred wanted to know when we would have supper.

9. The robin flew from the sidewalk to the window sill.

10. Did you apply salve to the sore finger?

11. Did you enjoy your summer by the sea?

12. The scenery in that part of the country may be called sublime.

13. The soot from the chimney soiled the dining-room ceiling.

14. The boy lived at Seventy-five Cedar Lane.

15. Helen enjoyed a sight-seeing trip around the city of Savannah.

16. The sound of the sea can be soothing and sad.

17. We had supper at the "Sign of the Peacock."

18. A sailor is a seafaring man.

19. He sang as he had never sung before.

20. Solomon sailed for Port Said.

21. We will have both hot and cold cereal.

22. The woman in the sable coat soothed the sobbing child.

23. They planted a Lebanon cedar by the cellar door.

24. The senator celebrated the victory with a great deal of ceremony.

25. Helen sang a sentimental song.

26. "In sooth, I know not why I am so sad."

27. "The sea! the sea! the open sea!
The blue, the fresh, the ever free!"

28. "I hear a solemn murmur
. . . of the mighty sea."

29. "Now deep in ocean sunk the lamp of light,
And drew behind the cloudy veil of night."

30. "Sing, seraph, poet! Sing on equally."

z [z] as in *zodiac, buzz, puzzle*

zeal	zoom	hussy	Tuesday	has	pause
zebra	zero	fizzle	bees	learns	raise
zinc	zone	muzzle	fizz	whose	sighs
zipper	busy	puzzle	cares	buzz	tease
zest	drizzle	visit	says	foes	vines

1. Zero weather seems to prevail this season.

2. Mad dogs should be muzzled for public safety.

3. The bees were buzzing busily in the garden.

4. Did you see the zebra at the zoo?

5. Could you solve the puzzle in Tuesday's paper?

6. I visited Stratford because I desired to see the Shakespearean plays.

7. Both girls and boys were carrying trays in the cafeteria.

8. Business men realize that it pays to advertise.

9. John was one of the members of the ways and means committee.

10. The lightning zig-zagged across the heavens.

11. The writer's design was to expose vice and crime.

12. It always pleases Susan to do kind deeds.

13. The president of the debating society resigned because his speech was criticized.

14. "These are pearls that were his eyes."

15. "I am always very well pleased with a country Sunday."

16. "And then my heart with rapture thrills,
And dances with the daffodils."

17. "For men must work and women must weep,
Though storms be sudden and waters deep."

18. "Tell me not in mournful numbers,
Life is but an empty dream,
For the soul is dead that slumbers,
And things are not what they seem."

19. "There's music in the sighing of a reed;
There's music in the rushing of a rill;
There's music in all things, if men had ears;
Their earth is but an echo of the spheres."

20. "Labor with what zeal we will,
Something still remains undone,
Something uncompleted still
Waits the rising of the sun."

sp [sp] as in *spin, clasp, rasping*

speak	span	spoke	spear	crisp	clasping
spin	spurn	spawn	spout	grasp	gasping
spend	spun	spot	spoil	lisp	grasping
spare	spoon	spar	spine	rasp	lisping
spat	spool	spare	spire	wasp	rasping

1. Try to speak without lisping.

2. The spider spun a silken web.

3. The second speech was splendid.

4. That car struck ours and sped by.

5. The spiteful child spurned the spinach.

6. The sparrow sang in the spreading chestnut tree.

7. The English navy swept the Spanish Armada from the sea.

8. Spencer stared speechlessly at the spot.

9. The baby grasped the silver spoon.

10. The teacher spoke with a rasping voice.

11. As the man raised the spear, the whale spouted.

12. "Woodman, spare that tree!
Touch not a single bough!
In youth it sheltered me,
And I'll protect it now."

13. Speak the speech, I pray you, as I pronounced it to you, trippingly, on the tongue."

14. "Spring, Spring, beautiful Spring,
Laden with glory and light you come."

15. "Fled now the sullen murmurs of the North,
The splendid raiment of the Spring peeps forth."

16. "But if thou spare to sling Excalibur,
I will arise and slay thee with my hands."

17. "The silver vessels sparkle clear."

18. "Ye swelling hills and spacious plains!
Besprent from shore to shore with steeple towers,
And spires whose 'silent finger points to heaven.'"

sw [sw] as in *swing*

sweep	swish	swam	swollen	swallow
sweet	sweat	swirl	swore	swine
swim	swell	swerve	swap	swipe
swing	swear	swoon	swat	sway

1. The sportsman swung along with a swagger.

2. Some children were swinging on the swings; others were swimming in the pool.

3. *Swing Low, Sweet Chariot* is a Negro Spiritual.

4. The swimmer smote the swollen current with his strong arms.

5. The swallows were swirling through the air.

6. It is pleasant to go swimming on a sweltering hot day.

7. The swarm of bees hummed over the swaying reeds.

8. There was a ground swell which made the steamer rock gently.

9. The car swerved madly as it swished by.

10. "Sweets to the sweet."

11. "The sweetest song, the loudest string,
Should pour a welcome to beautiful Spring."

12. "The stately-sailing swan
Gives out his snowy plumage to the gale."

13. "I go, I go; look how I go;
Swifter than arrow from the Tartar's bow."

14. "But if you swear by that that is not, you are not forsworn: no more was this knight, swearing by his honor, for he never had any."

15. "See how in a living swarm they come
From the chambers beyond that misty veil;
Some hover awhile in the air, and some
Rush prone from the sky like summer hail.
All, dropping swiftly, or settling slow,
Meet, and are still in the depths below;
Flake after flake
Dissolved in the dark and silent lake."

sm [sm] as in *small; zm* [zm] as in *prism*

smitten	smug	smart	chasm
smell	smooth	smile	prism
smack	smoke	smite	schism
smirch	small	smear	truism

1. The fishing smack sailed smoothly over the sea.

2. A smirk is an affected smile.

3. The old pitcher was smashed to smithereens.

4. There was a plume of smoke emerging from the smokestack.

5. It is a truism that a sneak has a smooth manner.

6. Smith smuggled the diamonds through the Customs Office.

7. The fire smoked and smouldered on the hearth.

8. The boy smelled smoke and smothered the flame with his smock.

9. The mother smiled as she listened to the small girl's catechism.

10. There was a smooth wall of rock on one side of the deep chasm.

11. The smartly dressed woman smiled pleasantly at the small children.

12. Some people like to smell the smoke of a cigar.

13. The careless painter smeared the beautiful crystal prism.

14. "One may smile, and smile, and be a villain."

15. "The smith, a mighty man is he,
With large and sinewy hands."

sn [sn] as in *snap, fasten*

sneak	snag	snob	sniper	chasten
snip	snub	snack	snout	fasten
snare	snoop	snarl	sneer	listen
snap	snow	snake	assassin	mason

1. The small boy stumbled over the snare and fell into the chasm.

2. The sneak-thief snatched the watch from the man's wrist.

3. It is best to fasten the dress with snaps.

4. Mary took some snapshots of the snow drifts last winter.

5. The bully sneered and sneaked away.

6. *The Tailor of Gloucester* had snippets of silk.

7. The snake had risen swiftly from the path and was about to strike.

8. I will not listen to such snobbish ideas.

9. The kittens played with the yarn until it was soiled and snarled.

10. The sniper killed the slithering snake.

11. The girl had some snowdrops in the pocket of her coat.

12. The teacher chastened Tom for being a snob and snubbing the new student.

13. The assassin was sentenced to life imprisonment.

14. "Silent, and swift, and slow,
Descends the snow."

15. "And out of that frozen mist the snow
In wavering flakes begins to flow;
Flake after flake,
They sink in the dark and silent lake."

sk [sk] as in *skill, risk, asking*

scheme	skirt	scald	ask	asking
skim	scum	Scot	bisque	frisky
schedule	school	scar	rascal	husking
scat	scold	sky	task	husky
scan	scope	scout	whisk	risking

1. The skater schemed to get a full schedule.

2. The teacher asked John to scan the line of poetry.

3. Jane wrote a vivid description of the sky at sunset.

4. The children suddenly stopped skipping rope, and ran helter-skelter up the street.

5. Sarah asked if she might go skating or skiing after school.

6. The teacher scolded the children for screaming in the school room.

7. The cook said to add a scant cup of skim milk to make the batter smooth.

8. The Boy Scouts asked permission to give a program at the school.

9. Mary spilled tomato bisque on her new skirt.

10. The landscape architect made a sketch of his plans for the garden.

11. "Sculpture is more than painting."

12. "When to outstrip thy skyey speed,
Scarce seemed a vision."

13. "He jests at scars that never felt a wound."

14.   "Alas to make me
The fixed figure of the time, for scorn
To point his slow and moving finger at."

15. "I 'scotched not killed' the Scotchman in my blood,
And love the land of mountain and of flood."

sl [sl] as in *slur, nestle*

sleep	slam	slope	sleigh	mistletoe
slim	slur	slogan	slower	muscle
sled	slum	slot	slave	nestle
slat	sloop	sly	missile	wrestle

1. The boy slipped a penny in the slot machine.

2. Select the slang phrases in the following sentences.

3. The sidewalks in the slum district were dangerously slippery.

4. The actress spoiled the "sleep-walking scene" by speaking too slowly.

5. Tom's brother slipped out to gather holly and mistletoe for Christmas.

6. The sloop was painted slate-gray.

7. The little village nestled against the sloping hillside.

8. The children were sliding on the slippery floor.

9. The slave wrestled skilfully with the slim boy.

10. The sled swerved dangerously when the boy was sliding down the steep slope.

11. "'Tis the voice of the sluggard; I hear him complain,
'You have waked me too soon, I must slumber again.'"

12. "Sloth, like rust, consumes faster than labor wears, while the used key is always bright."

13. "There is nothing more shameful than slavery."

14. "The little white town of Bideford slopes upwards from . . .
the river, paved with yellow sands."

st [st] (*initial*) as in *stun*

steed	stab	stood	stop	style	stream
still	stack	stone	star	stifle	strip
stick	stir	stoke	stark	stout	strap
stem	stern	story	stain	stare	struggle
step	stuck	stork	steak	steer	structure

1. The student had a stern but stimulating teacher.

2. Sam stubbed his toe and stumbled into the study.

3. Stratford-on-Avon stands in a beautiful section of England.

4. Stephen stood on the porch staring at the mettlesome steed.

5. The student did an amusing stunt in fine style.

6. The stout man steered the steed into the stall.

7. Steak and stew were on the table at the stroke of twelve.

8. It will not storm tomorrow as the evening star is shining brightly.

9. Sarah stepped on a stone and strained her ankle.

10. Sam stole a sterling silver spoon.

11. The structure stood at the edge of the stream.

12. Sally struggled stormily with her skate strap.

13. The starving man stopped to beg a slice of stale bread.

14. The stout steward was stranded on the deck in the storm.

15. Will you have steak and strawberry shortcake for supper?

16. Susan stood at the stove stirring the soup.

17. We stopped at the stile as the storm broke over the mountain.

18. Saul strolled along the stone wall and by the haystack.

19. The storm made the static so strong that we stopped the radio.

20. Sally was startled and stunned by the shock.

21. "The strawberry grows underneath the nettle."

22. "He would drown the stage with tears
And cleave the general air with horrid speech."

st [st] as in *star, best, instead, twists*

stall	step	distraught	mystic	just	wrists
stare	stern	disturb	restive	list	bastes
start	stick	extend	rustic	must	casts
static	stout	extinct	beast	nest	fasts
stay	stunt	instead	cost	pest	fists
steam	bestow	instill	dust	twist	lists
steer	distill	instinct	first	west	masts

1. The static disturbed the stern man who wished to listen to the speech.

2. Sam twisted his wrist when he stumbled and fell in the street.

3. The best teachers attempt to instill respect for high standards of speech.

4. The dusty trip made us all thirsty.

5. This prehistoric monster has been extinct for many centuries.

6. When the list of successful candidates was published, Dick's name came first.

7. It is difficult to stimulate interest in a subject that is dry as dust.

8. The young fencer parried his opponent's thrust dexterously.

9. There are many places of historic interest in the United States.

10. This summer resort attracts many artists and novelists.

11. The Sunday evening service was held in the First Baptist Church.

12. "Some books are to be tasted, others to be swallowed, and some few to be chewed and digested."

13. "When the sun is in the west,
The lazy work the best."

14. "Golden lads and girls all must
As chimney-sweepers come to dust."

15. "The long-remembered beggar was his guest,
Whose beard descending swept his aged breast."

16. "I stood in the midst of the temple and threw my eyes round on the walls filled with the statues, the inscriptions and the monuments of the dead."

17. "In the stillness of the night,
Quick rays of intermingling light
Sparkle from star to star."

18. "Just laws are no restraint upon the freedom of the good."

19. "Poetry is the record of the best and happiest moments of the happiest and best minds."

20. "Next to being a poet is the power of understanding one."

21.   "Stars
Which stand as thick as dewdrops on the fields
Of heaven."

22. "He thrusts his fists
Against the post,
And still insists
He sees the ghost."

23. "For weeks the goblin weird and wild
That noble stripling haunted;
For weeks the stripling stood and smiled
Unmoved and all undaunted."

24. "For several years the ghostly twain
These Britons bold have haunted,
But all their efforts are in vain—
The victims stand undaunted.
This very day, the imp, and ghost,
Whose powers the imp derided,
Stand each at his allotted post—
The bet is undecided."

s [s] (*general*)

seal	base	bustle	muscle	best	lisps
sick	dose	docile	nestle	chest	mists
sent	face	fossil	pencil	disk	nests
some	horse	gossip	pestle	gist	pests
soot	mice	hustle	Sicily	hist	rasps
solve	peace	lesson	vicissitude	just	rusts
sought	loss	listen	whistle	musk	subsists
psalm	valise	missile	wrestle	wrist	tasks

1. Rose belongs to a secret society.

2. Tickets are for sale at the box office.

3. "Safety first" is a sensible slogan.

4. Sparkling water is best to quench the thirst.

5. The shop is situated in the center of the city.

6. This is the most unpleasant season of the year.

7. San Francisco is on the west coast of California.

8. There are poisonous snakes in those mountains.

9. After the sleet storm the trees were covered with ice.

10. Did James empty the waste-paper baskets Thursday?

11. This story ran in serial form in one of the magazines.

12. Sam has been seriously ill ever since Christmas.

13. The white fence was visible through the mist.

14. It does not seem possible that summer has come so soon.

15. We spoke to the superintendent about an increase in wages yesterday.

16. The senator's house was almost entirely surrounded by bandits.

17. Please send several samples of silk at once.

18. Sarah left the room and returned with gifts for the six children.

19. He sang as he had never sung before.

20. Patience and perseverance are important assets when striving to overcome speech defects.

21. Tom's father has gone deep-sea fishing and hopes to catch some sea bass.

22. "From the sublime to the ridiculous" is a hackneyed expression.

23. *Sense and Sensibility* was written by Jane Austen.

24. We shall have celery soup and salmon sandwiches for lunch.

25. "Sail on, O Ship of State."

26. "And the sails did sigh like sedge."

27. "White his skin, as the summer snow."

28. "And here were forests, ancient as the hills."

29. "Satan finds some mischief still for idle hands to do."

30. "Sleep that sometimes shuts up sorrow's eye."

31. "Eternal summer gilds them yet,
But all except their sun is set."

32. "Swiftly, swiftly flew the ship,
Yet she sailed softly, too."

33. "Sweet, sweet, sweet, O Pan!
Piercing sweet by the river!"

34. "And the three passed over the white sands, between the rocks, silent as the shadows."

35. "She sent the gentle sleep from Heaven,
That slid into my soul."

36. "Sometimes a-dropping from the sky,
I heard a skylark sing."

37. "True ease in writing comes from art, not chance,
As those move easiest, who have learned to dance."

38. "And till my ghastly tale is told,
This heart within me burns."

39. "The day is done; and slowly from the scene
The stooping sun upgathers his spent shafts,
And puts them back into his golden quiver."

40. "Shine out, fair sun, till I have bought a glass,
That I may see my shadow as I pass."

41. "All the world's a stage
And all the men and women merely players.
They have their exits and their entrances;
And one man in his time plays many parts,
His acts being seven ages."

42. "This is the forest primeval. The murmuring pines and the
hemlocks,
Bearded with moss, and in garments green, indistinct in the
twilight,
Stand like Druids of eld, with voices sad and prophetic,
Stand like harper's hoar, with beards that rest on their bosoms.
Loud from its rocky caverns, the deep-voiced neighboring ocean
Speaks, and in accents disconsolate, answers the wail of the
forest."

sh [ʃ] as in *shoe*

she	shut	sharp	leash	cashier	ocean
ship	shoe	shine	wish	crucial	promotion
shed	sugar	shout	fresh	impression	racial
share	shone	sure	rush	lotion	rasher
shir	shawl	shore	wash	motion	usher

zh [ʒ] as in *pleasure*

collision	decision	evasion	illusion
conclusion	derision	exclusion	lesion
confusion	erasure	fusion	persuasion

Note: See *sh* [ʃ] and *zh* [ʒ], page 37.

Read the following pairs of columns horizontally and vertically:

azure	assure	garage	garish	pleasure	pressure
delusion	delicious	measure	meshes	treasure	threshing
erosion	notion	mirage	marshes	vision	vicious

1. She came to the conclusion that the shoe salesman had fitted her foot incorrectly.

2. The cashier wished for a rasher of bacon for breakfast.

3. The crucial moment came; there was a shot and another sharp report.

4. It was a pleasure to see the treasure ship on the ocean.

5. He shouted that the shed had been shut in order to insure the safety of the sugar and other provisions.

6. She was under the impression that the dog broke his leash and rushed at the ash man.

7. The usher wished to make sure that his shoes were properly shined.

8. The soldiers stood at attention when the national anthem was played at the legation.

9. The garage was freshly painted a garish red.

10. There was a crowd at the police station when the sheriff made his sensational arrest.

11. A mirage is an optical illusion that sometimes occurs on the ocean.

12. The many erasures on the boy's examination paper gave an indication of his lack of preparation.

13. " 'Mongst horrid shapes and shrieks and sights unholy."

14. "Hath not a Jew hands, organs, dimensions, senses, affections, passions?"

15. "A true and noble friendship shrinks not at the greatest of trials."

16. "Great men are never sufficiently shown but in struggles."

17. "What shadows we are, and what shadows we pursue."

18. "Men's lives like oceans change
In shifting tides, and ebb from either shore."

j [dʒ] as in *judge; ch* [tʃ] as in *church*

Jim	chin	jar	char	ridge	rich
jet	chess	James	chase	serge	search
jam	chat	jibe	chime	siege	beseech
jerk	church	jowl	chow	fidget	hatchet
judge	chum	joist	choice	ledges	latches
June	choose	jeer	cheer	pigeon	pitching
joke	choke	budge	bunch	smudges	smirches
jot	chop	large	larch	trudging	trencher

Note: See *j* [dʒ] and *ch* [tʃ], page 37.

1. "Haste thee, nymph, and bring with thee,
   Jest and youthful jollity."

2. "The hungry judges soon the sentence sign,
   And wretches hang that jurymen may dine."

3. "It is jealousy's peculiar nature
   To swell small things to great; nay out of nought
   To conjure much. . . . "

4. "Man is unjust, but God is just; and finally justice triumphs."

5. " 'Tis with our judgments as our watches, none
   Go just alike, yet each believes his own."

6. "If a Jew wrong a Christian, what is his humility? Revenge. If a Christian wrong a Jew, what should his sufferance be by Christian example? Why, revenge."

7. "It requires a surgical operation to get a joke well into a Scotch understanding."

8. "A good judge should never boast of his power, because he can do nothing but what he can do justly . . . Authority without virtue is a very dangerous state."

9. "It is impossible to be just if one is not generous."

10. "Much has been said of the wisdom of old age."

11. "Judge not that ye be not judged."

12.   "Therefore, Jew,
   Though justice be thy plea, consider this,
   That in the course of justice, none of us
   Should see salvation. . . . "

13. "By the margin, willow-veil'd
   Slide the heavy barges trailed
   By slow horses. . . . "

14. "Rejoice, you men of Angiers, ring your bells;
   King John, your king and England's, doth approach."

15. "Such tricks hath strong imagination,
   That, if it would but apprehend some joy,
   It comprehends some bringer of that joy;
   Or in the night imagining some fear,
   How easy is a bush supposed a bear."

Exercises for the Correction of Cognate Substitutions

In the following exercise for cognate substitutions,[5] you will find seven double columns; read each double column horizontally, as, for instance: *bay-pay, bee-pea,* and so forth.

---

[5] See *Note,* page 33.

bay	pay	dad	tat	seize	cease
bee	pea	seed	seat	advise	advice
bib	pip	deem	team	because	course
bet	pet	rend	rent	laws	loss
bear	pear	dare	tear	lose	loose
bat	pat	durst	terse	prize	price

of	off	wine	whine
five	fife	weather	whether
vine	fine	were	whirr
believe	belief	witch	which
sieve	sift	wile	while
loaves	loaf	watt	what

judge	chuck	girl	curl
jerk	church	good	could
adjourn	churn	gone	corn
junk	chunk	bag	back
ridges	riches	leg	lake
smudge	much	frog	frock

1. James says it is dangerous to drive without chains today.

2. The buttons on my coat are so loose that I shall lose them if I do not sew them on at once.

3. The boy lost his pay check on the ferry crossing the bay.

4. One of the boys must get off at once.

5. You must judge for yourself and choose accordingly.

6. The little princess was very angry when the frog prince jumped up on her frock.

7. Will you please drive to the police court at once?

8. The little tots wore white dresses with red dots.

9. The kitten purrs as his mistress removes the burrs from his coat.

10. There are many of the rich people from the Ridge playing cards in the garden.

11. We make it a rule not to pay high prices for prizes in our club.

12. The policeman seized the boys and told them to cease their noise.

13. The boy got a cramp in his leg when swimming in the lake.

14. I believe there were five boys playing fifes in the village.

15. The naughty children cringed when the beggar struck at them with his crutch.

16. This boy tries so hard that he will have his lessons done in a trice.

17. If you will tell me the precise size, I can easily fit your sister to a pair of shoes.

18. I am taking this course because I think I will derive a great deal of benefit from it.

19. Will you please look in the paper to see whether fine weather is predicted for tomorrow?

20. While some worked, others whiled away the time in the garden.

Further Exercises for Difficult Sounds

ă [æ] as in *man*

Your self-made man, whittled into shape with his own jack-knife, deserves more credit, if that is all, than the regular engine-turned article, shaped by the most approved pattern, and French-polished by society and travel.   But as to saying that one is every way the equal of the other, that is another matter.   The right of strict social discrimination of all things and persons, according to their merits, native or acquired, is one of the most precious republican privileges.   I take the liberty to exercise it, when I say, that, *other things being equal,* in most relations of life I prefer a man of family.

—OLIVER WENDELL HOLMES.

* * *

A Fox was boasting to a Cat of its clever devices for escaping its enemies.   "I have a whole bag of tricks," he said, "which contains a hundred ways of escaping my enemies."

"I have only one," said the Cat; "but I can generally manage with that."   Just at that moment they heard the cry of a pack of hounds coming towards them, and the Cat immediately scampered up a tree and hid herself in the boughs.   "This is my plan," said the Cat. "What are you going to do?"   The Fox thought first of one way, then of another, and while he was debating, the hounds came nearer and nearer, and at last the Fox in his confusion was caught up by the hounds and soon killed by the huntsmen.   Miss Puss who had been looking on, said:

"Better one safe way than a hundred on which you cannot reckon."

—*Aesop's Fables.*

So all day long the noise of battle roll'd
Among the mountains by the winter sea;
Until King Arthur's Table, man by man,
Had fall'n in Lyonnesse about their lord,
King Arthur.   Then, because his wound was deep,
The bold Sir Bedevere uplifted him,
And bore him to a chapel nigh the field,
A broken chancel with a broken cross,
That stood on a dark strait of barren land:
On one side lay the Ocean, and on one
Lay a great water, and the moon was full.

—ALFRED LORD TENNYSON.

* * *

I suppose that a man being tried for his life must be more uncomfortable than an undergraduate being examined for his degree, and that to be hung—perhaps even to be pilloried—must be worse than to be plucked.   But after all, the feelings in both cases must be essentially the same, only more intense in the former, and an institution which can examine a man once a year for two or three days at a time, has nothing to complain of, though it has no longer the power of hanging him at once out of hand.

—T. HUGHES.

ī [aɪ] as in *ice*

The beautiful metropolis of America is by no means so clean a city as Boston, but many of its streets have the same characteristics; except that the houses are not quite so fresh-colored, the sign-boards are not quite so gaudy, the gilded letters not quite so golden, the bricks not quite so red, the stone not quite so white, the blinds and area railings not quite so green, the knobs and plates upon the street doors not quite so bright and twinkling.   There are many by-streets, almost as neutral in clean colors, and positive in dirty ones, as by-streets in London; and there is one quarter, commonly called the Five Points, which in respect of filth and wretchedness may be safely backed against Seven Dials, or any other part of the famed St. Giles.

The great promenade and thoroughfare, as most people know, is Broadway; a wide and bustling street, which from the Battery Gardens to its opposite termination in a country road, may be four miles long. Shall we sit down in an upper floor of the Carlton House Hotel . . . and when we are tired of looking down upon the life below, sally forth arm-in-arm and mingle with the stream?

—CHARLES DICKENS.

* * *

All these are items in the description of a winter evening, which must surely be familiar to everybody born in a high latitude.   And it is evident that most of these delicacies, like ice-cream, require a very low temperature of the atmosphere to produce them: they are fruits which cannot be ripened without weather stormy or inclement in some way or other. I am not *particular*, as people say, whether it be snow or black frost, or wind so strong, that "You may lean your back against it like a post"; I can put up even with rain, provided it rains cats and dogs; but something of the sort I must have; and if I have it not, I think myself in a manner ill-used; for why am I called on to pay so heavily for winter, in coals, in candles, and various privations that will occur even to gentlemen, if I am not to have the article good of its kind? . . . Indeed, so great an epicure am I in this matter, that I cannot relish a winter night fully if it be much past St. Thomas's day, and have degenerated into disgusting tendencies to vernal appearances; no it must be divided by a thick wall of dark nights from all return of light and sunshine . . . But here to save myself the trouble of too much verbal description, I will introduce a painter, and give him directions for the rest of the picture. Painters do not like white cottages, unless a good deal weather-stained; but as . . . it is a winter's night, his services will not be required, except for the inside of the house.

—Thomas De Quincey.

* * *

The nights are pleasant in May, short and pleasant for travel. We will leave the ancient city asleep, and do our flight in the night to save time. Trust yourselves, then to the story-teller's aerial machine. It is but a rough affair, I own, rough and humble, unfitted for high or great flights . . . still there is much to be learned in a third class carriage, if we will only not look while in it for cushions, and fine panels and forty miles an hour travelling . . . The fares are holiday fares, the tickets, return tickets . . . May you have a pleasant journey.

—T. Hughes.

* * *

So he ran away and went into the woods, and thence to the margin of Shadow Brook, where he could hear the streamlet grumbling along, under the great overhanging banks of snow and ice, which would scarcely let it see the light of day. There were adamantine icicles glittering around all its little cascades. Thence he strolled to the shore of the lake, and beheld a white, untrodden plain before him, stretching from his own feet to the foot of Monument Mountain. And, it being now sunset, Eustace thought that he had never beheld anything so fresh and beautiful as the scene. He was glad that the children were not with him; for their lively spirits and tumble-about activity would quite have chased away his higher and graver mood, so that he would merely have been merry . . . and wouldn't have known the loveliness of the winter sunset among the hills.

—NATHANIEL HAWTHORNE.

ow [aʊ] as in *gown*

We walked together to the crown
Of a high mountain, which looked down
Afar from its proud natural towers
Of rock and forest, on the hills—
The dwindled hills, whence amid bowers
Her own fair hand had reared around,
Gushed shoutingly a thousand rills,
Which as it were, in fairy bound
Embraced two hamlets—those our own.—
Peacefully happy—yet alone.

—EDGAR ALLAN POE.

* * *

But what are these grave thoughts to thee?
Out, out! into the open air!
Thy only dream of liberty,
Thou carest little how or where.
I see thee eager at thy play,
Now shouting to the apples on the tree,
With cheeks as round and red as they;
And now among the yellow stalks,
Among the flowering shrubs and plants,
As restless as the bee.

—HENRY WADSWORTH LONGFELLOW.

* * *

The cry of "Town! Town!" now rose on all sides. The Gownsmen in a compact body . . . pushed rapidly across the open space in which the caravans were set up and gained the street. Here they were comparatively safe: they were followed close, but could not be surrounded by the mob. Three or four pushed rapidly on, and were out of sight in no time. The greater part, without showing any signs of actual fear, kept steadily on at a good pace. Close behind these, a Gownsman struggled violently . . . and shouted defiance to the town; while a small and silent rear guard . . . walked slowly and . . . carelessly behind, within a few yards of shouting boys who headed the advancing Town.

—T. HUGHES.

And now it would have fared hardly with him, and he would scarcely have reached college with sound bones—for, I am sorry to say, an Oxford mob is a cruel and brutal one, and a man who is down has no chance with it,—but that for one moment he and his prostrate foes were so jumbled together that the town could not get at him, and the next cry of "Gown! Gown!" rose high above the din and the Town were swept back again by the reinforcement of the Gownsmen.

—T. Hughes.

s [s]

The St. Ambrose undergraduates at one time had carried off almost all the university prizes, and filled the class lists, while maintaining at the same time the highest character for manliness and gentlemanly conduct. This had lasted long enough to establish the fame of the college, and great lords and statesmen had sent their sons there; headmasters had struggled to get the names of their best pupils on the books; in short, everyone who had a son, ward, or pupil, whom he wanted to push forward in the world . . . left no stone unturned to get him into St. Ambrose's; and thought the first, and a very long, step gained when he had succeeded.

—T. Hughes.

* * *

One bright summer's afternoon, in the year of grace 1575, a tall and fair boy came lingering along the quay, in his scholar's gown, with satchel and slate in hand, watching wistfully the shipping and the sailors, till, just after he had passed the bottom of High Street, he came opposite to one of the many taverns which looked out upon the river. In the open bay window sat merchants and gentlemen, discoursing over their afternoon's draught of sack; and outside the door was gathered a group of sailors, listening earnestly to someone who stood in the midst. The boy, all alive for any sea-news, must needs go up to them, and take his place among the sailor-lads who were peeping and whispering under the elbows of the men; and so came in for the following speech, delivered in a loud, bold voice, with a strong Devonshire accent, and a fair sprinkling of oaths.

—Charles Kingsley.

* * *

This King Midas was fonder of gold than of anything else in the world. He valued his royal crown chiefly because it was composed of that precious metal. If he loved anything better, or half so well, it was the one little maiden who played so merrily around her father's footstool. But the more Midas loved his daughter, the more did he desire and seek for wealth. He thought that the best thing that he could possibly do for this dear child would be to bequeath her the most immense pile of yellow, glistening coin that had ever been heaped together, since the world was made.   Thus, he gave all his thoughts, and all his time to this one purpose.   If ever he happened to gaze for an instant at the gold-tinted clouds of the sunset, he wished that they were real gold, and that they could be squeezed safely into his strong box.

—Nathaniel Hawthorne, *A Wonder Book.*

* * *

The mighty forests are sparkling with myriad fireflies.   The lazy mist which lounges around the inner hills shines golden in the sunset rays; and nineteen thousand feet aloft, the mighty peaks cleave the abyss of air, rose red against the dark-blue vault of heaven.   The stars flash out one by one, and Venus, like another moon, tinges the eastern snows with gold, and sheds across the bay a long, yellow line of rippling light.   Everywhere is glory and richness.

—Charles Kingsley.

* * *

And then the summer twilight came on, and the birds disappeared, and the hush of night settled down on the river, and copse, and meadow —cool and gentle summer twilight after the hot, bright day.   He welcomed it, too, as it folded up the landscape, and the trees lost their outline and settled into soft, black masses rising here and there out of the white mist which seemed to have crept up . . . unawares. There was no sound now but the gentle murmur of the water, and an occasional rustle of reeds, or of the leaves over his head, as a stray wandering puff of air passed through them on its way home to bed. Nothing to listen to, and nothing to look at; for the moon had not risen, and the light mist hid everything except a star or two, right up above him.   So, the outside world having left him for the present, he was turned inwards on himself.

—T. Hughes.

* * *

A man's first care should be to avoid the reproaches of his own heart; his next, to escape the censures of the world: if the last inter- feres with the former, it ought to be entirely neglected; but otherwise there cannot be a greater satisfaction to an honest mind, than to see those approbations which it gives itself, seconded by the applauses of the public . . . My worthy friend, Sir Roger, is one of those who is not only at peace within himself, but beloved and esteemed by all about him.   He receives a suitable tribute for his universal benevolence to mankind, in the returns of affection and good will, which are paid him by everyone that lives within his neighborhood.

—Joseph Addison.

The perfect historian is he in whose work the character and spirit of an age is exhibited in miniature. He relates no fact, he attributes no expression to his characters, which is not authenticated by sufficient testimony. But, by judicious selection, rejection, and arrangement, he gives to truth those attractions which have been usurped by fiction. In his narrative a due subordination is observed: some transactions are prominent; others retire. But the scale on which he represents them is increased, or diminished, not according to the dignity of the persons concerned in them, but according to the degree in which they elucidate the condition of society and the nature of man. He shows us the court, the camp, and the senate. But he shows us also the nation. He considers no anecdote, no peculiarity of manner, no familiar saying, as too insignificant for his notice, which is not too insignificant to illustrate the operation of laws, of religion, and of education, and to mark the progress of the human mind. Men will not merely be described, but will be made intimately known to us. The changes of manners will be indicated, not merely by a few general phrases or a few extracts from statistical documents, but by appropriate images presented in every line.

—THOMAS BABINGTON MACAULAY.

* * *

I've fought them all, these ghosts of mine,
But the weapons I've used are sighs and brine,
And now that I'm nearly forty-nine,
  Old age is my chiefest bogy;
For my hair is thinning away at the crown,
And the silver fights the worn-out brown;
And the general verdict sets me down,
  As an irreclaimable fogy.

—W. S. GILBERT.

* * *

Sitting, on a bright September morning, among my books and papers at my open window on the cliff overhanging the sea beach, I have the sky and ocean framed before me like a beautiful picture. A beautiful picture, but with such movement in it, such changes of light upon the sails of ships and wake of steamboats, such dazzling gleams of silver far out at sea, such fresh touches on the crisp wave-tops as they break and roll towards me—a picture with such music in the billowy rush upon the shingle, the blowing of morning wind through the corn-sheaves where the farmer's wagons are busy, the singing of the larks, and the distant voices of children at play—such charms of sight and sound as all the Galleries on earth can but poorly suggest.

—CHARLES DICKENS.

It was a miserable day; chilly and raw; a damp mist falling; and the trees in that northern region quite bare and wintry.   Whenever the train halted, I listened for the roar; and was constantly straining my eyes in the direction where I knew the Falls must be, from seeing the river rolling on towards them; every moment expecting to behold the spray.   Within a few minutes of our stopping, not before, I saw two great white clouds rising up slowly and majestically from the depths of the earth.   That was all.   At length we alighted: and then for the first time, I heard the mighty rush of water, and felt the ground tremble underneath my feet.

The bank is very steep, and was slippery with rain, and half-melted ice.   I hardly know how I got down, but I was soon at the bottom, and climbing, with two English officers who were crossing and had joined me, over some broken rocks, deafened by the noise, half-blinded by the spray, and wet to the skin.   We were at the foot of the American Fall.   I could see an immense torrent of water tearing headlong down from some great height, but had no idea of shape, or situation, or anything but vague immensity.

—CHARLES DICKENS.

th (*voiced*) [ð]; *th* (*voiceless*) [θ]

Toiling, rejoicing, sorrowing,
Onward through life he goes;
Each morning sees some task begin,
Each evening sees it close;
Something attempted, something done,
Has earned a night's repose.

Thanks, thanks to thee, my worthy friend,
For the lesson thou hast taught!
Thus at the flaming forge of life
Our fortunes must be wrought;
Thus on its sounding anvil shaped
Each burning deed and thought.

—HENRY WADSWORTH LONGFELLOW.

* * *

I'll example you with thievery:
The sun's a thief, and with his great attraction
Robs the vast sea: the moon's an arrant thief,
And her pale fire she snatches from the sun:
The sea's a thief, whose liquid surge resolves
The moon into salt tears: The earth's a thief,
. . . each thing's a thief.

—SHAKESPEARE.

In my school-days, when I had lost one shaft,
I shot his fellow of the self-same flight
The self-same way with more advised watch,
To find the other forth; and by adventuring both,
I oft found both: I urge this childhood proof,
Because what follows is pure innocence.
I owe you much; and, like a wilful youth,
That which I owe is lost: but if you please
To shoot another arrow that self way
Which you did shoot the first, I do not doubt,
As I will watch the aim, or to find both,
Or bring your latter hazard back again,
And thankfully rest debtor for the first.
—SHAKESPEARE.

* * *

The quality of mercy is not strain'd,
It droppeth as the gentle rain from heaven
Upon the place beneath: it is twice blest;
It blesseth him that gives, and him that takes:
'Tis mightiest in the mightiest: it becomes
The throned monarch better than his crown;
His sceptre shows the force of temporal power,
The attribute to awe and majesty,
Wherein doth sit the dread and fear of kings;
But mercy is above this sceptred sway;
It is enthroned in the hearts of kings,
It is an attribute to God himself;
And earthly power doth then show likest God's
When mercy season's justice.   Therefore, Jew,
Though justice be thy plea; consider this,
That, in the course of justice, none of us
Should see salvation: we do pray for mercy;
And that same prayer doth teach us all to render
The deeds of mercy.
—SHAKESPEARE.

* * *

Thanks for the heavenly message brought by thee,
          Child of the wandering sea,
          Cast from her lap forlorn!
From thy dead lips a clearer note is born
Than ever Triton blew from wreathed horn!
          When on mine ear it rings,
Through the deep caves of thought I hear a voice that sings:—

Build thee more stately mansions, O my soul,
    As the swift seasons roll!
    Leave thy low-vaulted past!
Let each new temple, nobler than the last,
Shut thee from heaven with a dome more vast,
    Till thou at length art free,
Leaving thy outgrown shell by life's unresting sea!
                        —OLIVER WENDELL HOLMES.

ng [ŋ] as in *ring*

It seems as if our schools were doomed to be the sport of change.
We have faint recollections of a Preparatory Day-School, which we
have sought in vain, and which must have been pulled down to make
a new street, ages ago.   We have dim impressions, scarcely amounting
to a belief, that it was over a dyer's shop.   We know that you went
up steps to it; that you frequently grazed your knees in doing so; that
you generally got your leg over the scraper, in trying to scrape the mud
off a very unsteady, little shoe.   The mistress of the Establishment
holds no place in our memory; but rampant on one eternal door-mat,
in an eternal entry, long and narrow, is a puffy pug-dog with a personal
animosity towards us, who triumphs over time.   The barking of that
baleful Pug, a certain radiating way he had of snapping at our unde-
fended legs, the ghastly grinning of his moist black muzzle and white
teeth, and the insolence of his crisp tail curled like a pastoral crook,
all live and flourish.

                        —CHARLES DICKENS.

                    * * *

Ding, Clash, Dong, Bang, Boom, Rattle, Clash, Bang, Clink, Bang,
Dong, Bang, Clatter, bang, bang, BANG!   This is, or soon will be,
the Achilles, iron, armor-plated ship.   Twelve hundred men are
working on her now; twelve hundred men working on stages over her
sides, over her bows, over her stern, under her keel, between her decks,
down in her hold, within her and without, crawling and creeping into
the finest curves of her lines wherever it is possible for men to twist.
Twelve hundred hammerers, caulkers, armorers, forgers, smiths,
shipwrights; twelve hundred dingers, clashers, dongers, rattlers,
clinkers, bangers, bangers, bangers!   Yet all this stupendous uproar
around the rising Achilles is as nothing to the reverberations with
which the perfected Achilles shall resound upon the dreadful day when
the full work is in hand for which this is but note of preparation—the
day when the scuppers, that are now fitting like great, dry, thirsty
conduit pipes, shall run red.   All these busy figures between decks,
dimly seen bending at their work in smoke and fire, are as nothing to
the figures that shall do another kind of work in smoke and fire that
day.

                        —CHARLES DICKENS.

Soon leaving the calm Italian villages behind us, sleeping in the moonlight, the road began to wind among dark trees, and after a time emerged upon a barer region, very steep and toilsome, where the moon shone bright and high. By degrees, the roar of water grew louder; and the stupendous track, after crossing the torrent by a bridge, struck in between two massive walls of rock that quite shut out the moonlight, and only left a few stars shining in the narrow strip of sky above. Then, even this was lost, in the thick darkness of a cavern in the rock, through which the way was pierced; the terrible cataract thundering and roaring close below it, and its foam and spray hanging, in a mist about the entrance . . . Thus we went, climbing on our rugged way, higher and higher all night, without a moment's weariness: lost in the contemplation of the black rocks, the tremendous heights and depths, the fields of smooth snow lying in the clefts and hollows, and the fierce torrents thundering headlong down the deep abyss.

—CHARLES DICKENS.

* * *

The day was a very fine one, a bright sun shining, and a nice fresh breeze blowing across the stream, but not enough to ruffle the water seriously. Some heavy storms . . . had cleared the air, and swollen the stream at the same time; in fact, the river was as full as it could be without overflowing its banks—a state in which, of all others, it is the least safe for boating experiments . . . If any ordinary amount of bungling could have done it, Tom's voyage would have terminated very shortly. While he had been sitting quiet and merely paddling, and almost letting the stream carry him down, the boat had trimmed well enough; but, now, taking a long breath, he leaned forward, and dug his skulls into the water, pulling them through with all his strength. The consequence of this feat was that the handles of the skulls came into violent collision in the middle of the boat, the knuckles of his right hand were barked, his left skull unshipped, and the head of his skiff almost blown round by the wind before he could restore order on board.

—T. HUGHES.

* * *

Rip Van Winkle was coming up the road humming a song. He had heard some dwarfs singing that same tune on the mountain the night he disappeared. They had sung at a great rate of speed and in a language he could not understand. The church bells were ringing in the village this Sunday morning, as he came walking up the street. Rip fingered his long and flowing beard, wondering at the changes he saw about him. He was to find changes at home too. There would be no more scolding, and ranting, and henpecking, as his wife had died many years before, while he was sleeping on the mountain.

—ANON.

The chief difficulty Alice found at first was in managing her flamingo: she succeeded in getting its body tucked away, comfortably enough, under her arm, with its legs hanging down, but generally, just as she had got its neck nicely straightened out and was going to give the hedgehog a blow with its head, it *would* twist itself around and look up in her face, with such a puzzled expression that she could not help bursting out laughing; and, when she had got its head down and was going to begin again, it was very provoking to find that the hedgehog had unrolled itself, and was in the act of crawling away: besides all this, there was generally a ridge or a furrow in the way . . . and, as the doubled-up soldiers were always getting up and walking off to other parts of the ground, Alice soon came to the conclusion that it was a very difficult game indeed.

The players all played at once, without waiting for turns, quarreling all the while and fighting over the hedgehogs; and in a very short time the Queen was in a furious passion, and went stamping about, and shouting "Off with his head!" or "Off with her head!" about once in a minute.

—LEWIS CARROLL.

* * *

It was small tyranny for a respectable wind to go wreaking its vengeance on such poor creatures as the fallen leaves, but this wind happening to come upon a great heap of them . . . did so disperse and scatter them that they fled away pell-mell, some here, some there, rolling over each other, whirling around and around on their thin edges, taking frantic flights into the air, and playing all manner of extraordinary gambols in the extremity of their distress. Nor was this enough for its malicious fury: for not content with driving them abroad, it charged small parties of them and hunted them into the wheelwright's saw-pit, and below the planks and timbers in the yard, and, scattering all the sawdust in the air, it looked for them underneath, and when it did meet with any . . . how it drove them on and followed at their heels.

—CHARLES DICKENS.

* * *

Perhaps he was the more curious about these bells, because there were points of resemblance between himself and them. They hung there, in all weathers, with the wind and rain driving in upon them; facing only the outsides of all those houses; never getting any nearer to the blazing fires that gleamed and shone upon the windows, or came puffing out of the chimney tops; and incapable of participation in any of the good things that were constantly being handed, through the street doors and area railings, by prodigious cooks.

—CHARLES DICKENS.

For the night wind has a dismal trick of wandering around and round a building of that sort, and moaning as it goes; and of trying, with its unseen hand, the windows and the doors; and seeking out some crevices by which to enter. And when it has got in, as one not finding what it seeks, whatever that may be, it wails and howls to issue forth again: and not content with stalking through the aisles, and gliding around and round the pillars, and tempting the deep organ, soars up to the roof, and strives to rend the rafters: then flings itself despairingly upon the stones below, and passes, muttering, into the vaults. Anon it comes up stealthily, and creeps along the walls, seeming to read in whispers, the inscriptions sacred to the dead . . . It has a ghostly sound, too, lingering within the altar, where it seems to chant, in its wild way, of wrong and murder done . . . It has an awful voice, that wind at midnight, singing in a church.

—CHARLES DICKENS.

Exercises for Articulation

Willows whiten, aspens quiver,
Little breezes dusk and shiver
Thro' the wave that runs forever
By the island in the river
 Flowing down to Camelot.
Four gray walls and four gray towers,
Overlook a space of flowers,
And the silent isle imbowers
 The Lady of Shalott.

By the margin, willow-veiled,
Slide the heavy barges trailed
By slow horses; and unhailed
The shallop flitteth silken-sailed,
 Skimming down to Camelot;
But who hath seen her wave her hand?
Or at the casement seen her stand?
Or is she known in all the land,
 The Lady of Shalott?

—ALFRED LORD TENNYSON.

* * *

This is the house that Jack built.

This is the malt that lay in the house that Jack built.

This is the rat that ate the malt, that lay in the house that Jack built.

This is the cat that chased the rat, that ate the malt, that lay in the house that Jack built.

This is the dog that worried the cat, that chased the rat, that ate the malt, that lay in the house that Jack built.

This is the cow with the crumpled horn, that tossed the dog, that worried the cat, that chased the rat, that ate the malt, that lay in the house that Jack built.

This is the maiden all forlorn, that milked the cow with the crumpled horn, that tossed the dog, that worried the cat, that chased the rat, that ate the malt, that lay in the house that Jack built.

This is the man all tattered and torn, that loved the maiden all forlorn, that milked the cow with the crumpled horn, that tossed the dog, that worried the cat, that chased the rat, that ate the malt, that lay in the house that Jack built.

This is the priest all shaven and shorn, that married the man all tattered and torn and the maiden all forlorn, that milked the cow with the crumpled horn, that tossed the dog, that worried the cat, that chased the rat, that ate the malt, that lay in the house that Jack built.

This is the cock that crowed in the morn, that waked the priest all shaven and shorn, that married the man all tattered and torn and the maiden all forlorn, that milked the cow with the crumpled horn, that tossed the dog, that worried the cat, that chased the rat, that ate the malt, that lay in the house that Jack built.—*Folk tale.*

* * *

Through the deep gulf of the chimney wide
Wallows the Yule-log's roaring tide;
The broad flame pennons droop and flap
And belly and tug as a flag in the wind;
Like a locust shrills the imprisoned sap,
Hunted to death in its galleries blind;
And swift little troops of silent sparks,
Now pausing, now scattering away as in fear,
Go threading the soot-forest's tangled darks
Like herds of startled deer.
—JAMES RUSSELL LOWELL.

* * *

THE FOUNTAIN

Into the sunshine,
Full of light,
Leaping and flashing
From morn till night.

Into the moonlight,
Whiter than snow,
Waving so flower-like
When the winds blow!

Into the starlight,
Rushing in spray,
Happy at midnight,
Happy by day!

Ever in motion
Blythesome and cheery,
Still climbing heavenward,
Never aweary;—

Glad of all weathers,
Still seeming best,
Upward or downward,
Motion thy rest;—

. . .

Glorious fountain!
Let my heart be
Fresh, changeful, constant,
Upward like thee.
                    —JAMES RUSSELL LOWELL.

* * *

Christmas time! That man must be a misanthrope, indeed, in whose breast something like a jovial feeling is not roused—in whose mind some pleasant associations are not awakened—by the recurrence of Christmas. There are people who will tell you that Christmas is not to them what it used to be; that each succeeding Christmas has found some cherished hope, or happy prospect of the year before, dimmed or passed away; that the present only serves to remind them of reduced incomes and straightened circumstances—of the feasts they once bestowed on hollow friends, and of the cold looks that meet them now, in adversity and misfortune. Never heed such dismal reminiscences. There are few men who have lived long enough in the world, who cannot call up such thoughts any day in the year. Then do not select the merriest of the three hundred and sixty five, for your doleful recollections, but draw your chair near the blazing fire—fill the glass and send round the song—and if your room be smaller than it was a dozen years ago, or if your glass be filled with reeking punch, instead of sparkling wine, put a good face on the matter, and empty it off-hand and fill another, and troll off the old ditty you used to sing, and thank heaven it's no worse . . . Reflect upon your present blessings . . . Fill your glass again with a merry face and contented heart. Our life on it, but your Christmas shall be merry, and your new year a happy one.
                    —CHARLES DICKENS.

Oh but he was a tight-fisted hand at the grindstone. Scrooge! a squeezing, wrenching, scraping, grasping, clutching, covetous, old sinner! Hard and sharp as flint, from which no steel had ever struck out generous fire; secret and self-contained, and solitary as an oyster. The cold within him froze his old features, nipped his pointed nose, shrivelled his cheek, stiffened his gait; made his eyes red; his thin lips blue; and spoke out shrewdly in his grating voice. A frosty rime was on his head, and on his eye-brows, and his wiry chin. He carried his own low temperature always about with him; he iced his office in the dog days, and didn't thaw it one degree at Christmas.

External heat and cold had little influence on Scrooge. No warmth could warm, no wintry weather chill him. No wind that blew was bitterer than he, no falling snow was more intent upon its purpose, no pelting rain less open to entreaty. Foul weather didn't know where to have him. The heaviest rain, and snow, and hail, and sleet could boast of the advantage over him in only one respect. They often came down handsomely and Scrooge never did.

—CHARLES DICKENS.

* * *

It is an ancient Mariner,
And he stoppeth one of three.
"By thy long grey beard and glittering eye,
Now wherefore stopp'st thou me?

The Bridegroom's doors are opened wide,
And I am next of kin;
The guests are met, the feast is set:
May'st hear the merry din."

He holds him with his skinny hand,
"There was a ship," quoth he.
"Hold off! unhand me, grey-beard loon!"
Eftsoons his hand dropt he.

He holds him with his glittering eye—
The Wedding-Guest stood still,
And listens like a three years' child:
The Mariner hath his will.

The Wedding-Guest sat on a stone:
He cannot choose but hear;
And thus spake on that ancient man,
The bright-eyed Mariner.

—SAMUEL TAYLOR COLERIDGE.

The clock struck nine when I did send the nurse. In half an hour she promised to return. Perchance she cannot meet him:—that's not so. O, she is lame! Love's herald should be thoughts, that ten times faster glide than the sun's beams, driving back shadows over lowering hills:—therefore do nimble-pinioned doves draw love, and therefore hath the wind-swift cupid wings. Now is the sun upon the highmost hill of this day's journey; and from nine till twelve is three long hours,—and yet she is not come. Had she affections, and warm, youthful blood, she'd be as swift in motion as a ball; my words would bandy her to my sweet love, and his to me.

—SHAKESPEARE.

* * *

Speak the speech, I pray you, as I pronounced it to you, trippingly on the tongue; but if you mouth it, as many of our players do, I had as lief the town-crier spoke my lines.

Nor do not saw the air too much with your hand, thus; but use all gently; for in the very torrent, tempest, and (as I may say) whirlwind of your passion, you must acquire and beget a temperance that may give it smoothness. O, it offends me to the soul to hear a robustious periwig-pated fellow tear a passion to tatters, to very rags, to split the ears of the groundlings, who for the most part are capable of nothing but inexplicable dumb shows and noise. I would have such a fellow whipped for o'erdoing Termagant; it out-herods Herod. Pray you avoid it.

—SHAKESPEARE.

* * *

Thoughts black, hands apt, drugs fit, and time agreeing,
Confederate season, else no creature seeing;
Thou mixture rank, of midnight weeds collected,
With Hecate's ban thrice blasted, thrice infected,
Thy natural magic and dire property
On wholesome life usurp immediately.

—SHAKESPEARE.

* * *

Haste thee, Nymph, and bring with thee
Jest and youthful Jollity,
Quips and Cranks, and wanton Wiles,
Nods and Becks and wreathed Smiles,
Such as hang on Hebe's cheek,
And love to live in dimple sleek;
Sport that wrinkled Care derides
And Laughter holding both his sides.
Come, and trip it, as you go,
On the light fantastic toe.

—MILTON.

Hear the loud alarum bells—
   Brazen bells!
What a tale of terror, now, their turbulency tells!
  In the startled ear of night
  How they scream out their affright!
   Too much horrified to speak,
   They can only shriek, shriek,
    Out of tune,
In the clamorous appealing to the mercy of the fire
In a mad expostulation with the deaf and frantic fire,
   Leaping higher, higher, higher,
   With a desperate desire,
  And a resolute endeavour.
  Now—now to sit or never,
By the side of the pale-faced moon.
   Oh, the bells, bells, bells!
   What a tale their terror tells
    Of Despair!
How they clang, and clash, and roar
What a horror they outpour
On the bosom of the palpitating air!
  Yet the ear it fully knows,
   By the twanging,
   And the clanging,
  How the danger ebbs and flows:
  Yet the ear distinctly tells,
   In the jangling,
   And the wrangling,
  How the danger sinks and swells,
By the sinking or the swelling in the anger of the bells—
   Of the bells—
  Of the bells, bells, bells, bells,
   Bells, bells, bells—
In the clamour and the clangor of the bells!
            —EDGAR ALLAN POE.

* * *

Once upon a midnight dreary, while I pondered weak and weary,
Over many a quaint and curious volume of forgotten lore,
While I nodded, nearly napping, suddenly there came a tapping,
As of some one gently rapping, rapping at my chamber door.
" 'Tis some visitor," I muttered, "tapping at my chamber door—
  Only this, and nothing more."

Ah, distinctly I remember it was in the bleak December,
And each separate dying ember wrought its ghost upon the floor.

Eagerly I wished the morrow;—vainly I had sought to borrow
From my books surcease of sorrow—sorrow for the lost Lenore—
For the rare and radiant maiden whom the angels name Lenore—
    Nameless here for evermore.

And the silken sad uncertain rustling of each purple curtain
Thrilled me—filled me with fantastic terrors never felt before;
So that now, to still the beating of my heart, I stood repeating,
" 'Tis some visitor entreating entrance at my chamber door;—
    This it is, and nothing more."

Presently my soul grew stronger; hesitating then no longer,
"Sir," said I, "or Madam, truly your forgiveness I implore;
But the fact is I was napping, and so gently you came rapping,
And so faintly you came tapping, tapping at my chamber door,
That I scarce was sure I heard you"—here I opened wide the door;—
    Darkness there, and nothing more.

Deep into that darkness peering, long I stood there wondering, fearing,
Doubting, dreaming dreams no mortals ever dared to dream before;
But the silence was unbroken, and the stillness gave no token,
And the only word there spoken was the whispered word, "Lenore!"
This I whispered, and an echo murmured back the word, "Lenore!"—
    Merely this, and nothing more.

—EDGAR ALLAN POE.

Exercises for Volume and Energy of Tone

Wherefore rejoice?   What conquest brings he home?
What tributaries follow him to Rome,
To grace in captive bonds his chariot-wheels?
You blocks, you stones, you worse than senseless things!
O you hard hearts, you cruel men of Rome,
Knew you not Pompey?   Many a time and oft
Have you climb'd up to walls and battlements,
To towers and windows, yea, to chimney-tops,
Your infants in your arms, and there have sat
The live-long day with patient expectation
To see great Pompey pass the streets of Rome;
And when you saw his chariot but appear,
Have you not made an universal shout,
That Tiber trembled underneath her banks
To hear the replication of your sounds
Made in her concave shores?
And do you now put on your best attire?
And do you now cull out a holiday?
And do you now strew flowers in his way

That comes in triumph over Pompey's blood?
Be gone!
Run to your houses, fall upon your knees,
Pray to the gods to intermit the plague
That needs must light on this ingratitude.

—SHAKESPEARE.

* * *

All this! ay more: fret till your proud heart break;
Go show your slaves how choleric you are,
And make your bondmen tremble.   Must I budge?
Must I observe you? must I stand and crouch
Under your testy humour?   By the gods,
You shall digest the venom of your spleen,
Though it do split you; for, from this day forth,
I'll use you for my mirth, yea, for my laughter,
When you are waspish.

—SHAKESPEARE.

* * *

Once more unto the breach, dear friends, once more;
Or close the wall up with our English dead!
In peace there's nothing so becomes a man
As modest stillness and humility:
But when the blast of war blows in our ears,
Then imitate the action of the tiger;
Stiffen the sinews, summon up the blood,
Disguise fair nature with hard-favour'd rage;
Then lend the eye a terrible aspect;
Let it pry through the portage of the head
Like the brass cannon; let the brow o'erwhelm it
As fearfully as doth a galled rock
O'erhang and jutty his confounded base,
Swill'd with the wild and wasteful ocean.
Now set the teeth and stretch the nostril wide,
Hold hard the breath and bend up every spirit
To his full height.   On, on, you noblest English,
Whose blood is fet from fathers of war-proof!
Fathers that, like so many Alexanders,
Have in these parts from morn till even fought,
And sheathed their swords for lack of argument:
Dishonour not your mothers; now attest
That those whom you call'd fathers did beget you.
Be copy now to men of grosser blood,
And teach them how to war.   And you good yeomen,
Whose limbs were made in England, show us here
The mettle of your pasture; let us swear

That you are worth your breeding; which I doubt not;
For there is none of you so mean and base,
That hath not noble lustre in your eyes.
I see you stand like greyhounds in the slips,
Straining upon the start.   The game's afoot:
Follow your spirit, and upon this charge
Cry "God for Harry, England, and Saint George!"

—SHAKESPEARE.

* * *

More than I have said, loving countrymen,
The leisure and enforcement of the time
Forbids to dwell upon: yet remember this,
God and our good cause fight upon our side;
The prayers of holy saints and wronged souls,
Like high-rear'd bulwarks, stand before our faces.
Richard except, those whom we fight against
Had rather have us win than him they follow:
For what is he they follow? truly, gentlemen,
A bloody tyrant and a homicide;
One raised in blood, and one in blood establish'd;
One that made means to come by what he hath,
And slaughter'd those that were the means to help him;
A base foul stone, made precious by the foil
Of England's chair, where he is falsely set;
One that hath ever been God's enemy:
Then, if you fight against God's enemy,
God will in justice ward you as his soldiers;
If you do sweat to put a tyrant down,
You sleep in peace, the tyrant being slain;
If you do fight against your country's foes,
Your country's fat shall pay your pains the hire;
If you do fight in safeguard of your wives,
Your wives shall welcome home the conquerors;
If you do free your children from the sword,
Your children's children quit it in your age.
Then, in the name of God and all these rights,
Advance your standards, draw your willing swords.
For me, the ransom of my bold attempt
Shall be this cold corpse on the earth's cold face;
But if I thrive, the gain of my attempt
The least of you shall share his part thereof.
Sound drums and trumpets boldly and cheerfully;
God and Saint George!   Richmond and victory!

—SHAKESPEARE.

Marching Along

I

Kentish Sir Byng stood for his King,
Bidding the crop-headed Parliament swing:
And, pressing a troop unable to stoop
And see the rogues flourish and honest folk droop,
Marched them along, fifty-score strong,
Great-hearted gentlemen, singing this song.

II

God for King Charles! Pym and such carles
To the Devil that prompts 'em their treasonous parles!
Cavaliers, up! Lips from the cup,
Hands from the pasty, nor bite take nor sup
Till you're—
  (Chorus) *Marching along, fifty-score strong,*
  Great-hearted gentlemen, singing this song.

III

Hampden to Hell, and his obsequies' knell
Serve Hazelrig, Fiennes, and young Harry as well!
England, good cheer! Rupert is near!
Kentish and loyalists, keep we not here
  (Cho.) *Marching along, fifty-score strong,*
  Great-hearted gentlemen, singing this song!

IV

Then, God for King Charles! Pym and his snarls
To the Devil that pricks on such pestilent carles!
Hold by the right, you double your might;
So, onward to Nottingham, fresh for the fight.
  (Cho.) *March we along, fifty-score strong,*
  Great-hearted gentlemen, singing this song!
                              —Robert Browning.

* * *

Boot and Saddle

I

Boot, saddle, to horse, and away!
Rescue my Castle, before the hot day
Brightens to blue from its silvery gray.
  (Cho.) *"Boot, saddle, to horse, and away!"*

II

Ride past the suburbs, asleep as you'd say;
Many's the friend there, will listen and pray
"God's luck to gallants that strike up the lay,
(Cho.) *"Boot, saddle, to horse, and away!"*

—ROBERT BROWNING.

* * *

French Herald

You men of Angiers, open wide your gates,
And let young Arthur, Duke of Bretagne, in,
Who by the hand of France this day hath made
Much work for tears in many an English mother,
Whose sons lie scattered on the bleeding ground:
Many a widow's husband grovelling lies,
Coldly embracing the discoloured earth;
And victory, with little loss, doth play
Upon the dancing banners of the French,
Who are at hand, triumphantly display'd,
To enter conquerors, and to proclaim
Arthur of Bretagne England's king and yours.

* * *

English Herald

Rejoice you men of Angiers, ring your bells;
King John, your king and England's, doth approach,
Commander of this hot malicious day:
Their armours, that march'd hence so silver-bright,
Hither return all gilt with Frenchmen's blood;
There stuck no plume in any English crest
That is removed by a staff of France;
Our colours do return in those same hands
That did display them when we first march'd forth;
And, like a jolly troop of huntsmen, come
Our lusty English, all with purpled hands,
Dyed in the dying slaughter of their foes:
Open your gates and give the victors way.

—SHAKESPEARE.

* * *

Rebellious subjects, enemies to peace,
Profaners of this neighbour-stained steel,—
Will they not hear? What, ho! you men, you beasts,
That quench the fire of your pernicious rage
With purple fountains issuing from your veins,

On pain of torture, from those bloody hands
Throw your mistemper'd weapons to the ground,
And hear the sentence of your moved prince.
Three civil brawls, bred of an airy word,
By thee, old Capulet, and Montague,
Have thrice disturb'd the quiet of our streets,
And made Verona's ancient citizens
Cast by their grave beseeming ornaments,
To wield old partisans, in hands as old,
Canker'd with peace, to part your canker'd hate;
If ever you disturb our streets again,
Your lives shall pay the forfeit of the peace.
For this time, all the rest depart away:
You, Capulet, shall go along with me;
And Montague, come you this afternoon,
To know our farther pleasure in this case,
To old Free-town, our common judgement-place.
Once more, on pain of death, all men depart.
—SHAKESPEARE.

* * *

I perceive, here in my majesty,
How that all creatures be to me unkind,
Living without fear in worldly prosperity.
In spiritual vision the people be so blind,
Drowned in sin, they know me not for their God;
In worldly riches is all their mind;

. . .

Every man liveth so after his own pleasure,
And yet of their lives they be nothing sure.
The more I them forbear, I see
The worse from year to year they be;

. . .

I proferred the people great multitude of mercy,
And few there be that ask it heartily.
They be so cumbered with worldly riches, thereto
I must needs upon them justice do
On every man living without fear.
—*Everyman.*

Exercises for Round, Free Tone

Romans, countrymen, and lovers! hear me for my cause, and be silent, that you may hear; believe me for mine honour, and have respect to mine honour, that you may believe: censure me in your wisdom, and awake your senses, that you may the better judge. If there be any in this assembly, any dear friend of Caesar's, to him I say that Brutus' love to Caesar was no less than his. If then that friend demand why Brutus rose against Caesar, this is my answer; not that I loved Caesar less, but that I loved Rome more. Had you rather Caesar were living, and die all slaves, than that Caesar were dead, to live all freemen? As Caesar loved me, I weep for him; as he was fortunate, I rejoice at it; as he was valiant, I honour him; but as he was ambitious I slew him. There is tears for his love; joy for his fortune; honour for his valour; and death for his ambition. Who is here so base that would be a bondman? If any, speak; for him have I offended. Who is here so rude that would not be a Roman? If any, speak; for him have I offended. Who is here so vile that will not love his country? If any, speak; for him have I offended. I pause for reply.

—SHAKESPEARE.

* * *

Roll on, thou deep and dark blue Ocean—roll!
Ten thousand fleets sweep over thee in vain;
Man marks the earth with ruin—his control
Stops with the shore;—upon the watery plain
The wrecks are all thy deed, nor doth remain
A shadow of man's ravage, save his own,
When, for a moment, like a drop of rain,
He sinks into thy depths with bubbling groan,
Without a grave, unknelled, uncoffined, and unknown.

—LORD BYRON.

* * *

Now, my co-mates and brothers in exile,
Hath not old custom made this life more sweet
Than that of painted pomp? Are not these woods
More free from peril than the envious court?
Here feel we but the penalty of Adam,
The seasons' difference; as the icy fang
And churlish chiding of the winter's wind,
Which, when it bites and blows upon my body,
Even till I shrink with cold, I smile and say
"This is no flattery; these are counsellors
That feelingly persuade me what I am.
Sweet are the uses of adversity,
Which, like the toad, ugly and venomous,
Wears yet a precious jewel in his head;
And this our life exempt from public haunt
Finds tongues in trees, books in the running brooks,
Sermons in stones and good in everything."

—SHAKESPEARE.

O thou that rollest above, round as the shield of my fathers!
whence are thy beams, O sun! thy everlasting light?

—JAMES MACPHERSON.

* * *

How sweet the moonlight sleeps upon this bank!
Here will we sit, and let the sounds of music
Creep in our ears: soft stillness and the night
Become the touches of sweet harmony.
Sit, Jessica.   Look how the floor of heaven
Is thick inlaid with patines of bright gold:
There's not the smallest orb which thou behold'st
But in his motion like an angel sings,
Still quiring to the young-eyed Cherubims;
Such harmony is in immortal souls;
But whilst this muddy vesture of decay
Doth grossly close it in, we cannot hear it.

—SHAKESPEARE.

* * *

And slowly answered Arthur from barge:
"The old order changeth, yielding place to new,
And God fulfills himself in many ways,
Lest one good custom should corrupt the world.
Comfort thyself: what comfort is in me?
I have lived my life, and that which I have done
May He within himself make pure! but thou,
If thou shouldst never see my face again,
Pray for my soul.   More things are wrought by prayer
Than this world dreams of.   Wherefore, let thy voice
Rise like a fountain for me night and day.
For what are men better than sheep or goats
That nourish a blind life within the brain,
If, knowing God, they lift not hands of prayer
Both for themselves and those who call them friend?
For so the whole round earth is every way
Bound by gold chains about the feet of God."

—ALFRED LORD TENNYSON.

* * *

The splendor falls on castle walls
    And snowy summits old in story:
The long light shakes across the lakes,
    And the wild cataract leaps in glory.
Blow, bugle, blow, set the wild echoes flying,
Blow, bugle; answer, echoes, dying, dying, dying.

O hark, O hear! how thin and clear,
  And thinner, clearer, farther going!
O sweet and far from cliff and scar
  The horns of Elfland faintly blowing!
Blow, let us hear the purple glens replying:
Blow, bugle; answer, echoes, dying, dying, dying.

O love they die in yon rich sky,
  They faint on hill or field or river;
Our echoes roll from soul to soul,
  And grow for ever and for ever.
Blow, bugle, blow, set the wild echoes flying,
And answer, echoes, answer, dying, dying, dying.
                    —ALFRED LORD TENNYSON.

* * *

Now is the winter of our discontent
Made glorious summer by this sun of York;
And all the clouds that lour'd upon our house
In the deep bosom of the ocean buried.
Now are our brows bound with victorious wreaths;
Our bruised arms hung up for monuments;
Our stern alarums changed to merry meetings,
Our dreadful marches to delightful measures.
                    —SHAKESPEARE.

* * *

This is the forest primeval. The murmuring pines and the hemlocks,
Bearded with moss, and in garments green, indistinct in the twilight,
Stand like Druids of eld, with voices sad and prophetic,
Stand like harpers hoar, with beards that rest on their bosoms.
Loud from its rocky caverns, the deep-voiced neighboring ocean
Speaks, and in accents disconsolate answers the wail of the forest.

This is the forest primeval; but where are the hearts that beneath it
Leaped like the roe, when he hears in the woodland the voice of the
                    huntsman?
Where is the thatch-roofed village, the home of Acadian farmers,—
Men whose lives glided on like rivers that water the woodlands,
Darkened by shadows of earth, but reflecting an image of heaven?

Ye who believe in affection that hopes, and endures, and is patient,
Ye who believe in the beauty and strength of woman's devotion,
List to the mournful tradition still sung by the pines of the forest;
List to a Tale of Love in Acadie, home of the happy.
                    —HENRY WADSWORTH LONGFELLOW.

Breathes there the man, with soul so dead,
Who never to himself hath said,
  This is my own, my native land!
Whose heart hath ne'er within him burned,
As home his footsteps he hath turned
  From wandering on a foreign strand!
If such there be, go, mark him well;
For him no Minstrel raptures swell;
High though his titles, proud his name,
Boundless his wealth as wish can claim;
Despite those titles, power, and pelf,
The wretch, concentred all in self,
Living, shall forfeit fair renown,
And doubly dying, shall go down
To the vile dust, from whence he sprung,
Unwept, unhonoured, and unsung.

                —SIR WALTER SCOTT.

PART IV

Contracts

CONTRACT SHEET
Careless Speech

1. Control of the organs of articulation.

2. Clear enunciation of initial consonants, *th voiced* [ð] and *th voiceless* [θ].

3. Clear enunciation of final consonants.

4. Clear enunciation of middle consonants.

5. Correct pronunciation of difficult sound combinations.

6. Correction of mispronunciations due to (1) omission of sounds, (2) addition of sounds, (3) sound substitutions.

7. Clear articulation in sentences.

8. Clear articulation in the reading of brief stanzas of poetry.

9. Clear articulation in the reading of prepared paragraphs.

10. Clear articulation in a prepared talk.

11. Clear articulation in sight reading, extemporaneous speaking, and general conversation.

CONTRACT 1

Objective:

Control of the organs of articulation.

Procedure:

See tongue, lip, and jaw exercises given on pages 68 and 69. Do these exercises conscientiously several times a day.

Caution:

Be sure that you always practice with a mirror.

Be sure that your tongue, lips, and jaw always take the position indicated in the exercise.

When doing the tongue exercises, be sure to have approximately the distance of two fingers' space between the teeth, in order that the tongue may get the maximum exercise.

When you are asked to point the tongue, be sure that it is pointed and not blunt.

Be sure to use the lips and jaw vigorously when doing the lip and jaw exercises.

Practice Material:

Stand or sit before a mirror, and do the tongue exercises (page 68) carefully. Go slowly at first; accuracy is more important than speed.

Next do the lip and jaw exercises.

Do the following exercises, using the lips and jaw vigorously:

ah ē o͞o [ɑ: i: u:]	po͞o pē pah [pu: pi: pɑ:]
o͞o ē ah [u: i: ɑ:]	bo͞o bē bah [bu: bi: bɑ:]
ē ah o͞o [i: ɑ: u:]	mo͞o mē mah [mu: mi: mɑ:]
pah pē po͞o [pɑ: pi: pu:]	pē pah po͞o [pi: pɑ: pu:]
bah bē bo͞o [bɑ: bi: bu:]	bē bah bo͞o [bi: bɑ: bu:]
mah mē mo͞o [mɑ: mi: mu:]	mē mah mo͞o [mi: mɑ: mu:]
wah wē wo͞o [wɑ: wi: wu:]	wē wah wo͞o [wi: wɑ: wu:]
hwah hwē hwo͞o [ʍɑ: ʍi: ʍu:]	hwē hwah hwo͞o [ʍi: ʍɑ: ʍu:]

pĭppity păppity pŏppity po͞o   wĭppity wăppity wŏppity wo͞o
bĭbbity băbbity bŏbbity bo͞o   hwĭppity hwăppity hwŏppity hwo͞o
mĭbbity măbbity mŏbbity mo͞o   pĭbbity bĭbbity wĭbbity mĭbbity hwo͞o

Test:

1. Can you point your tongue?

2. Can you bulge your tongue?

3. Can you groove your tongue? Can you blow through the groove?

4. Can you rotate your tongue carefully, smoothly, slowly, not omitting to touch any surface?

5. Can you snap your lips together for *p* [p], making a popping noise like a motor boat?

6. Can you open your mouth wide for *ah* [ɑ:]? Can you round your lips closely for *ōō* [u:]? Can you spread your lips in a broad grin for *ē* [i:]? Do you feel the lips move from one position to another?

CONTRACT 2

Objective:

Clear pronunciation of initial sounds *th voiced* [ð] and *th voiceless* [θ].

Procedure:

See page 34 for the correct pronunciation of these sounds.

Say the following syllables, using great care in placing the tongue for *th*:

thē thē thē [ði:]	thā thā thā [θeтɪ]
thā thā thā [ðeтɪ]	then then then ['ðeтn]
thah thah thah [ðɑ:]	thin thin thin ['θɪn]
thē thē thē [θi:]	thah thah thah [θɑ:]

Continue practicing in this manner, placing *th voiced* [ð] and *th voiceless* [θ] before all vowel sounds.

Caution:

In making these sounds, be sure:

1. That your tongue is not on your upper gum.

2. That your tongue is not on your upper teeth.

3. That your tongue is not thrust out beyond your teeth.

4. That your tongue protrudes very slightly beyond the edge of your upper teeth.

Speak slowly at first in order that you may never allow yourself to make these sounds incorrectly.

Practice Material:

Say each of the following words three times:

th voiced [ð]		*th voiceless* [θ]	
then	this	thin	thumb
there	though	thank	thread
thus	than	third	throne
the	thou	theatre	three
that	thy	thick	thrive

Say the following sentences slowly and then more quickly, using great care in the pronunciation of the *th* sounds:

1. He sat in the middle of the room.

2. The thin man stood at the foot of the stairs.

3. The theatre was about a third of the way down the street.

4. There was a large throne at the front of the banquet hall.

5. There were three thin trees on that side of the lawn.

6. The beggar stopped at the front of the house to thank his benefactor.

Read the following paragraph, using great care in the pronunciation of the *th* sounds:

When his mother was away, Theodore was obliged to sew a button on his coat. When he attempted to thread the needle, he felt that his "fingers were all thumbs." He held that thoroughly tantalizing needle up to the light to be sure that it really contained an eye. He thought that the eye of the needle was too fine, or that the thread was too coarse and thick. He tried another needle and another spool of thread. Finally he had a bright idea: he thought he would use a darning needle and very fine thread. This plan was a success, and the button stayed in place until Theodore's mother returned.

Test:

1. Can you read the words in the Practice Material, pronouncing the *th* sounds correctly?

2. Can you pronounce the *th* sounds correctly in the sentences given above?

3. Can you pronounce the *th* sounds correctly in the sentences given on page 35?

4. Can you pronounce the *th* sounds correctly in the paragraph given above?

5. Can you pronounce the *th* sounds correctly when reading *The House that Jack Built* (page 135)?

6. Can you pronounce the *th* sounds correctly in the sentences given for those sounds in Part III (pages 95–96)?

7. Can you pronounce the *th* sounds correctly in the paragraphs and stanzas of poetry given for those sounds in Part III (pages 130–132)?

CONTRACT 3

Objective:

Clear enunciation of all final consonants.

Procedure:

Consult Part II, Chapter IV, for the correct production of any consonants about which you are in doubt.

Say the following syllables pronouncing the final consonants clearly and distinctly:

ăt ăt ăt [æt]
ĕt ĕt ĕt [eᴛt]
ĭt ĭt ĭt [ɪt]
ŏt ŏt ŏt [ɒt]
ŭt ŭt ŭt [ʌt]
ăt ĕt ĭt ŏt ŭt [æt eᴛt ɪt ɒt ʌt]

ăd ăd ăd [æd]
ĕd ĕd ĕd [eᴛd]
ĭd ĭd ĭd [ɪd]
ŏd ŏd ŏd [ɒd]
ŭd ŭd ŭd [ʌd]
ăd ĕd ĭd ŏd ŭd [æd eᴛd ɪd ɒd ʌd]

ăg ăg ăg [æg]
ĕg ĕg ĕg [eᴛg]
ĭg ĭg ĭg [ɪg]
ŏg ŏg ŏg [ɒg]
ŭg ŭg ŭg [ʌg]
ăg ĕg ĭg ŏg ŭg [æg eᴛg ɪg ɒg ʌg]

Proceed in this manner with other vowel and consonant sounds.

Caution:

Be sure to pronounce all final sounds clearly and distinctly.
Be sure not to *overdo* the pronunciation of the final consonants.
Remember:

1. That the voiceless plosives *p* [p], *t* [t], *k* [k] are aspirated (followed by a slight puff of breath) when preceding a vowel, or when final in a phrase.

2. That p [p], t [t], k [k] are *never* aspirated before another consonant.[1]

3. That there is no off glide on the voiced plosives b [b], d [d], g [g] when preceding another consonant.

Practice Material:

Say the following three times:

> tit for tat [tɪt fə tæt]
> tit tat toe [tɪt tæt toɾʊ]
> tick tack toe [tɪk tæk toɾʊ]
> ăk ăt ăct [æk æt ækt]

Say the following words, pronouncing the final consonants clearly and distinctly:

cricket	trite	cold	fifth
chilled	trap	tallest	hives
looked	cribbed	act	drag
twisted	tripped	draft	clap
tossed	five	lack	club

Read the following sentences clearly and distinctly:

1. Did you hear the cricket sing?

2. The boys caught the rabbit in the snare.

3. Would you like some chilled tomato juice?

4. We drank from a cracked cup.

5. The cub tripped as he walked through the forest.

6. The pilot glanced nervously at the black cloud.

7. The child wanted five cents' worth of licorice candy.

8. Kate wore her hair in a twist at the top of her head.

9. The soldiers tramped down the hot, dark road.

10. "Now I am cabined, cribbed, confined."

Read the following paragraph clearly and distinctly, but not pedantically:

> Washington's Birthday, the twenty-second of February, was the coldest day of winter that year. There was a blizzard in which the snow drifted to the depth of eight feet; the wind blew at the rate of seventy miles an hour, and the temperature dropped to eight below zero. Many people had to stay at home because of the storm. The more hardy ones,

---

[1] See page 32.

however, made an attempt to get to their places of business, and, for the most part, were successful, although they suffered great discomfort and delay. The children enjoyed the excitement, but wished that it might have occurred on a school day instead of on Washington's Birthday.

Test:

1. Can you pronounce clearly and distinctly the words given in the Practice Material?

2. Can you read the sentences in the Practice Material, clearly and distinctly, but not pedantically?

3. Can you read the sentences on pages 73–74, pronouncing the final consonants distinctly?

4. Can you read the paragraph given above clearly and distinctly?

5. Can you read one or more of the paragraphs given in the Exercises for Articulation in Part III, clearly and distinctly but not pedantically?

CONTRACT 4

Objective:

Clear enunciation of middle consonants.

Procedure:

Say the following syllables, pronouncing the middle consonants clearly and distinctly:

ăbba ăbba ăbba ['æbə]
ĕbba ĕbba ĕbba ['eɪbə]
ĭbba ĭbba ĭbba ['ɪbə]
ŏbba ŏbba ŏbba ['ɒbə]
ŭbba ŭbba ŭbba ['ʌbə]
ăbba ĕbba ĭbba ŏbba ŭbba ['æbə 'eɪbə 'ɪbə 'ɒbə 'ʌbə]

ăppa ăppa ăppa ['æpə]
ĕppa ĕppa ĕppa ['eɪpə]
ĭppa ĭppa ĭppa ['ɪpə]
ŏppa ŏppa ŏppa ['ɒpə]
ŭppa ŭppa ŭppa ['ʌpə]
ăppa ĕppa ĭppa ŏppa ŭppa ['æpə 'eɪpə 'ɪpə 'ɒpə 'ʌpə]

ătta ătta ătta ['ætə]
ĕtta ĕtta ĕtta ['eɪtə]
ĭtta ĭtta ĭtta ['ɪtə]
ŏtta ŏtta ŏtta ['ɒtə]
ŭtta ŭtta ŭtta ['ʌtə]
ătta ĕtta ĭtta ŏtta ŭtta ['ætə 'eɪtə 'ɪtə 'ɒtə 'ʌtə]

ădda ădda ădda ['ædə]
ĕdda ĕdda ĕdda ['eɪdə]
ĭdda ĭdda ĭdda ['ɪdə]
ŏdda ŏdda ŏdda ['ɒdə]
ŭdda ŭdda ŭdda ['ʌdə]
ădda ĕdda ŏdda ŭdda ['ædə 'eɪdə 'ɪdə 'ɒdə 'ʌdə]

Proceed in like manner with other vowels and consonants.

Caution:

Be sure to differentiate carefully between voiced and voiceless consonants in the middle of a word.

Remember that a consonant in the middle of a word is generally pronounced with the following syllable; that is, the word *kitten* is divided as follows: *ki—tn* ['kɪ tn̩] not *kit—n* ['kɪt n̩]—the *t* is pronounced with the second syllable, not the first.

Remember that a double consonant in the spelling of a word is pronounced as one sound.

Practice Material:

Read the following words, pronouncing the middle consonants clearly and distinctly:

city	carpenter	beautiful
little	glimmering	satisfactory
Latin	children	partner
atom	huddle	opponent
utter	mortal	winter
pretty	middle	kettle
kitten	water	opportunity

Read the following pairs of words, differentiating carefully between the voiced and unvoiced middle consonants:

addict	attic	wading	waiting
candor	canter	riding	writing
ribbon	ripping	madder	matter
soggy	soccer	ladder	latter
egging	aching	raiding	rating

Read the following sentences, pronouncing all consonant sounds clearly and distinctly:

1. Kitty lived in the middle west.
2. Watertown is a pretty little city.
3. The mittens were beautifully knitted.
4. The tea kettle was shining brightly.

5. The students were uttering difficult sentences.

6. The children's toys were cluttering up the room.

7. The bridge player doubled his opponent's bid.

8. Herbert and Donald were partners in the new enterprise.

9. The children were waiting to go wading in the water.

10. Tom was writing to his mother about his riding lesson.

Read the following paragraph, making all consonant sounds clearly and distinctly:

> The students found great difficulty in pronouncing the sounds *t* and *d* distinctly. The teacher told them to try pointing the tip of the tongue on the middle of the upper gum in order to make these sounds correctly. She said if they would practice the tongue exercises faithfully every day, they would find themselves better able to utter these sounds. She said they moved their tongues so little, and opened their mouths so slightly when they talked, that it was no wonder it was difficult to understand them. She advised them to spend much more time practicing tongue and articulation exercises if they desired to have beautiful speech.

Test:

1. Can you pronounce the words given in the Practice Material clearly and distinctly?

2. Can you read the sentences given in the Practice Material, pronouncing the consonant sounds clearly and distinctly?

3. Can you read the sentences on pages 98–99, pronouncing all consonant sounds clearly and distinctly?

4. Can you read the paragraph given above, pronouncing all consonant sounds clearly and distinctly?

5. Can you read one or two of the selections given for articulation in Part III, pronouncing all consonant sounds clearly and distinctly?

CONTRACT 5

Objective:

Clear pronunciation of difficult sound combinations, such as: *nt, nd, mp, tl, pt, ft, st, kt, th, sts, fts, pts, ths, thz.*

Procedure:

See the consonant section of Chapter IV, Part II, for the correct production of the sounds concerned: *m* [m], *p* [p], *th* [ð] and [θ], *f* [f], *n* [n], *d* [d], *t* [t], *l* [l], *s* [s], *k* [k], *g* [g].

Say the following syllables, pronouncing the consonant sounds clearly and distinctly:

ēast	ēast	ēast	[i·st]	ĕpts	ĕpts	ĕpts	[eгpts]
ĭst	ĭst	ĭst	[ɪst]	ĕths	ĕths	ĕths	[eгθs]
ănt	ănt	ănt	[ænt]	ănta	ănta	ănta	['æntə]
ănd	ănd	ănd	[ænd]	ĕnda	ĕnda	ĕnda	['eгndə]
ăft	ăft	ăft	[æft]	ăfta	ăfta	ăfta	['æftə]
ĭft	ĭft	ĭft	[ɪft]	ăkta	ăkta	ăkta	['æktə]
ăkt	ăkt	ăkt	[ækt]	ŏmpa	ŏmpa	ŏmpa	['ɒmpə]
ĭmp	ĭmp	ĭmp	[ɪmp]	ĭlta	ĭlta	ĭlta	['ɪltə]
ăfts	ăfts	ăfts	[æfts]	ĕfta	ĕfta	ĕfta	['eгftə]
ăkts	ăkts	ăkts	[ækts]	ĭntly	ĭntly	ĭntly	['ɪntlɪ]

Proceed in like manner, placing various vowel sounds before these difficult consonant combinations.

Caution:

Be sure that each consonant is pronounced clearly and distinctly. Remember that voiceless consonants *p* [p], *t* [t], and *k* [k] are not aspirated before another consonant.

Practice Material:

Read the following words, pronouncing the consonant sounds clearly and distinctly:

act	eminently	last	secondary	facts
apparently	evidently	left	shouldn't	fifths
artist	fact	length	sift	fists
breadth	fifth	lintel	slept	fits
candidate	fist	list	swept	ghosts
candle	gentleman	lost	temptation	gifts
competently	ghost	mantle	tentative	lasts
complicated	gift	middle	test	lengths
complimented	government	momentously	thrust	lists
confidently	hadn't	month	twenty	months
consequently	handle	mountain	wanted	oaths
consistently	insists	pedantic	width	presents
couldn't	intermittent	permanently	wouldn't	rasps
decently	kept	presently	acts	sifts
defect	kettle	preventable	artists	tests
depths	kindly	providently	breadths	thrusts
didn't	lamentably	riddle	depths	truths
eighth	landlord	rift	eights	widths

Read the following sentences clearly and distinctly:

1. Rip Van Winkle spent twenty years on the mountain.

2. Lester lived in the eastern part of the state.

3. The candidate for election was fond of talking in riddles.

4. The artist apparently didn't have the money to buy his materials.

5. The gentleman bought his clothes in Bond Street when he was in London.

6. The problem was complicated by several factors.

7. Pedantic people are apt to have stilted speech.

8. The refugees were discovered to be lamentably poor.

9. The landlord reduced the rent because the tenant was an intimate friend.

10. "How far that little candle throws its beams.
So shines a good deed in a naughty world."

Read the following paragraph clearly and distinctly:

The successful candidate for the mayoralty compiled lists of the predilections of his constituents, and, as a result, was better able to treat them with consideration and tact. Probably because of this, he received four-fifths more votes than his opponent. If he redeems his campaign pledges and is true to his extravagant promises, he will be worthy of the confidence of the voters, and will become the best mayor any city has ever had.

Test:

1. Can you pronounce the words given in the Practice Material clearly and distinctly? Can you do so in your general conversation?

2. Can you read the sentences given above clearly and distinctly?

3. Can you read the paragraph given above clearly and distinctly?

4. Can you read several of the exercises for articulation in Part III clearly and distinctly?

CONTRACT 6

Objective:

Correction of mispronunciations due to (1) omission of sounds, (2) addition of sounds, (3) sound substitutions.

Procedure:

Look at each word carefully and be sure (1) that you do not omit any sound which should be pronounced, (2) that you do not insert any sound, (3) that you neither substitute an incorrect sound for the sound indicated, nor change the position of the sound in a word.

Practice the exercises in the Procedure and Practice Material of Contracts 3, 4, and 5.

Caution:

Be sure to look up in the *most recent* edition of an approved dictionary the pronunciation of any word about which you are not absolutely sure.

Practice Material:

Pronounce the following words carefully (these words frequently have a sound *omitted* by careless speakers).

actually	duke	geometry	only	temperature
Arctic	duty	giant	our	terrible
barbarous	eleven	government	particularly	tube
champion	family	huge*	police	Tuesday
comfortable	February	human*	probably	tumult
company	finally	humble*	quarrel	tune
cruel	five	library	recognize	usually
diamond	gentleman	new	Saturday	violet

Pronounce the following words carefully (these words frequently have a sound *added* by careless speakers):

athletic	drawing	forehead	law
attacked	drowned	grievous	often
chimney	elm	height	sawing
comma	film	helm	umbrella

Pronounce the following words correctly. These words frequently have an incorrect sound substituted for the desired sound, such as *wale* [ˈweɪl] for *whale* [ˈʌeɪl], or the position of a sound changed about in the word, as *bronical* [ˈbɹɒnɪkl] for *bronchial* [ˈbɹɒŋkɪəl].

American	data	length	sandwich	wharf	whether
architect	engineer	open	status	what	whip
aviator	fellow	piano	strength	wheat	white
bronchial	just	picture	such	wheel	window
chasm	larynx	radiator	whale	where	yesterday

Read the following sentences, making sure that all words are correctly and clearly pronounced:

1. Be sure to take your umbrella, because it will probably rain.

2. The members of the Athletic Association had their pictures taken on Tuesday.

---

* The omission of the *h* in these words is probably due to lack of understanding of the phonetic rule rather than to carelessness. (See "Silent Letters," page 18.)

3. The architect suggested that the house needed a larger fireplace in the library.

4. The American government is democratic in form.

5. Many policemen will probably attend the picnic on Saturday.

6. The tall fellow was striding excitedly toward the city.

7. There was a film of moisture on the picture over the piano.

8. The larynx and bronchial tubes are parts of man's breathing apparatus.

9. The only excuse for such a lengthy quarrel was that both gentlemen had terrible tempers.

10. He was particularly anxious that his eleven-year-old son should study geometry this February.

Read the following paragraph, making sure that all words are correctly and clearly pronounced:

> The champion of the swimming team was president of the Athletic Association. He was also captain of the Young American basketball team, and played football and baseball as well; in short, he was an all-round athlete. He was popular with his classmates, and in his senior year was elected president of the Student Government Association. He did excellent work in his studies, particularly in Latin, mathematics, and English. He enjoyed music, and, although he certainly could not be called an artist, he played the piano with skill. He was fond of singing and dancing, and was considered a good-fellow at all school parties. Therefore, it was not surprising to discover that, in the opinion of everyone in the school, from the Principal down to the newest freshman, he was an outstanding citizen of the Centerville High School, and was worthy of their recognition and love.

Test:

1. Can you pronounce all the words in the Practice Material correctly? Do you pronounce them correctly in general conversation?

2. Can you read the sentences in the Practice Material, pronouncing all words correctly and clearly?

3. Can you read the paragraph given above, pronouncing all the words correctly and clearly?

CONTRACT 7

Objective:

Clear enunciation in the reading of sentences.

Procedure:

See Contracts 3, 4, and 5.

Caution:

Be sure to speak clearly and distinctly at all times.

Practice Material:

Read the following sentences clearly and distinctly:

1. The Civic Center was situated in the middle of the city.

2. Tom couldn't be persuaded to go to the party.

3. Mary insisted that her guests should stay for five months.

4. Katherine apparently didn't want to go to the theatre that evening in February.

5. The radio announcer said that there would be momentous news in the afternoon broadcast.

6. The twenty gentlemen slept soundly that night after climbing the mountain.

7. "The Acts of the Apostles" is the fifth book of the *New Testament.*

8. The artist sold the beautiful picture for two thousand dollars.

9. There was an old-fashioned pitcher in the middle of the mantle in the dining room.

10. The speech of the eminent gentleman was sometimes pedantic and always a little labored.

11. I thought I recognized Jim when he passed me in the library last Tuesday.

12. The little bride had received furniture, carpets, sheets, pillow-cases, cut-glass water-bottles, and many new clothes for wedding gifts.

13. It didn't seem possible that a candidate with so few constituents could speak so confidently of election.

14. The teacher is thoroughly competent to decide whether the student should go into the eighth grade or remain in the seventh.

15. Ted wanted to enter a first-class secondary school in order that he might receive excellent preparation for college.

16. The little boy was heart-broken because he hadn't been invited to go to the motion pictures with the others that afternoon.

17. "This division, by distracting the attention of the combatants, put an end to the strife."

18. "All their cares, hopes, joys, affections, virtues, and associations seemed to be melted down into dollars."

19. "Once or twice, when there was a pause, Martin asked . . . about the national poets, the theatre, literature or the arts."

20. "The glitter of gold or of diamonds will but hurt sore eyes, instead of curing them; and an aching head will no more be eased by wearing a crown than a common nightcap."

Test:

1. Can you read the sentences given above clearly and distinctly?

2. Can you read the sentences in the exercises for careless speech (pages 73–74) clearly and distinctly?

3. Do you speak clearly and distinctly in your conversation?

CONTRACT 8

Objective:

Clear articulation in the reading of brief stanzas of poetry.

Procedure:

See Contract 7.

Caution:

Be sure to speak clearly and distinctly at all times.
Never allow yourself to speak in a slovenly manner.

Practice Material:

Read the following stanzas clearly and distinctly:

> "But this remark, I grieve to state,
> Came just a little bit too late;
> For as I framed it in my head,
> I woke and found myself in bed."
> —W. S. GILBERT.

* * *

> "Mine are horrible, social ghosts,—
> Speeches and women, and guests and hosts.
> Weddings and morning calls and toasts,
>   In every bad variety;
> Ghosts who hover about the grave
> Of all that's manly, free, and brave;
> You'll find their names on the architrave
>   Of that charnel house, Society."
> —W. S. GILBERT.

"Not a word to each other; we kept the great pace
Neck by neck, stride by stride, never changing our place;
I turned in my saddle and made its girths tight,
Then shortened each stirrup, and set the pique right,
Rebuckled the cheek-strap, chained slacker the bit,
Nor galloped less steadily Roland a whit."
—BROWNING.

* * *

"All that I know
Of a certain star,
Is, it can throw
(Like the angled spar)
Now a dart of red,
Now a dart of blue,
Till my friends have said
They would fain see, too,
My star that dartles the red and the blue!
Then it stops like a bird,—like a flower, hangs furled;
They must solace themselves with the Saturn above it.
What matter to me if their star is a world?
Mine has opened its soul to me; therefore I love it."
—BROWNING.

Test:

1. Can you read the stanzas given in the Practice Material clearly and distinctly, but not pedantically?

2. Can you read two other stanzas clearly and distinctly?

3. Can you read the stanzas in the Exercises for Articulation (pages 135–141) clearly and distinctly?

4. Are you always careful to speak distinctly?

CONTRACT 9

Objective:

Clear articulation in the reading of prepared paragraphs.

Procedure:

See Contract 7.

Caution:

Remember that you must never allow yourself to revert to slovenly habits of speech.

Practice Material:

Read the following paragraph from *Martin Chuzzlewit* by Dickens, speaking clearly and distinctly, but not pedantically:

Pursuing his inquiries, Martin found that there were no fewer than four majors present, two colonels, one general, and a captain, so that he could not help thinking how strongly officered the American militia must be; and wondering very much whether the officers commanded each other; or if they did not, where on earth the privates came from. There seemed to be no man there without a title: for those who had not attained to military honors were either doctors, professors, or reverends. Three very hard and disagreeable gentlemen were on missions from neighboring states; one on monetary affairs, one on political, one on sectarian. Among the ladies . . . there was a wiry-faced old damsel who held strong sentiments touching the rights of women, and had diffused the same in lectures—the rest were strangely devoid of individual traits of character, insomuch that any one of them could have changed minds with the other and nobody would have found out.

Test:

1. Can you read the paragraph given above clearly and distinctly?

2. Can you read the paragraphs in the Exercises for Articulation (pages 135–141) clearly and distinctly?

3. Do you speak clearly and distinctly in conversation?

CONTRACT 10

Objective:

Clear articulation when presenting a prepared talk or speech.

Procedure:

See Contract 7.

Caution:

Make careful notes which will guide you in giving your speech.

Practice talking the speech aloud (but do not memorize it) when preparing to give it before the class.

Be sure that you speak clearly and distinctly.

Practice Material:

Prepare a five-minute talk on any subject in which you are interested. The following suggested subjects may help you to decide upon a subject about which you wish to talk:

A brief review of a book you have enjoyed.

A brief review of a movie or a play which you have seen recently.

Hobbies.

An overnight camping trip.

Test:

1. Can you speak for five minutes before the class, using clear distinct articulation?

2. Can you give a talk at your club meetings, professional meetings, or in another class, speaking clearly and distinctly?

3. Do you speak clearly and distinctly on all occasions?

CONTRACT 11

Objective:

Clear articulation in sight reading, extemporaneous speaking, and general conversation.

Procedure:

Review in the preceding contracts the practice material for any sounds with which you still have difficulty. If you are occasionally careless about your final consonants, review Contract 3. If middle consonants still trouble you, review Contract 4, and so forth.

Caution:

Remember that you must speak clearly and distinctly in every situation if you do not wish to revert to careless speech.

Practice Material:

Pick up a newspaper and read aloud the first article which meets your eye.

Talk to the class upon any subject suggested to you by your teacher.

Carry on a conversation with your classmates.

In doing all of these things, be careful to speak clearly and distinctly.

Test:

1. Can you read at sight, speaking clearly and distinctly?

2. Can you give a brief, extemporaneous talk clearly and distinctly?

3. Can you speak clearly and distinctly in general conversation?

Foreign Accent*

---

1. The following consonants correctly made: *t* [t], *d* [d], *n* [n], *l* [l].

The following vowels correctly made: *ē* [i:] as in *see*, *ōō* [u:] as in *too*.

The above sounds combined in syllables, words, phrases, and conversation.

---

2. The following consonants correctly made: *b* [b], *m* [m], *p* [p], *th* (voiced) [ð], *th* (voiceless) [θ].

The following vowels correctly made: *ĭ* [ɪ] as in *it*, *ŏŏ* [ʊ] as in *book*.

The above sounds combined in syllables, words, phrases, short sentences, and conversation.

---

3. The following consonants correctly made: *g* [g], *k* [k], *ng* [ŋ] as in *song*.

The following vowels correctly made: *ĕ* [eᴛ] as in *let*, *ô* [ɔ:] as in *all*, *ä* [ɑ:] as in *father*.

The following diphthong correctly made: *ā* [eᴛɪ] as in *ate*.

The above sounds combined in syllables, words, phrases, short sentences, and conversation.

---

4. The following consonants correctly made: *f* [f], *v* [v], *s* [s], *z* [z].

The following vowels correctly made: *ă* [æ] as in *at*, *à* [a] as in *ask*.

The following diphthongs correctly made: *ō* [oᴛʊ] as in *go*, *ow* [aʊ] as in *now*.

The above sounds combined in syllables, words, short sentences, and conversation.

---

* At the beginning of every practice period, do Contract 1 under "Careless Speech."

5. The following consonants correctly made: *w* [w] and *wh* [ʍ].

The following vowels correctly made: *û* [ɜ:] as in *bird*, *ȧ* [ə] as in *about*.

The following diphthongs correctly made: *ī* [aɪ] as in *ice*, *oi* [ɔɪ] as in *boy*.

The above sounds combined in syllables, words, short sentences, and conversation.

6. The following consonants correctly made: *y* [j] and *h* [h].

The following vowels correctly made: *ŏ* [ɒ] as in *coffee*, *ŭ* [ʌ] as in *up*.

The following digraph correctly made: *ū* [ju:] as in *tune*.

The following diphthongs correctly made: *ę* [ɪə] as in *here*, *â* [ɛə] as in *care*.

The above sounds combined in syllables, words, short sentences, and conversation.

7. The following consonants correctly made: *sh* [ʃ] and *zh* [ʒ]

The following digraphs correctly made: *ch* [tʃ] and *j* [dʒ]

The following diphthongs correctly made: *o͝or* [ʊə] as in *poor*, *ōr* [ɔə] as in *floor*.

The above sounds combined in syllables, words, short sentences, and conversation.

8. The following consonant correctly made: *r* [ɹ].

This sound correctly pronounced in syllables, words, short sentences, and conversation.

9. All sounds correctly pronounced with special attention to middle consonants.

10. The correct pronunciation of voiced and voiceless consonants (with special attention to final consonants) in syllables, words, sentences, and conversation.

11. Strong and weak forms correctly used in phrases, sentences, paragraphs, and conversation.

12. Intonation in phrases, short sentences, questions, and conversation.

13. Intonation in longer sentences, paragraphs, and conversation.

14. Reading of a paragraph with all sounds correctly made, correct intonation, and correct use of strong and weak forms.

15. Correct sounds, correct intonation, and correct use of strong and weak forms in sight-reading and conversation.

CONTRACT 1

Objective:

The following consonants correctly made: *t* [t], *d* [d], *n* [n], *l* [ll].
The following vowels correctly made: *ē* [i:] as in *see*, *ōō* [u:] as in *too*.
The above sounds combined in syllables, words, phrases, and short sentences.

Procedure:

See Consonant section of Part II, Chapter IV, for the correct production of the consonants given above.

See Vowel section, Part II, Chapter IV, for the correct production of the vowels given above.

When you are sure that the individual sounds are correctly made, combine them as follows:

tē	tē	tē [ti:]
dē	dē	dē [di:]
tē	dē	tē [ti: di: ti:]
nē	nē	nē [ni:]
lē	lē	lē [li:]
nē	lē	nē [ni: li: ni:]
tōō	tōō	tōō [tu:]
dōō	dōō	dōō [du:]
dōō	tōō	dōō [du: tu: du:]
nōō	nōō	nōō [nu:]
lōō	lōō	lōō [lu:]
nōō	lōō	nōō [nu: lu: nu:]
ēt	ēt	ēt [i·t]
ēd	ēd	ēd [i:d]
ōōt	ōōt	ōōt [u·t]
ōōd	ōōd	ōōd [u:d]
ēl	ēl	ēl [i:l]
ōōl	ōōl	ōōl [u:l]
ēn	ēn	ēn [i:n]
ōōn	ōōn	ōōn [u:n]

Caution:

Be sure that the tip of the tongue touches the middle of the upper gum when making *t* [t] and *d* [d]. Be sure that the tip of the tongue is *pointed* when making these sounds.

Practice Material:

Pronounce the following words correctly:

deed	tea	eat	need
do	to	lead	loot

Read the following phrases and short sentences, pronouncing all sounds correctly:

1. Need to do.
2. Do a deed.

3. Eat at noon.
4. Neat dean.

Test:

1. Can you do the exercises suggested in the Procedure, making all sounds correctly?

2. Can you read the words, phrases, and sentences in the Practice Material, pronouncing all sounds correctly?

3. If you speak slowly, can you use the sounds listed above correctly in your conversation?

4. Can you read all the words and sentences for *n* [n] (pages 99–100) and *ē* [i:](page 75), pronouncing those sounds correctly?

CONTRACT 1A

Objective:

See Contract 1.

Procedure:

See Contract 1.

Caution:

Be sure that the lips are spread when making the sound *ē* [i:]. Be sure that the lips are very round when making the sound *ōō* [u:].

Practice Material:

Read the following words, pronouncing all sounds correctly:

dean	loot	noon	eel
neat	deal	too	kneel

Read the following phrases, pronouncing all sounds correctly:

1. Kneel at noon.
2. Lead a dean.
3. Tea at noon.

4. Need a neat dean.
5. Eat an eel.

Test:

1. Can you read the words and phrases given in the Practice Material, making all sounds correctly?

2. Can you read the words and sentences given for the sound *l* [l] (page 101) and *ōō* [u:] (pages 81–82), making these sounds correctly?

3. If you speak slowly, can you pronounce these sounds correctly in your conversation?

CONTRACT 1B

Objective:

The sounds *t* [t] and *d* [d] correctly pronounced.

Procedure:

Point the tip of the tongue on the middle of the upper gum to make the sounds *d* [d] and *t* [t].

Say the following syllables, making sure that these sounds are correctly pronounced:

tē	tē	tē [ti:]	dōō	dōō	dōō [du:]
dē	dē	dē [di:]	tōō	tōō	tōō [tu:]
tē	dē	tē [ti: di: ti:]	tōō	dōō	tōō [tu: du: tu:]
dē	tē	dē [di: ti: di:]	dōō	tōō	dōō [du: tu: du:]
ēt	ēt	ēt [i·t]	ōōd	ōōd	ōōd [u: d]
ēd	ēd	ēd [i: d]	ōōt	ōōt	ōōt [u·t]

tēed	tēed	tēed [ti: d]
tōōt	tōōt	tōōt [tu·t]

Caution:

Be sure that the tip of the tongue is placed directly on the middle of the upper gum in making the sounds *d* [d] and *t* [t]. (If the tip of the tongue is placed too high, or too low, the resulting sound will be incorrect.)

Be sure that the tip of the tongue is *pointed* when making these sounds.

Practice Material:

Read the words in the following columns horizontally and vertically, giving special attention to the sounds *d* [d] and *t* [t]:

dip	tip	dirk	turkey	add	at	road	rote
den	ten	dug	tug	bead	beat	seed	seat
dad	tat	darn	tar	mode	moat	tend	tent

Read the following words, pronouncing the middle sounds with great care:

better	later	budding	peddle
dated	mitten	lending	sending
grated	tattle	muddy	tender

Differentiate between the mid consonants in the following words; read across and then down:

bidden	bitten		lading	later
cedar	seating		riding	writing
hiding	heighten		wading	waiting

Read the following sentences, using great care in the pronunciation of *t* [t] and *d* [d]:

1. I do not intend to do it.
2. Tom didn't want Don to go.
3. Mary hadn't had time to dust the dining-room.
4. The seating capacity of the stadium is twenty thousand.
5. The deadline for the article is September twenty-second.
6. I haven't seen Douglas for ten days.
7. It is better to use butter for the cake batter.
8. It is Betty's turn to wash the dishes.
9. Do you want to ride to Portland today?
10. The little tot was waiting patiently to go wading.
11. The incoming tide evidently tore down the sand-castle.
12. It is unpleasantly cold at night, but mild in the daytime.
13. The knitted garments were exhibited in the window of the department store.
14. The beautiful saddle horse belonged to Dan.
15. The cut-glass bottles gleamed on the polished mahogany sideboard.
16. Have you read the latest dispatch in *The Times?*
17. The members of the congregation were glad to pay tribute to the popularity of the pastor.
18. The writing table was littered with riding whips, cigarettes, lead pencils, and twine.
19. There was apparently no reason for Teddy to go to Texas.
20. *A Tale of a Tub* was written by Jonathan Swift in the eighteenth century.

Test:

1. Can you do the exercises in the Procedure, pronouncing *d* [d] and *t* [t] correctly?

2. Can you read the words and sentences given in the Practice Material, pronouncing *d* [d] and *t* [t] correctly?

3. Can you read the words and sentences on pages 98–99, pronouncing *d* [d] and *t* [t] correctly?

4. If you speak slowly, can you pronounce these sounds correctly in your conversation?

> *Note to instructor:* This contract contains, of necessity, many sounds not yet studied by the student. It will therefore have to be used at your discretion.

CONTRACT 2

Objective:

The following consonants correctly made: *p* [p], *b* [b], *m* [m], *th* voiced [ð], *th* voiceless [θ].

The following vowels correctly made: *ĭ* [ɪ] as in *it*, *ŏŏ* [ʊ] as in *put*.

The above sounds combined in syllables, words, phrases, short sentences, and conversation.

Procedure:

See Part II, Chapter IV, Consonant section, for the correct production of the consonant sounds concerned.

See Part II, Chapter IV, Vowel section, for the correct production of the two vowels to be studied in this contract.

When you think the individual sounds are correctly made, combine them as follows:

pĭ	pĭ	pĭ [pɪ]
bĭ	bĭ	bĭ [bɪ]
pĭ	bĭ	pĭ [pɪ bɪ pɪ]
pŏŏ	pŏŏ	pŏŏ [pʊ]
bŏŏ	bŏŏ	bŏŏ [bʊ]
pŏŏ	bŏŏ	pŏŏ [pʊ bʊ pʊ]
mĭ	mĭ	mĭ [mɪ]
mŏŏ	mŏŏ	mŏŏ [mʊ]
thĭ	thĭ	thĭ (*th* voiced) [ðɪ]
thĭ	thĭ	thĭ (*th* voiceless) [θɪ]
pĭth	pĭth	pĭth (*th* voiceless) [pɪθ]
mĭth	mĭth	mĭth (*th* voiceless) [mɪθ]

Caution:

Remember that *b* [b] and *p* [p] are made in the same way, except that *p* [p] is voiceless, whereas *b* [b] is voiced.

Be sure that the tip of the tongue touches the edge of the teeth for *th* [ð-θ].

Practice Material:

Say the following words, pronouncing all sounds correctly:

pith	tip	thin	thee
myth	leap	bull	teeth

Read the following phrases and short sentences, pronouncing all sounds correctly:

1. To meet the team.

2. To need a thimble.

3. Thin neat teeth.

4. The bull leaped into the pool.

5. Billy pulled two teeth.

Test:

1. Can you do the exercises given in the Procedure, pronouncing all sounds correctly?

2. Can you read the words, phrases, and sentences given in the Practice Material, pronouncing all sounds correctly?

3. Can you read the words and phrases for *p* [p] and *b* [b] (pages 92–93) and *ĭ* [ɪ] (pages 75–76), pronouncing these sounds correctly?

4. If you speak slowly can you pronounce all sounds, studied thus far, correctly in your conversation?

CONTRACT 2A

Objective:

See Contract 2.

Procedure:

Combine the sounds studied in this contract in the following manner:

ĭp	ĭp	ĭp [ɪp]	o͝op	o͝op	o͝op [ʊp]
ĭb	ĭb	ĭb [ɪb]	o͝ob	o͝ob	o͝ob [ʊb]
ĭm	ĭm	ĭm [ɪm]	o͝om	o͝om	o͝om [ʊm]

thĭb	thĭb	thĭb (*th voiceless*) [θɪb]
thĭp	thĭp	thĭp (*th voiceless*) [θɪp]
thĭm	thĭm	thĭm (*th voiced*) [ðɪm]

Caution:

Be sure that the front of the tongue is held very high when making the sound ĭ [ɪ].

Be sure that the lips are closely rounded when making the sound ŏŏ [ʊ].

Practice Material:

Read the following words, pronouncing all sounds correctly:

deep	theme	leal	pool
lip	thimble	till	put

Read the following phrases and sentences, pronouncing all sounds correctly:

1. The moonlit pool.
2. The leaping bull.
3. Put it in the deep pit.
4. The dean put the theme in the pool.
5. The moonbeam lit the booth.

Test:

1. Can you do the exercises given in the Procedure, pronouncing all sounds correctly?

2. Can you read the words, phrases, and sentences in the Practice Material, pronouncing all sounds correctly?

3. Can you read the words and sentences for m [m] (pages 93–94) and ŏŏ [ʊ] (pages 81–82), pronouncing those sounds correctly?

4. If you speak slowly, can you pronounce correctly in your conversation all sounds studied thus far?

CONTRACT 2B

Objective:

Correct pronunciation of th voiced [ð] and voiceless [θ].

Procedure:

Place the tip of the tongue lightly against the edge of the upper teeth in order to make the sound th. This sound may be both voiced [ð] and voiceless [θ].

Do the following exercises:

thē	thē	thē (th voiced) [ðiː]
thĭ	thĭ	thĭ (th voiced) [ðɪ]
thŏŏ	thŏŏ	thŏŏ (th voiced) [ðuː]

ēth	ēth	ēth (*th* voiceless) [i·θ]
ĭth	ĭth	ĭth (*th* voiceless) [ɪθ]
ēth	ēth	ēth (*th* voiced) [i:ð]
ĭth	ĭth	ĭth (*th* voiced) [ɪð]
o͞oth	o͞oth	o͞oth (*th* voiced) [u:ð]
o͝oth	o͝oth	o͝oth (*th* voiced) [ʊð]
o͞oth	o͞oth	o͞oth (*th* voiceless) [u·θ]
o͝oth	o͝oth	o͝oth (*th* voiceless) [ʊθ]

Caution:

Place the tongue *lightly* against the edge of the upper teeth for the sound *th*.

Practice Material:

Say the following words, giving special attention to the *th* sounds:

Initial Voiced	*Initial Voiceless*		*Mid Voiced*
these	theme	thumb	other
thus	three	thump	hither
this	thin	thud	whither
them	thing	threw	whether
then	thick	throat	weather
there	thimble	throw	bother
that	theorem	thwart	mother
than	thread	thought	father
the	thank	think	gather
though	thirst	thousand	either
those	Thursday	thew	together

Final Voiced		*Final Voiceless*	
with	scythe	teeth	cloth
soothe	lathe	myth	mouth (*n.*)
loathe	bathe	earth	south
smooth	writhe	bath	north

Read the following sentences, giving special attention to the *th* sounds:

1. This is the house that Jack built.

2. They lived at Nine thousand four hundred and fifty-five Fifth Avenue.

3. Do this, then do that, then do the other thing.

4. The theater was at Fourteenth Street and Sixth Avenue.

5. To the thief, the idea of "mine and thine" is thoroughly theoretical.

6. The three thickets had very thick undergrowths.

7. Then the band played *Over There*.

8. There were thousands of people in the other amphitheater although the weather was cloudy.

9. Arthur went with his father, but the others went with their mother.

10. The bathers were having a fine bath in the ocean.

Read the following paragraph, giving special attention to the *th* sounds:

> Thursday the three students wrote a thousand-word theme on the subject of Thessaly. They gathered their material from a theatrical performance and did not bother to think through the subject thoroughly. They confused the myths of the north with those of the south. They said that heather and thistles grew together. As a result, they were loath to see their grades, and writhed when they were thrust upon them.

Test:

1. Can you say all the words in the Practice Material correctly?

2. Can you read the sentences and the paragraph in the Practice Material, pronouncing the *th* sounds correctly?

3. Can you prepare ten other sentences and read them, pronouncing the *th* sounds correctly?

4. Can you read all the sentences for *th* voiced [ð] and *th* voiceless [θ] (pages 95–96), pronouncing all the *th* sounds correctly?

5. If you speak slowly, can you pronounce the *th* sounds correctly in your conversation?

> *Note to instructor:* This contract, of necessity, contains many sounds that the student has not studied, and therefore will have to be used at your discretion.

CONTRACT 3

Objective:

The following consonant sounds correctly made: *g* [g], *k* [k], *ng* [ŋ] as in *song*.

The following vowels correctly made: *ĕ* [eτ] as in *let*, *ô* [ɔ:] as in *all*, *ä* [ɑ:] as in *father*.

The following diphthong correctly made: *ā* [eτɪ] as in *ate*.

These sounds combined in syllables, words, phrases, short sentences, and conversation.

Procedure:

See Part II, Chapter IV, Consonant section, for the correct production of the sounds *g* [g], *k* [k], and *ng* [ŋ].

See Part II, Chapter IV, Vowel section, for the correct production of the vowels studied in this contract.

See Part II, Chapter IV, section on Diphthongs, for the correct production of the diphthong *ā* [erĬ].

Learn the rules for the pronunciation of ng.

Do the following exercises:

gĕ	gĕ	gĕ [gerʈ]	kĕg	kĕg	kĕg [kerg]
gaw	gaw	gaw [gɔ:]	āk	āk	āk [erĬk]
kĕ	kĕ	kĕ [kerʈ]	ĕg	ĕg	ĕg [erg]
kaw	kaw	kaw [kɔ:]	ĕng	ĕng	ĕng [erŋ]
gawk	gawk	gawk [gɔ·k]	awng	awng	awng [ɔ:ŋ]

Proceed in this manner with all sounds studied in this contract.

Caution:

Be sure that the lips remain rounded until you have ceased to voice the sound *ô* [ɔ:] in order that the vowel may not be fractured.

Be sure that you know your rules for the pronunciation of *ng* (see page 39).

Be sure that no voiced or unvoiced click follows the production of the sound [ŋ].

Practice Material:

Say the following words; be careful that all sounds are correctly pronounced:

keg	length	thing	lard
law	day	ail	pawn
get	name	bake	dig

Read the following phrases; be sure that all sounds are correctly pronounced:

1. Getting all.
2. Baking cake.
3. Cooking all day.
4. Parking law.

Read the following sentences; be sure that all sounds are correctly pronounced:

1. The cook baked cake all day.
2. Put the keg of ale in the pool.
3. Paul ate lean meat.
4. The king paid the pale, thin guard.

Test:

1. Can you do the exercises in the Procedure, pronouncing all sounds correctly?

2. Do you know the rules for the pronunciation of *ng*?

3. Can you do the exercises given in the Practice Material, pronouncing all sounds correctly?

4. Can you read the words and sentences in the exercises for *g* [g] and *k* [k] (pages 103–104) and *ā* [eгĭ] (page 87), pronouncing those sounds correctly?

5. If you speak slowly, can you pronounce correctly in your conversation all the sounds studied thus far?

CONTRACT 3A

Objective:

See Contract 3.

Procedure:

See Contract 3.

Caution:

Be sure that the lips are *not* rounded when making the sound *ä* [ɑ:].

Be sure that the back of the tongue rests very gently against the soft palate when making the sound *ng* [ŋ].

Practice Material:

Say the following words; be sure that all sounds are pronounced correctly:

king	blade	bleed	lame
nail	lawn	pay	ale
gay	bed	gain	gnarled

Read the following phrases; be sure that all sounds are correctly pronounced:

1. Playing ball.

2. Digging all day.

3. Gay blade.

4. Lame paw.

5. Gaining all.

Read the following sentences; be sure that all sounds are correctly pronounced:

1. The king ate the plain cake.

2. The lame paw made the kitten ill.

3. Ted played ball in the lane.

4. Paul played a card game.

5. Billy came to the aid of the mate.

Test:

1. Can you read the words in the Practice Material, pronouncing all sounds correctly?

2. Can you read the phrases and sentences in the Practice Material, pronouncing all sounds correctly?

3. Can you read the words and sentences given for ĕ [eɪ] (pages 76–77), ô [ɔ:] (pages 83–84), ä [ɑ:] (pages 78–79), pronouncing those sounds correctly?

4. If you speak slowly, can you use the sounds you have studied to date correctly in general conversation?

CONTRACT 3B

Objective:

The correct pronunciation of the sound *ng* [ŋ].

Procedure:

Place the back of the tongue gently against the lowered soft palate and say the sound *ng* [ŋ].

Do the following exercises:

ŭng	ŭng	ŭng [ʌŋ]	sung	sung	sung ['sʌŋ]
ĭng	ĭng	ĭng [ɪŋ]	ring	ring	ring ['ɹɪŋ]
ĕng	ĕng	ĕng [eɪŋ]	length	length	length ['leɪŋθ]
ŏng	ŏng	ŏng [ɒŋ]	song	song	song ['sɒŋ]
ăng	ăng	ăng [æŋ]	rang	rang	rang ['ɹæŋ]

ng—ē	ng—ē	ng—e [ŋ—i:]
ng—ä	ng—ä	ng—ä [ŋ—ɑ:]
ng—ōō	ng—ōō	ng—ōō [ŋ—u:]
ng—ē	ng—ä	ng—ōō [ŋ—i: ŋ—ɑ: ŋ—u:]

> *Note:* The sound *ng* [ŋ] never occurs at the beginning of a word. This is a valuable exercise, however, as a word ending in *ng* [ŋ] often precedes a word beginning with a vowel—as in *boiling oil* or *reading a book.*

Caution:

The combination *ng* is sometimes pronounced with a single sound as in *sing, singer, singing,* and sometimes with two sounds as in *finger* and *English.* It is easier to distinguish between the two pronunciations if you use the phonetic symbol [ŋ] to indicate the single sound, and [ŋg] to indicate the two sounds. Look up the rules for the pronunciation of *ng* (page 39) and learn them.

Practice Material:

Say the following words, paying special attention to the pronunciation of *ng* sounds:

thing	song	thank	clang	English
swing	bringer	having	rang	language
singing	tongue	losing	bringing	younger
bring	ringer	sling	finger	longer

Read the following phrases, paying special attention to the pronunciation of *ng*:

[ŋ]

1. Attending a lecture.
2. Long, long ago on Long Island.
3. Looking at a picture.
4. Planning an attack.
5. Running around town.
6. Signing up for a course.
7. Living a long time.
8. Burning a book.
9. Climbing a mountain.
10. Hearing Young America singing.
11. Tuning a piano.
12. Forgetting our appointment.

[ŋ] and [ŋg]

13. The hungry children.
14. The ringless fingers.
15. The English language.
16. Fingering a tie.
17. A single thing.
18. Lingering along a road.
19. An angry bull.
20. An unsatisfied hunger.
21. Helping a younger child.
22. Searching for the strongest argument.
23. Encountering a stronger opponent.
24. Using finger bowls.

Read the following phrases, remembering that *nge* is pronounced *nj* [ndʒ]:

1. Cringing from fear.
2. Fitting a flange.
3. Trimming with fringe.
4. Impinging upon.
5. Lunging to the right.
6. A harbinger of spring.
7. Plunging into the water.

8. Looking at a mountain range.

9. Taking revenge.

10. A singed chicken.

11. Using a syringe.

12. Just a tinge of color.

Read the following sentences, paying special attention to the *ng* sounds:

1. Skating and skiing and tobogganing are winter sports.

2. Children enjoy swimming and paddling in the ocean.

3. The boys were coming up in the midst of the heavy traffic.

4. The children were swinging and singing a song.

5. The messenger was a bringer of good tidings.

6. Every single member of the team mingled with the onlookers.

7. The bell ringer and the street singer sang a duet.

8. The boys were ringing a bell to celebrate the coming of the troops.

9. The young American is playing football with his English cousins.

10. The cadets were marching around the parade ground.

11. The girl was practicing finger exercises on the piano, and singing as she practiced.

12. The dashing of the rain and the howling of the wind and the grumbling of the thunder made those nights things of terror.

Read the following paragraph, paying special attention to *ng* sounds:

After a concert tour of Long Island, the English Singers decided to take a sight-seeing trip through New England. They crossed by ferry from Long Island to Connecticut, and lingered along the beautiful country roadside. They drove north to the White Mountains, and gazed longingly at the Presidential range. Then turning about, and going in a southeasterly direction, they visited Boston and Cape Cod. They were particularly interested in Provincetown, where the bell-ringer or town-crier rings his bell and announces the news. At the close of this delightful trip, the English Singers voted unanimously that New England, as well as England, could boast of beautiful country.

Test:

1. Can you pronounce correctly all the words given in the Practice Material?

2. Prepare a list of fifteen more words containing *ng* and then pronounce them correctly.

3. Can you read the sentences and the paragraph given in the Practice Material, pronouncing the sounds of *ng* correctly?

4. Prepare ten more sentences containing words with *ng* and then read them with correct pronunciation.

5. If you speak slowly, can you pronounce *ng* correctly in your conversation?

6. Are you sure of the rules for the pronunciation of *ng*?

7. Can you read the words and ten of the sentences given for *ng* (pages 105–106), pronouncing the sounds correctly?

8. Can you read some of the paragraphs devoted to *ng* in Part III, pronouncing the sounds correctly?

Note: See Note, Contract 2B.

CONTRACT 4

Objective:

The consonants *f* [f], *v* [v], *s* [s], *z* [z] correctly pronounced.

The vowels *ă* [æ] as in *at* and *à* [a] as in *ask* correctly pronounced.

The diphthongs *ō* [oтU] as in *go* and *ow* [aʊ̆] as in *now* correctly pronounced.

Procedure:

See Part II, Chapter IV, Consonant section, for the correct production of the consonants to be studied in this contract.

See Part II, Chapter IV, Vowel section, for the vowel sounds to be studied in this contract.

See Part II, Chapter IV, section on Diphthongs, for the correct production of the diphthongs to be studied in this contract.

As there is a great deal of confusion in regard to the difference between the pronunciation of *ă* [æ] as in *man* and *à* [ɑ] as in *ask*, ask your teacher to pronounce these sounds for you. Then ask her to check your pronunciation of these sounds when you read the words in the following columns.

[æ]	[ɑ]	[æ]	[ɑ]
at	after	fad	fast
add	ask	lass	last
ban	basket	mad	mast
bat	bath	pan	past
cat	class	tan	task

Do the following exercises:

fă	fă	fă	fan	['fæn]
fȧ	fȧ	fȧ	fast	['fɑst]
vă	vă	vă	van	['væn]
vȧ	vȧ	vȧ	vast	['vɑst]
fă	vă	fă		[fæ væ fæ]
vow	vow	vow	vow	['vaʊ]
sō	sō	sō	so	['soʊ]
zō	zō	zō	zone	['zoʊn]
sō	zō	sō		[soʊ zoʊ soʊ]
sow	zow	sow		[saʊ zaʊ saʊ]
ăz	ăz	ăz	as	['æz]
ōz	ōz	ōz	owes	['oʊz]

Continue in this manner, using all sounds to be studied in this contract.

Note: If the sounds *s* [s] and *z* [z] are incorrectly pronounced, take the "Contracts for Lisping," pages 219–251.

Caution:

Be sure that final *v* [v] and *z* [z] are voiced.
Be sure that you hear the difference between *ă* [æ] and *ȧ* [a].
Be sure that the diphthong *ow* [aʊ] is made on the back of the tongue.

Practice Material:

Read the following words; be sure that all sounds are correctly pronounced.

fad	van	sew	pave	sound
fat	vast	owes	laugh	down
fan	zone	lose	last	count

Read the following phrases; be sure that all sounds are correctly pronounced:

1. Zoning laws.
2. Fattening foods.
3. Maddening laugh.
4. Losing pounds.
5. Sloping mast.

Read the following sentences; be sure that all sounds are correctly pronounced:

1. The man made a vow.
2. The class is dismissed.
3. The clown laughs last.

4. The sound *o* is made with rounded lips.

5. The town allows no parking in this zone.

6. The fat man is standing in the lane.

7. Zoning and parking laws are enforced in this city.

8. Potatoes and peas are fattening foods.

9. The old man sailed the boat skilfully.

10. The singers are singing down town.

Test:

1. Can you hear the difference between ă [æ] and à [ɑ]? Can you make each of these sounds correctly?

2. Can you do the exercises in the Practice Material, pronouncing all sounds correctly?

3. Can you do the exercises for *ow* [aʊ] (pages 89–90) and ă [æ] (pages 77–78), pronouncing those sounds correctly?

4. If you speak slowly, can you use the sounds studied to date correctly in conversation?

CONTRACT 4A

Objective:

See Contract 4.

Procedure:

See Contract 4.
Do the following exercises:

ăf	ăf	ăf [æf]
ăv	ăv	ăv [æv]
ăf	ăv	ăf [æf æv æf]
ăv	ăf	ăv [æv æf æv]
ows	ows	ows [aʊs]
owz	owz	owz [aʊz]
owz	ows	owz [aʊz aʊs aʊz]

Proceed in like manner for all sounds studied in this contract.

Caution:

See Contract 4.

Practice Material:

Read the following words; be sure that all sounds are correctly pronounced:

lad	sat	loss	found
land	sad	lose	town
last	sand	zinc	mount

Read the following phrases; be sure that all sounds are correctly pronounced:

1. Mounting a pony.
2. Seeing the town.
3. Playing in the sand.
4. Landing the boat.
5. Looking at the tan cat.
6. Thinking about the past.

Read the following sentences; be sure that all sounds are correctly pronounced:

1. This is the last class.
2. The van is going too fast.
3. The black cat is playing in the sand.
4. Please get a pound of tea for me.
5. Ask the sick man to sit down.
6. The old man sat in the garden thinking about the past.
7. Ted lost count of the passing cars.
8. Please save a seat at the table for me.
9. Betty felt sad about leaving her classmates.
10. Nancy plans to spend the month of May in Maine.

Test:

1. Can you do the exercises given in the Procedure, pronouncing all sounds correctly?

2. Can you do the exercises given in the Practice Material, pronouncing all sounds correctly?

3. Can you do the exercises for *f* [f] and *v* [v] (page 97) and *ō* [oᴛŭ] (pages 88–89), pronouncing those sounds correctly?

4. If you speak slowly, can you pronounce correctly all the sounds studied thus far?

CONTRACT 5

Objective:

The following consonants correctly made: *w* [w] *wh* [ᴍ].

The following vowels correctly made: *û* [ɜ:] as in *bird, a* [ə] as in *about*.

The following diphthongs correctly made: *ī* [aɪ] as in *ice, oi* [ɔɪ] as in *boy*.

The above sounds combined in syllables, words, short sentences, and conversation.

Procedure:

See Part II, Chapter IV, Consonant section, for the correct production of the sounds *w* [w] and *wh* [ʍ].

See Part II, Chapter IV, Vowel section, for the correct production of the vowel sounds given above.

See Part II, Chapter IV, for the correct production of the diphthongs given above.

Do the following exercises:

wû	wû	wû	were ['wɜ:]
wī	wī	wī	wide ['waɪd]
whû	whû	whû	whirr ['ʍɜ:]
whī	whī	whī	whine ['ʍaɪn]
wī	whī	wī	[waɪ ʍaɪ waɪ]
wû	whû	wû	[wɜ: ʍɜ: wɜ:]
oi	oi	oi	oil ['ɔɪl]
û	û	û	earn ['ɜ:n]
ī	ī	ī	ice ['aɪs]

Caution:

Remember that the neutral vowel *ǎ* [ə] is found in many unstressed syllables in English; remember also that it is *never* found in a stressed position.

Be careful not to substitute the sound *w* [w] for *wh* [ʍ].

Practice Material:

Say the following words, remembering that *ǎ* [ə] occurs in unstressed syllables:

above	bother	confound
about	father	convey
allow	mother	supply
assault	sofa	sustain

Read the following columns horizontally and vertically; be careful to differentiate between the paired words:

were—whirr	earl—oil
wide—why	curl—coil
wine—whine	surly—soil
woe—whoa	turn—toil

Read the following sentences, pronouncing all sounds correctly:

1. The earl had oily, black hair.

2. Ida burned her hand on the pan of boiling water.

3. The early bird finds the worm.

4. The front window was wide open.

5. The surly boy turned away.

6. We were frightened by the whirring of the plane.

7. Why does the baby whine?

8. Do you know whether the girl will go downtown today?

9. We are concerned about the weather.

10. The nurse thanked the boy for finding the baby's toy.

Test:

1. Can you do the exercises in the Procedure, making all sounds correctly?

2. Can you read the words and sentences in the Practice Material, pronouncing all sounds correctly?

3. Can you read the sentences for *w* [w] and *wh* [ʍ] (pages 94–95) and *oi* [ɔɪ] (pages 87–88), pronouncing those sounds correctly?

4. Can you pronounce correctly when you are conversing all sounds studied thus far?

CONTRACT 5A

Objective:

See Contract 5.

Procedure:

See Contract 5.

Caution:

Be careful not to confuse the sounds *û* [ɜ:] and *oi* [ɔɪ].
Be sure that the sound *ī* [aɪ] is made in the *front* of the mouth.

Practice Material:

Read the following words; be sure that the diphthong *ī* [aɪ] is made on the front of the tongue:

bind	height	might	sight
bite	hide	mine	sign
guile	life	night	tight
guide	line	nine	time

Read the following columns horizontally and vertically; be sure to differentiate between the paired words:

weather—whether	learn—loin
wither—whither	mercy—moist
wight—white	pearl—poise
watt—what	turtle—toy

Read the following sentences; be sure to pronounce all sounds correctly:

1. It is time to go down to the mine.

2. Pearls are found in oysters.

3. The white cat seemed to have nine lives.

4. The little boys were flying kites in the park.

5. Can the small girl do this exercise?

6. What time did Ted leave for Canada?

7. Can Ida find out whether the flowers in the garden are withered?

8. The girl with the pearl necklace had plenty of poise.

9. The life-guard swam out and saved Carl's life.

10. The play will be given at nine tonight.

Test:

1. Can you do the exercises given in the Practice Material, pronouncing all sounds correctly?

2. Can you do the exercises for the sounds *û* [ɜ:] (pages 79–80) and *ī* [aɪ] (pages 85–86), pronouncing those sounds correctly?

3. If you speak slowly, can you pronounce correctly all sounds studied thus far?

CONTRACT 6

Objective:

Correct pronunciation of the following consonants: *y* [y], *h* [h].

Correct pronunciation of the following vowels: *ŏ* [ɒ] as in *coffee*, *ŭ* [ʌ] as in *up*.

Correct pronunciation of the following diphthongs: *ẹ̄* [ɪ̌] as in *here*, *â* [ɛ̌] as in *care*.

Correct production of the digraph *ū* [ju:] as in *tune*.

Procedure:

See Part II, Chapter IV, Consonant section, for the correct production of the consonants given above.

See Part II, Chapter IV, Vowel section, for the correct production of the vowels and digraph given above.

See Part II, Chapter IV, section devoted to diphthongs, for the correct production of the diphthongs given above.

Do the following exercises:

hŏ	hŏ	hŏ [hɒ]
yŏ	yŏ	yŏ [jɒ]
yŏ	hŏ	yŏ [jɒ hɒ jɒ]
hū	hū	hū [ˈhjuː]
here	here	here [ˈhɪ̆ə̆]
hare	hare	hare [ˈhɛ̆ə̆]
year	year	year [ˈjɪ̆ə̆]

Continue in this manner, placing all consonant sounds studied thus far before the above vowels, digraph, and diphthongs.

Caution:

Study carefully the rules for the use of the digraph *ū* [juː] (see page 25).

When making the vowel *ŏ* [ɒ], remember to open your mouth almost as wide as for *ä* [ɑː] then round your lips slightly.

Practice Material:

Read the following words; be sure that all sounds are pronounced correctly:

here	yield	bottle	but	dear	bare	duke
hare	year	coffee	compass	fear	care	futile
hot	young	got	gull	gear	dare	lute
hut	yellow	lot	mud	jeer	fare	new
hue	yawn	office	nut	leer	lair	puny

Read the following sentences; be sure to pronounce all sounds correctly:

1. The sky is perfectly blue and clear.

2. Would you like a cup of hot cocoa?

3. The duke asked Howard to go to the theatre with him.

4. Where would you like to go tonight?

5. We're going to hear the concert at Town Hall.

6. The little girl had beautiful, long, curly hair.

7. The copper coffee pot is on the stove.

8. The boys in Tom's office gave him a traveling bag for his birthday.

9. Are you comfortable on the sofa, or would you like to move over here?

10. Tom took his compass with him when he went camping last summer.

Test:

1. Can you do the exercises in the Procedure and Practice Material, pronouncing all sounds correctly?

2. Can you do the exercises given for *y* [j] (page 103), *ŏ* [ɒ] (pages 84–85), and *ū* [ju:] (pages 82–83), pronouncing those sounds correctly?

3. Can you use correctly in your conversation all sounds studied thus far?

CONTRACT 6A

Objective:

See Contract 6.

Procedure:

See Contract 6.

Caution:

See Contract 6.

Practice Material:

Read the following words; be sure that all sounds are pronounced correctly:

hobby	yeast	cog	bud	mere	mare	dew
humble	yesterday	dog	comfort	peer	pear	few
huge	yet	not	company	tear	tares	nuisance
hair	yacht	upon	money	veer	vary	pew
heat	yawl	top	pun	we're	wear	tune

Read the following sentences; be sure that all words are correctly pronounced:

1. Dogs are good companions.

2. Tom sailed over to Long Island on his new yacht yesterday.

3. The boat veered about and came in to the pier.

4. The glee-club sang some new tunes.

5. The weather was so hot that we decided not to go.

6. Stamp-collecting is a fairly expensive hobby.

7. There must have been a heavy dew last night, because the lawn is very wet this morning.

8. The heat in the subway and tube was severe on Tuesday.

9. Our companions from the country marvelled at the sights of the city.

10. "Company halt!" commanded the captain.

Test:

1. Can you do the exercises given in the Practice Material, pronouncing all sounds correctly?

2. Can you do the exercises for *h* [h] (pages 107–108), pronouncing all sounds correctly?

3. Can you do the exercises for *ŭ* [ʌ] (pages 80–81), pronouncing all sounds correctly?

4. Are you careful to pronounce all sounds correctly in your conversation?

CONTRACT 7

Objective:

The correct pronunciation of the consonants *sh* [ʃ] and *zh* [ʒ].

The correct pronunciation of the diphthongs *ŏŏr* [ʊə] as in *poor* and *ōr* [ɔə] as in *floor.*

The correct pronunciation of the digraphs *ch* [tʃ] and *j* [dʒ].

The above sounds combined in syllables, words, short sentences, and conversation.

Procedure:

See Part II, Chapter IV, Consonant section, for the correct production of the consonants and digraphs given above.

See Part II, Chapter IV, section devoted to diphthongs, for the correct production of the diphthongs given above.

Do the following exercises:

shŏŏr	shŏŏr	shŏŏr	sure ['ʃʊə]
shōr	shōr	shōr	shore ['ʃɔə]
chōr	chōr	chōr	chore ['tʃɔə]
chōr	jōr	chōr	[tʃɔə dʒɔə tʃɔə]
chŏŏr	jŏŏr	chŏŏr	[tʃʊə dʒʊə tʃʊə]
shŏŏr	zhŏŏr	shŏŏr	[ʃʊə ʒʊə ʃʊə]
shōr	zhōr	shōr	[ʃɔə ʒɔə ʃɔə]

Caution:

Be sure that *zh* [ʒ] and *j* [dʒ] are both voiced.

Practice Material:

Read the following words; be sure that all sounds are pronounced correctly:

sheen	azure	chore	ginger	boor	core
shore	leisure	cheese	judge	moor	door
shin	measure	chest	jump	poor	four
shoot	pleasure	chin	just	tour	lore
sure	seizure	chop	jounce	your	more

Read the following sentences; be sure that all sounds are correctly pronounced:

1. Jim has a severe chest cold.

2. It is a pleasure to walk on the moors in summer.

3. The little girls sat on the floor playing with paper dolls.

4. The poor boy enjoyed the lunch of biscuits and cheese.

5. The church service lasted longer than usual this morning.

6. Stand erect and do not stick out your chin.

7. Be sure to sound your final consonants.

8. The four boys jumped at the chance to take a tour of the southern states.

9. Lincoln's Gettysburg speech begins with the words "Fourscore and seven years ago."

10. It was a pleasure to look at the azure sky and the blue sea.

Test:

1. Can you do the exercises in the Procedure and Practice Material, pronouncing all sounds correctly?

2. Can you do the exercises for *sh* [ʃ] and *zh* [ʒ] (pages 119–120), pronouncing all sounds correctly?

3. Can you do the exercises for *ẹ* [ɪɚ], *â* [ɛɚ], *o͝or* [ʊɚ], and *ōr* [ɔɚ] (pages 91–92), pronouncing all sounds correctly?

4. Are you careful to pronounce all sounds correctly in your conversation?

CONTRACT 7A

Objective:

See Contract 7.

Procedure:

See Contract 7.

Caution:

See Contract 7.

Practice Material:

Read the following sentences; be sure that all sounds are correctly pronounced:

1. Tom was doing his chores on the farm.

2. The judge sentenced the man to ten years of hard labor.

3. The shore line is more beautiful on this side of the lake.

4. It is almost sure to be clear for the picnic on Tuesday, because we have had so much storm of late.

5. Hobbies are helpful as leisure-time activities.

6. It is important that we have just laws in our community.

7. The poor boy has been selected to go on the student tour to Washington.

8. Have you any questions about today's lesson?

9. Adjectives, adverbs, nouns, and verbs are essential parts of speech.

10. Be sure to use enough sugar in the cake batter.

11. The girl's shoulders were badly sun-burned because she lay too long on the sand.

12. The leading feature at the motion pictures last evening was poor, but the acting was excellent.

13. Are you going to take a tour to the west coast this summer?

14. I should like to go to the seashore for the month of June.

15. December twenty-first is the shortest day of the year.

Test:

1. Can you read the sentences given above, pronouncing all sounds correctly?

2. Can you do the exercises for *ch* [tʃ] and *j* [dʒ] (pages 120–121), pronouncing all sounds correctly?

3. Are you careful to pronounce all sounds correctly in your conversation?

CONTRACT 8

Objective:

The consonant *r* [ɹ] correctly pronounced.

This sound correctly pronounced in syllables, words, sentences, and conversation.

Procedure:

See Part II, Chapter IV, Consonant section, for the correct production of the consonant r [ɹ].

Do the following exercises, pronouncing the sound r [ɹ] correctly:

rē	rē	rē	ream [ˈɹiːm]	rŏŏ	rŏŏ	rŏŏ	rook [ˈɹʊk]
rā	rā	rā	rain [ˈɹeɪɪn]	rō	rō	rō	road [ˈɹoɪʊ̆d]
rĭ	rĭ	rĭ	rice [ˈɹaɪs]	ery	ery	ery	very [ˈveɹɪɪ]
rōō	rōō	rōō	roof [ˈɹu·f]	ary	ary	ary	carry [ˈkæɹɪ]

Continue in this manner, using all vowels and diphthongs in relation to the sound r [ɹ].

Caution:

Remember that the tip of the tongue should be pointed and raised up toward the upper gum, then curled back slightly when making the sound r [ɹ].

Remember that the back of the tongue must not be raised when making this sound.

Remember that the lips must not be rounded for this sound.

Practice Material:

Read the following words; be sure that the sound r [ɹ] is pronounced correctly:

reap	root	raid	ferry	serious	grill
rill	rule	rout	garish	bring	prance
rent	robust	rear	lorry	cream	print
ran	raw	berry	merry	dry	trim
rasp	rot	cherry	period	drink	trot
run	ride	dairy	rarefy	green	trunk

1. The jolly children laughed and sang and rejoiced generally.

2. The snake was coiled and ready to strike as the child approached.

3. It is a great pleasure to hear the thrush's lilting song in the spring.

4. Robert and Mary were well versed in the lore of the village.

5. Would you prefer cherries or strawberries for dessert?

6. He raised the spear above his head and thrust savagely at the enemy.

7. The three-room apartment is rented to a family from Reading.

8. Are you ready to demonstrate the theorem to the geometry class?

9. April is the month when we rejoice at the return of spring.

10. Are you planning to spend the Christmas holidays with your friends in Richmond?

11. Henry Wadsworth Longfellow wrote the poem called *Paul Revere's Ride*.

12. The cow was grazing in the grassy meadow by the river.

13. The theatre is crowded tonight because a famous actress is to play the role of *Rosalind*.

14. Mary returned recently from a trip to Rhode Island.

15. The food in this restaurant is really excellent and the prices are reasonable.

Test:

1. Can you do the exercises in the Procedure, pronouncing the sound *r* [ɹ] correctly?

2. Can you read the words and sentences given in the Practice Material, pronouncing all sounds correctly?

3. Can you prepare ten more sentences containing words with *r* [ɹ], and pronounce all sounds correctly?

4. Can you read the exercises for *r* [ɹ] (pages 102–103), pronouncing all sounds correctly?

5. Can you pronounce this sound correctly in your conversation?

CONTRACT 8A

Objective:

See Contract 8.

Procedure:

See Contract 8.

Caution:

This is a difficult sound for the foreigner. If, after working on this contract, there is still difficulty with the sound, take Contracts 4 and 5 under "Defective Phonation."

Practice Material:

Read the following words; be sure that the sound *r* [ɹ] is correctly pronounced; do not confuse it with *w* [w].

ream	roof	rice	carry	marry	breast	prime
rich	room	ripe	diary	narrow	crisp	prince
rest	route	round	fairy	purring	drop	treat
rabbit	rock	rare	garage	terrify	grin	tremble
rubber	rotation	rain	herring	weary	grist	trick

Read the following sentences, pronouncing all sounds correctly:

1. Rhoda was pressing her dresses and getting ready to go on a trip.

2. Mrs. Wright and her son, Richard, are recent arrivals at the new hotel at Hot Springs.

3. The porter carried my travelling bag from the train to the taxi.

4. The people gathered on the roof to see the parade on Memorial Day.

5. It was a treat for Mary's parents to have her and her family at home for Christmas.

6. Richard kept a diary of his experiences during his first European trip.

7. There is plenty of room for three on the front seat of the car.

8. The guests made merry on the day that Robert and Mary were married.

9. The green-eyed cat was purring contentedly on the hearth-rug before the fire.

10. The three rooms are connected by very narrow passageways.

11. It is only reasonable to expect children to be high-spirited.

12. We crossed the Hudson River by ferry instead of driving over the bridge.

13. The children grinned as they watched the magician's tricks.

14. Hans Christian Andersen wrote many interesting fairy tales.

15. There are huge rocks across the roadway leading to the rich man's residence.

Test:

1. Can you read the words and sentences in the Practice Material, pronouncing the sound *r* [ɹ] correctly?

2. Can you read the paragraph on pages 265–266, pronouncing the sound *r* [ɹ] correctly?

3. Can you pronounce this sound correctly when you converse with your family and friends?

4. You have now had all the sounds of English. Can you pronounce these sounds correctly in your conversation?

CONTRACT 9

Objective:

All sounds correctly pronounced, with special attention to *middle* consonants.

Procedure:

Be sure you know the exact position of the organs of articulation for every sound.

Place the consonant between two vowels as follows:

ĭ—tĭ	ĭ—tĭ	ĭ—tĭ	pretty	['pɹɪtɪ]
ă—tĭ	ă—tí	ă—tĭ	chatty	['tʃætɪ]
ă—dĭ	ă—dĭ	ă—dĭ	caddy	['kædɪ]
ĭ—lĭ	ĭ—lĭ	ĭ—lĭ	lily	['lɪlɪ]
ĕnĭ	ĕnĭ	ĕnĭ	any	['eᴛnɪ]
ĕmĭ	ĕmĭ	ĕmĭ	semi	['seᴛmɪ]
ĕpĭ	ĕpĭ	ĕpĭ	tepid	['teᴛpɪd]
ărĭ	ărĭ	ărĭ	tarry	['tæɹɪ]

Caution:

Be sure that the mid consonants are clear.

Remember that in speaking, the consonant should begin the second syllable and not end the first one. (For instance, in writing we divide the word *stooping* into *stoop-ing*, but in speaking we actually say *stoo-ping* ['stu·pɪŋ].)

Remember that although the consonant may be doubled in the spelling, it occurs only once in the pronunciation. (*Happen* is pronounced *ha-pen* ['hæpən].)

Practice Material:

Say the following words:

baby	sugar	tobacco	hammer	toper
babble	haggle	baker	humming	interloper
rabid	wrangle	making	thumbing	popping
fumbling	single	soccer	hemming	paper
sable	gargle	cackle	rhymer	piper
pebble	bungle	lacquer	timing	simple
dinner	saddle	tearing	hissing	pretty
diner	peddle	hiring	sister	kitten
dinning	wheedle	shirring	presser	nettle
donate	middle	siren	listerine	battle
winner	ready	peering	mystery	prattle
finish	sediment	nearing	missing	mottled

Read the following sentences, paying particular attention to the middle consonants:

1. The baby was paddling in the babbling brook.

2. The workmen were hammering and pounding in the pretty little house.

3. "Peter Piper picked a peck of pickled peppers."

4. The dapper tourists donated coppers to the wheedling beggars.

5. Hattie had a pretty little mottled kitten.

6. A single cyclist was peddling rapidly through the teeming tempest.

7. "Night's candles are burnt out, and jocund day
   Stands tiptoe on the misty mountain tops."

8. They were eating dinner at the inn called "The Sign of the Copper Kettle."

9. The girl hunted for her missing sister through the Middle West.

10. The policemen battled with the interlopers in the middle of the night.

Test:

1. Can you pronounce all the words in the Practice Material correctly?

2. Can you read the sentences given in the Practice Material and pronounce all the sounds correctly?

3. Can you prepare ten more sentences stressing middle consonants and then read them, pronouncing all words correctly?

4. Can you pronounce all sounds correctly in conversation if you speak slowly and carefully?

CONTRACT 9A

Objective:

See Contract 9.

Procedure:

See Contract 9.

Caution:

See Contract 9.

Practice Material:

Do the following exercises; be sure to pronounce all sounds correctly:

ă—ta	ĕ—ta	ĭ—ta [æ—tə	eт—tə	ɪ—tə]
ă—da	ĕ—da	ĭ—da [æ—də	eт—də	ɪ—də]
ă—ba	ĕ—ba	ĭ—ba [æ—bə	eт—bə	ɪ—bə]
ă—va	ĕ—va	ĭ—va [æ—və	eт—və	ɪ—və]
ă—la	ĕ—la	ĭ—la [æ—lə	eт—lə	ɪ—lə]
ă—ka	ĕ—ka	ĭ—ka [æ—kə	eт—kə	ɪ—kə]
ă—ma	ĕ—ma	ĭ—ma [æ—mə	eт—mə	ɪ—mə]
ă—na	ĕ—na	ĭ—na [æ—nə	eт—nə	ɪ—nə]
ă—pa	ĕ—pa	ĭ—pa [æ—pə	eт—pə	ɪ—pə]
ă—ra	ĕ—ra	ĭ—ra [æ—ɹə	eт—ɹə	ɪ—ɹə]
	ŏ—ta	ŭ—ta [ɒ—tə	ʌ—tə]	
	ŏ—da	ŭ—da [ɒ—də	ʌ—də]	
	ŏ—ba	ŭ—ba [ɒ—bə	ʌ—bə]	
	ŏ—va	ŭ—va [ɒ—və	ʌ—və]	
	ŏ—la	ŭ—la [ɒ—lə	ʌ—lə]	
	ŏ—ka	ŭ—ka [ɒ—kə	ʌ—kə]	
	ŏ—ma	ŭ—ma [ɒ—mə	ʌ—mə]	
	ŏ—na	ŭ—na [ɒ—nə	ʌ—nə]	
	ŏ—pa	ŭ—pa [ɒ—pə	ʌ—pə]	
	ŏ—ra	ŭ—ra [ɒ—ɹə	ʌ—ɹə]	

pitter-patter	pitter-patter	pitter-patter
hugger-mugger	hugger-mugger	hugger-mugger

Read the following sentences:

1. The family sat at the supper table eating toast and sipping tea
2. "What is the matter," muttered the master at the meeting.
3. The three little kittens lost their mittens.
4. All this bickering must be stopped immediately.
5. The babies were paddling in the mud puddle.
6. Autumn is the season for canning, pickling, and preserving.
7. It is better to live in a little city.
8. The knotty problem puzzled the professor.
9. "The shattering trumpet shrilleth high."
10. "They bit the babies in the cradles,
    And licked the soup from the cook's own ladles."

Test:

1. Can you do all the exercises in the Practice Material, pronouncing all words correctly?
2. Can you pronounce all sounds correctly in your conversation?

CONTRACT 10

Objective:

The correct pronunciation of voiced and voiceless consonants (with special attention to final consonants) in syllables, words, sentences, and conversation.

Procedure:

Be sure you know the correct position of the organs of articulation for all sounds.

Combine vowels and consonants to make syllables as follows:

ăb	ĕb	ĭb	ŏb	ŭb	[æb	eᴛb	ɪb	ɒb	ʌb]
ăd	ĕd	ĭd	ŏd	ŭd	[æd	eᴛd	ɪd	ɒd	ʌd]
ăg	ĕg	ĭg	ŏg	ŭg	[æg	eᴛg	ɪg	ɒg	ʌg]
ăk	ĕk	ĭk	ŏk	ŭk	[æk	eᴛk	ɪk	ɒk	ʌk]
ăl	ĕl	ĭl	ŏl	ŭl	[æl	eᴛl	ɪl	ɒl	ʌl]
ăm	ĕm	ĭm	ŏm	ŭm	[æm	eᴛm	ɪm	ɒm	ʌm]
ăn	ĕn	ĭn	ŏn	ŭn	[æn	eᴛn	ɪn	ɒn	ʌn]
ăp	ĕp	ĭp	ŏp	ŭp	[æp	eᴛp	ɪp	ɒp	ʌp]
ăs	ĕs	ĭs	ŏs	ŭs	[æs	eᴛs	ɪs	ɒs	ʌs]
ăt	ĕt	ĭt	ŏt	ŭt	[æt	eᴛt	ɪt	ɒt	ʌt]

Caution:

Be sure that the voiced consonants are sufficiently voiced.

Be sure the voiceless consonants are not voiced.

Remember that vowel sounds are held longer before voiced consonants than before voiceless consonants.

Practice Material:

Read the following double columns of words horizontally:

pip	bib	half	have	mouth (*n*.)	mouth (*v*.)
pipe	imbibe	chief	achieve	breath	breathe
cape	babe	sift	sieve	cloth	clothe
rope	robe	golf	glove	loath	loathe
puppy	bubble	safe	save	teeth	teethe
police	please	precise	sighs	much	smudge
treatise	trees	ice	eyes	smirch	merge
cease	seize	pace	pays	lunch	lunge
loss	laws	course	cause	patch	badge
loose	lose	mace	maze	birch	dirge
	tight	died		duck	dug
	mate	made		frock	frog
	rite	ride		buck	bug
	suit	sued		hack	hag
	route	rude		pluck	plug

Read the following sentences:

1. The girls were in a rage because the doors of the house were locked.

2. The chief could not achieve the honor which the people were pleased to confer upon the rest of the police force.

3. The beasts in the fields were badly stung by bees and wasps.

4. Open your mouth, but make sure that you do not mouth your words.

5. That cloth will make very pretty clothes.

6. I changed my course because the professor was not precise in his assignments.

7. The dogs ceased their barking when their master seized them by their collars.

8. When Dick was digging in the garden, he dug up a gold piece.

9. The children's eyes brightened when they saw the ice cream on the table.

10. He trod on his sister's toes as she stood making the toast over the fire.

Test:

1. Can you do all the exercises in the Procedure and Practice Material, pronouncing all sounds correctly?

2. Can you prepare ten more sentences and then read them, pronouncing all sounds correctly?

3. Can you use all sounds correctly in conversation?

4. Are you careful to think about pronunciation when talking to your family and friends?

5. Can you do all the exercises given for cognate substitutions (pages 121–123), pronouncing all sounds correctly?

CONTRACT 10A

Objective:

See Contract 10.

Procedure:

See Contract 10.

Caution:

See Contract 10.

Practice Material:

Read the following columns of words horizontally:

dump	dub	laugh	lave	crutch	drudge
rip	rib	safe	save	such	budge
lope	lobe	gruff	grove	fetch	fudge
tap	tab	loaf	loaves	rich	ridge
nap	nab	off	of	church	judge

tight	tied	trait	trade	luck	lug
site	side	prate	parade	flock	fog
bite	bide	set	said	rack	rag
sot	sod	trite	tried	rick	rig
late	laid	boat	abode	peck	peg

bus	buzz	vice	vies
hiss	his	rice	rise
niece	knees	house (*n.*)	house (*v.*)
peace	peas	lace	lays
price	prize	rejoice	poise

Read the following sentences:

1. Did you ever see a Punch and Judy show?

2. "My good blade carves the casques of men."

3. The mate lunged out of the boat, perched on the rock, and ate his lunch.

4. Three black crows flew across the sky.

5. My niece stood up to her knees in the raging torrent.

6. The torn page was patched with court-plaster.

7. The soldier has leased this property on the leas for years.

8. "Perfume and flowers fall in showers,
That lightly rain from ladies' hands."

9. The child prated about the parade for many days.

10. We will grow peas and beans in the garden.

Test:

1. Can you do all the exercises in the Practice Material, pronouncing all words correctly, and paying special attention to voiced and voiceless sounds?

2. Can you prepare ten more sentences and then read them, pronouncing all words correctly?

3. Are you careful to differentiate between voiced and voiceless sounds in your conversation?

CONTRACT 11

Objective:

Strong and weak forms correctly used in phrases, sentences, paragraphs, and conversation.

Procedure:

See pages 41–43 for the discussion of strong and weak forms.

Caution:

Be careful to use weak forms when necessary in reading as well as talking.

Practice Material:

Read the following phrases, being careful to weaken forms that should be weakened:

1. Off and on.
2. Going to school.
3. Seeing the world.
4. Using all but one.
5. Coming home from school.
6. Taking a piece of paper.
7. Planning to have a party.
8. Buying more than one dress.
9. In the middle of the floor.
10. Seeing her sister.
11. Staying at home.
12. Looking for the children.
13. Driving faster and faster.
14. Wearing a black and white hat.
15. Having a fine time at the party.
16. Saying that *that* was true.

Read the following sentences, following the directions given above:

1. We are saving a place at the table for John.
2. Do you *have* to go to the party?
3. He was trying to find his hat.
4. I should like to go more than once.

5. Neither John nor Mary wishes to see the play.

6. I shall go shopping with her tomorrow.

7. What did you do with them?

8. I should like to go if you could go too.

9. Do you want to see her?

10. Here is an apple for the little boy.

11. John said that *that* was his coat.

12. This is the dress that Mary bought at the sale.

13. Is this the day we are to meet your friends from Chicago?

14. The letter was delayed because of insufficient postage.

15. Harold is the brother of a friend of mine.

Read the following paragraph from Washington Irving's *Stage Coach*, paying careful attention to the use of strong and weak forms:

Perhaps it might be owing to the pleasant serenity that reigned in my own mind that I fancied I saw cheerfulness in every countenance throughout the journey. A stage coach, however, carries animation always with it, and puts the world in motion as it whirls along. The horn sounded at the entrance of a village produces a general bustle. Some hasten forth to meet friends; some with bundles and bandboxes to secure places, and in the hurry of the moment can hardly take leave of the group that accompanies them. In the meantime, the coachman has a world of small commissions to execute. Sometimes he delivers a hare or a pheasant; sometimes jerks a small parcel or newspaper to the door of a public-house; and sometimes with knowing leer and words of sly import, hands to some half-blushing, half-laughing housemaid an odd-shaped billet-doux from some rustic admirer.

Test:

1. Can you read all the exercises in the Practice Material, making the proper use of weak forms?

2. Can you use strong and weak forms correctly in your reading and conversation?

CONTRACT 12

Objective:

Intonation in phrases, questions, and short sentences.

Procedure:

See pages 44–46 for the discussion of intonation.

Caution:

Intonation is a very important factor of your speech.   Remember that even though all sounds are correctly made, if the intonation is foreign, the speech is foreign.

Practice Material:

Read the following phrases with correct intonation:

1. Ready or unready.   5. Pale or red.
2. Hot or cold.   6. Off and on.
3. Up and down.   7. Sick or well.
4. Here and there.   8. This and that.

Read the following questions with correct intonation:

1. Are you here?   5. When do you leave?
2. Where are you going?   6. Have you seen the play?
3. Can you hear me?   7. Which is the older girl?
4. Is this the place?   8. Will six plates be enough?

Answer the questions listed above, using correct intonation.

Read the following sentences with correct intonation:

1. This is an old book.
2. The dogs are barking.
3. It is raining hard.
4. All the windows are closed.
5. The clock has stopped.
6. The plane flies too low.
7. The man is working hard.
8. The women are washing their clothes.
9. The birds are singing merrily.
10. This is a lovely day.

Read the following questions and answers with correct intonation.

1. Are you going to school?   Yes, I am.
2. What time do you plan to leave?
3. I expect to leave at nine o'clock.
4. Where are you going?
5. I am going to Maine and Vermont.

6. Have you finished your lessons?   Yes, I have.

7. What time do you have dinner?

8. We have dinner at twelve o'clock.

9. Isn't this a lovely day?

10. It's a beautiful day.

Test:

1. Can you do all the exercises in the Practice Material, using the proper intonation?

2. Can you prepare ten more questions and answers and then read them with the proper intonation?

CONTRACT 13

Objective:

Intonation in longer sentences and paragraphs.

Procedure:

See Contract 8.

Caution:

See Contract 8.

Practice Material:

Read the following sentences with proper intonation:

1. The children are playing a game in the garden.

2. The sound *t* is made with the tip of the tongue on the upper gum.

3. I visited friends in South Carolina for a month last winter.

4. Switzerland is beautiful because of its mountains and lakes.

5. In winter, the days are very short.

6. I have not seen him since college closed.

7. Did you arrange the books on the shelves in the library?

8. In the autumn, students in New England colleges have a holiday known as Mountain Day.

9. "Time and tide wait for no man," is a well-known saying.

10. Did you have an interesting time during your Christmas vacation?

Read with the proper intonation the following paragraphs from Dickens' *David Copperfield:*

It was with a singular jumble of sadness and pleasure that I used to linger about my native place, until the reddening winter sun admonished me that it was time to start on my returning walk. . . .

My nearest way to Yarmouth, in coming back from these long walks was by a ferry. It landed me on a flat between the town and the sea, which I could go straight across and so save myself a considerable circuit by the high road. Mr. Peggoty's house being on that waste place, and not a hundred yards out of my track, I always looked in as I went by. Steerforth was pretty sure to be there expecting me, and we went on together through the frosty air and gathering fog towards the twinkling lights of the town.

One dark evening, when I was later than usual—for I had, that day, been making my parting visit to Blunderstone, as we were now about to return home—I found him alone in Mr. Peggoty's house, sitting thoughtfully before the fire. He was so intent upon his own reflections that he was quite unconscious of my approach.

He gave such a start when I put my hand upon his shoulder, that he made me start too.

"You come upon me," he said almost angrily, "like a reproachful ghost!"

"I was obliged to announce myself somehow," I replied. "Have I called you down from the stars?"

"No," he answered. "No."

"Up from anywhere, then?" said I, taking my seat near him.

"I was looking at the pictures in the fire," he returned.

"But you are spoiling them for me," said I, as he stirred it quickly with a piece of burning wood, striking out of it a train of red-hot sparks that went careering up the little chimney, and roaring out into the air.

"You would not have seen them," he returned. "I detest this mongrel time, neither day nor night. How late you are! Where have you been?"

"I have been taking leave of my usual walk," said I.

Test:

1. Can you do the exercises in the Practice Material with proper intonation?

2. Can you find another selection, and read it with proper intonation?

3. Can you use proper intonation during your reading and conversation?

CONTRACT 14

Objective:

Reading of paragraphs with all sounds correctly made, correct intonation, and correct use of strong and weak forms.

Procedure:

See Contracts 11 and 12 and any other that you need to refer to.

Caution:

Read slowly at first in order to check up on possible errors, and then more rapidly.

Practice Material:

Read the following paragraphs from Dickens' *David Copperfield,* fulfilling the conditions of the objective:

On going down in the morning, I found my aunt musing so profoundly over the breakfast table, with her elbow on the tray, that the contents of the urn had overflowed the teapot and were laying the whole table-cloth under water, when my entrance put her meditations to flight. I felt sure that I had been the object of her reflections, and was more than ever anxious to know her intentions towards me. Yet I dared not express my anxiety, lest it should give her offence.

My eyes, however, not being so much under control as my tongue, were attracted towards my aunt very often during breakfast. I never could look at her for a few moments together but I found her looking at me—in an odd thoughtful manner, as if I were an immense way off, instead of being on the other side of the small round table. When she had finished her breakfast, my aunt very deliberately leaned back in her chair, knitted her brows, folded her arms, and contemplated me at her leisure, with such a fixedness of attention that I was quite overpowered with embarrassment. Not having as yet finished my own breakfast, I attempted to hide my confusion by proceeding with it; but my knife tumbled over my fork, my fork tripped up my knife, I chipped bits of bacon a surprising height into the air instead of cutting them for my own eating, and choked myself with my tea, which persisted in going the wrong way, instead of the right one, until I gave in altogether, and sat blushing under my aunt's close scrutiny.

Test:

1. Can you read the paragraphs given above, fulfilling the requirements of the Objective?

2. Find another paragraph and then read it, fulfilling the same requirements.

3. Can you fulfil these conditions in your daily conversation?

CONTRACT 15

Objective:

Correct sounds, correct intonation, and correct use of strong and weak forms in sight reading and conversation.

Procedure:

Consult any contract to which you need to refer.

Caution:

Always listen to your speech carefully, and correct any mistakes that you may make.

Practice Material:

See preceding contracts.

Test:

Can you fulfil the requirements of the Objective in sight reading and conversation?

CONTRACT SHEET
Lisping*

---

1. Correct production of the sounds *s* [s] and *z* [z].

---

2. Initial *s* [s] and *z* [z] in syllables, words, and phrases.

---

3. Initial *s* [s] and *z* [z] in sentences.
Initial *st* [st] and *sn* [sn] in syllables, words, and phrases.

---

4. Initial *s* [s], *z* [z], *st* [st], and *sn* [sn] in sentences.
Initial *sl* [sl] and *sk* [sk] in syllables, words, and phrases.

---

5. Initial *s* [s], *z* [z], *st* [st], *sn* [sn], *sk* [sk], and *sl* [sl] in sentences.
Initial *sp* [sp], *sw* [sw], and *sm* [sm] in syllables, words, and phrases.

---

6. All initial sibilant combinations in sentences.
The sounds *sh* [ʃ], *zh* [ʒ], *ch* [tʃ], and *j* [dʒ], in words, phrases, and sentences.

---

7. Final *s* [s] and *z* [z] in syllables, words, phrases, and short sentences.

---

8. Final *s* [s] and *z* [z] in more difficult sentences.
Final *st* [st] and *sk* [sk] in syllables, words, and phrases.

---

* At the beginning of every practice period, do Contract 1 under "Careless Speech."

9. Final *s* [s], *z* [z], *st* [st], and *sk* [sk] in sentences.

Final *sp* [sp], *sl* [sl̩], *zl* [zl̩], and *zm* [zm̩] in syllables, words, and phrases.

10. All final sibilant combinations in sentences, paragraphs, and conversation.

11. Medial sibilants in words, phrases, and sentences.

12. All sibilant sounds in sentences, paragraphs, and conversation.

13. Lists of words containing difficult combinations of sibilant sounds.

Use of these words in sentences, paragraphs, and conversation.

14. All sibilant sounds in prepared paragraphs (chosen by the student), sight reading, and conversation.

CONTRACT 1

Objective:

Individual sounds *s* [s] and *z* [z] correctly made.

Procedure:

Close the teeth slightly, or bring them together so that they just touch; place the tip of the tongue just behind the top of the upper teeth (in case of wide spaces between the upper teeth, the tongue may be placed just behind the upper gum); send the voiced *z* [z] or voiceless *s* [s] through a narrow groove in the middle of the tongue and out through the teeth.   It may help to rest the sides of the tongue lightly against the sides of the upper teeth, but *remember that the tip and the front of the tongue must be free.*   See pages 36–37 for the correct production of *s* [s] and *z* [z].

Caution:

Always practice with a mirror.

Be sure that the tip, front, or middle of the tongue does not touch the teeth.

Be sure that the tongue is just as close to the top of the upper teeth as it can be without actually touching them.

Be sure that the tongue is slightly grooved.

Let the sound flow softly; it is not a harsh sound.

Practice Material:

In the following exercise, prolong both the sibilant sounds a short time:

$$t—t—t—s$$
$$d—d—d—z$$

Do the following exercises:

z—ā	z—ā	z—ā	zā [zeɪɪ]
z—ē	z—ē	z—ē	zē [ziː]
s—ā	s—ā	s—ā	sā [seɪɪ]
s—ē	s—ē	s—ē	sē [siː]

Continue in this manner, placing *s* [s] and *z* [z] before other vowels and diphthongs.

Test:

1. Can you tell the difference between the correct and the incorrect production of z [z] and s [s] in the speech of others? in your own speech?

2. Can you make these sounds correctly?

CONTRACT 2

Objective:

Initial s [s] and z [z] combined with other sounds in syllables, words, and phrases.

Procedure:

Put the tongue in the correct position for t [t] (the tip of the tongue touching the upper gum lightly). Say the following exercise ten times, holding the s [s] sound as in Contract 1 and being sure that it is correctly made:

t—t—t—sssssss

Put the tongue in the correct position for th (the tip of the tongue protruding slightly beyond the upper teeth), and repeat the following exercises:

thā—sā	thā—sā	thā—sā–sā–sā [θeɪ̆—seɪ̆]
thah—sah	thah—sah	thah—sah–sah–sah [θɑː—sɑː]
thē—sē	thē—sē	thē—sē–sē–sē [θiː—siː]
thoo—soo	thoo—soo	thoo—soo–soo–soo [θuː—suː]
thē—sē	thah—sah	thoo—soo [θiː—si: θɑː—sɑ: θuː—suː]
thā—zā	thā—zā	thā—zā–zā–zā [ðeɪ̆—zeɪ̆]
thah—zah	thah—zah	thah—zah–zah–zah [ðɑː—zɑː]
thē—zē	thē—zē	thē—zē–zē–zē [ðiː—ziː]
thoo—zoo	thoo—zoo	thoo—zoo–zoo–zoo [ðuː—zuː]
thē—zē	thah—zah	thoo—zoo [ðiː—zi: ðɑː—zɑ: ðuː—zuː]

Caution:

Be sure the sibilant sounds are correctly made each time; you are forming a new habit, and you must never allow yourself to slip back into the old habit.

Practice Material:

Do the exercise given above, using a mirror.

Say the following words, being careful that the sibilant sounds are correctly made:

seem	surround	psalm	sower	zebra
sit	supper	so	same	zipper
set	soup	saw	sight	zealot
sat	soot	sour	seer	zero
sir	sop	soil	suit	zone

Read the following phrases, slowly at first and then more rapidly:

1. Sowing the seed.

2. Eating supper.

3. Seeing the country.

4. Reading a psalm.

5. Drinking sour milk.

6. Sawing a cedar tree.

7. Sitting on the seat.

8. Cleaning the soot out of the chimney.

9. Cultivating a beautiful zinnia.

10. Going to the Canal Zone.

Test:

1. Can you pronounce correctly all the words given in the Practice Material?

2. Can you pronounce correctly all the words given for initial *s* [s] (pages 108–109) and initial *z* [z] (page 110)?

3. Can you read with good, clear sibilant sounds all the phrases given in the Practice Material?

4. Can you prepare five more phrases and then read them without lisping?

CONTRACT 2A

Objective:

See Contract 2.

Procedure:

Take the correct position for *t* [t] and repeat the following exercise ten times:

t—t—t—sssssssss

Take the correct position for *d* [d], and repeat the following exercise ten times:

d—d—d—zzzzzzzzz

Take the correct position for *th* and do the following exercises:

thō—sō	thō—sō	thō—sō–sō–sō	[θoτŭ—soτŭ]
thī—sī	thī—sī	thī—sī–sī–sī	[θaɪ—saɪ]
thow—sow	thow—sow	thow—sow–sow–sow	[θaŭ—saŭ]
thoi—soi	thoi—soi	thoi—soi–soi–soi	[θɔɪ—sɔɪ]

sō—sō—sō   [soτŭ]
sī—sī—sī   [saĭ]
sow—sow—sow [saŭ]
soi—soi—soi [sɔĭ]

Take the correct position for *d* [d] and do the following exercises:

dō—zō   dō—zō   dō—zō–zō–zō   [doτŭ—zoτŭ]
dī—zī   dī—zī   dī—zī–zī–zī   [daĭ—zaĭ]
dow—zow   dow—zow   dow—zow–zow–zow   [daŭ—zaŭ]
doi—zoi   doi—zoi   doi—zoi–zoi–zoi   [dɔĭ—zɔĭ]
          zō—   zō—   zō   [zoτŭ]
          zī—   zī—   zī   [zaĭ]
          zow—zow—zow   [zaŭ]
          zoi— zoi— zoi [zɔĭ]

Caution:

Be sure that *every sound* is correctly made.

Practice Material:

Say the following words, giving special attention to the production of the sibilant sounds:

seed	serve	sod	sound	zeal
sip	supply	sold	sane	zed
settle	sup	saw	sign	zinc
sand	soon	sail	sight	zoo

Read the following phrases, giving special attention to the production of the sibilant sounds:

1. Sipping the tea.
2. Tilling the soil.
3. Seeding the ground.
4. Settling the land.
5. Sitting on the settle.

6. Playing the zither.
7. Going to the zoo.
8. Sawing wood.
9. Sounding the horn.
10. Following the sea.

Test:

1. Can you pronounce correctly all the words given in the Practice Material?

2. Can you pronounce correctly all the words given for initial *s* [s] (page 108) and initial *z* [z] (page 109)?

3. Can you read without lisping all the phrases given in the Practice Material?

4. Can you prepare six more phrases and then read them without lisping?

CONTRACT 3

Objective:

Initial *s* [s] and *z* [z] in sentences.
Initial *st* [st] and *sn* [sn] in syllables, words, and phrases.

Procedure:

Do the following exercise ten times:

t—t—t—sssssss

Make the sound *s* [s] clearly, and then raise the tongue to the gum
ridge for the sound *t* [t]:

s—t   s—t   s—t   s—t

Do this exercise very slowly until you are sure both sounds are
correctly made, and then say ten times:

st   st   st

Add the sound *ā* [erĭ] to *st* and say:

stā   stā   stā [sterĭ]

If this exercise causes trouble, try saying it in this fashion:

s—tā   s—tā   s—tā   sta [sterĭ]

Now raise the tip of the tongue to the gum ridge, allow the sound to
go out through the nose, and say *n* [n]; place *s* [s] before *n* [n] and say:

s—n   s—n   s—n
s—nā   s—nā   s—nā   snā [snerĭ]

Continue with this exercise, placing other vowels and diphthongs
after *st* [st] and *sn* [sn].

Caution:

Go slowly; it may be several days before you can combine these
sounds satisfactorily.

Remember that the sound *t* [t] must be made correctly if *st* [st] is
to be made correctly; if the *t* [t] is incorrectly made, take Contract
1B under "Foreign Accent."

Be sure that the tongue does not come into contact with the teeth
when going from *s* [s] to *t* [t] or *n* [n].

Practice Material:

Say the following words, paying special attention to the production
of the sibilant sounds:

steam	stir	stool	sneak	snake
stick	stumble	story	snip	snipe
step	stone	style	snap	snout
stare	stoop	stamen	snag	snore
static	stood	stout	snub	sneer

Say the following phrases without lisping:

1. Taking a steamboat trip.   4. Sitting on the step.
2. Stirring the soup.   5. Telling a sad story.
3. Making a statement.   6. Snipping the cloth.

7. Striking a snag.

Read the following sentences without lisping:

1. The man selected the top of the hill for a home.
2. They sat down to eat at "The Sign of the Peacock."
3. The workmen sang a merry song.
4. The boy got zero in zoölogy.
5. The woman seemed to be calm and serene.
6. The girl came running up the sand dune.

Test:

1. Can you read, without lisping, all the words given in the Practice Material?

2. Can you read without lisping all the words given for initial *st* [st] (page 115) and initial *sn* [sn] (page 112)?

3. Can you read, without lisping, all the phrases and sentences given in the Practice Material?

4. Can you prepare five more phrases and five more sentences and then read them without lisping?

CONTRACT 3A

Objective:

See Contract 3.

Procedure:

See Contract 3.

Caution:

See Contract 3.

Practice Material:

Do the following exercises:

st	st	st	
s—tō	s—tō	s—tō	stō [stoгŭ]
s—tōō	s—tōō	s—tōō	stōō [stu:]
s—tī	s—tī	s—tī	stī [staɪ]
s—tē	s—tē	s—tē	stē [sti:]
s—tah	s—tah	s—tah	stah [stɑ:]
s—tē	s—tah	s—tōō	stē stah stōō [sti: stɑ: stu:]
s—nē	s—nē	s—nē	snē [sni:]
s—nah	s—nah	s—nah	snah [snɑ:]
s—nōō	s—nōō	s—nōō	snōō [snu:]
s—nē	s—nah	s—nōō	snē snah snōō [sni: snɑ: snu:]

Read the following words, paying special attention to the production of the sibilant sounds:

steep	stand	stood	stain	snicker	snob
stint	stern	stoke	stave	snatch	snarl
stem	stunt	stall	start	snuggle	snare
stare	stoop	stifle	stop	snoop	sniper

Read the following phrases without lisping:

1. Stooping to pick up a book.
2. Driving by a steel mill.
3. Staring at the crowd.
4. Climbing a stone wall.
5. Putting the pony in the stall.
6. Cutting the stem of the flower.
7. Doing a stunt.
8. Sneering at the sight.
9. Snowing from dawn to dark.
10. Sneaking in for a snack of something to eat.

Read the following sentences without lisping:

1. The scene was weird at the zero hour.
2. He sold the hard-water soap.
3. The water seeped up through the cellar.
4. He sold the old settle for a song.
5. They sailed on the Sound in a sail boat.

6. The musician played the violin and the zither.

7. He said brown was a suitable color.

8. The gardener said the soil was sandy.

9. They served tea in the drawing-room.

10. I saw the sign from the sitting-room window.

Test:

1. Can you pronounce correctly all the words given in the Practice Material?

2. Can you read correctly the words in the Practice Material, placing the word *the* before each word?

3. Can you read all the phrases in the Practice Material without lisping?

4. Can you read all the sentences in the Practice Material without lisping?

5. Can you prepare five other sentences and then read them without lisping?

6. Can you read all the sentences for initial *s* [s] (pages 108–109) without lisping?

CONTRACT 4

Objective:

Initial *s* [s], *z* [z], *st* [st], and *sn* [sn] in sentences.
Initial *sl* [sl] and *sk* [sk] in syllables, words, and phrases.

Procedure:

Take the correct position for *s* [s]; make the sound correctly, then flatten the tongue against the gum ridge, pressing gently for the sound *l* [l]. (See page 36 for more detailed information concerning the production of *l* [l].)

Say the following exercises five times each:

sss—lll   sss—lll   sss—lll
  sl   sl   sl

Add the sound *ā* [eɪ] to *sl* [sl] and say:

slā   slā   slā   [sleɪl]

If you have any difficulty with this exercise, proceed as you did with *st* [st]:

s—lā   s—lā   s—lā   slā [sleɪl]

Make the sound *s* [s] correctly, then draw the back of the tongue back to the soft palate for *k* [k]; (see page 38 for production of *k* [k]). Proceed as with *l* [l].

Caution:

Remember that you must try very hard to pronounce *s* [s] correctly all the time; do not allow yourself to slip back into your former habit.

Practice Material:

Continue with the exercises suggested in the Procedure, adding all vowels and diphthongs to the sounds given above.

Say the following words without lisping:

sleep	slam	slow	scheme	scat	scald
slim	slur	slot	skill	skull	scold
sled	slum	slate	sketch	school	scorn
slap	sloop	sly	scare	scourge	scar

Read the following phrases without lisping:

1. Scooping up a bucket of sand.
2. Sketching the view from the second-story window.
3. Going for a sleigh ride.
4. Riding down the slope on the red sled.
5. Walking slowly into the school-room.
6. Scheming to get a longer holiday.
7. Sailing on the new sloop.
8. Slapping the slim boy.

Read the following sentences without lisping:

1. The zealot stood on the sand haranguing the throng.
2. The zebra had a beautiful striped coat.
3. The story told of a stirring adventure.
4. Seven able seamen landed from the sail boat.
5. The sailor snatched the boy out of the water.
6. The twig snapped under the weight of the snow.
7. The girl stood at the book stall.
8. The dog snarled when he saw the sneak thief.
9. Sarah stopped to look at the sea.
10. Our former home stood at the top of a steep hill.

Test:

1. Can you read all the words in the Practice Material without lisping?

2. Can you read the words given for *sn* [sn] on page 112, putting *but* before each word?

3. Can you read the phrases and sentences in the Practice Material without lisping?

4. Can you prepare ten more sentences and read them without lisping?

CONTRACT 4A

Objective:

See Contract 4.

Procedure:

See Contract 4.

Caution:

Be sure that the tongue does not touch the teeth when making *s* [s].

Practice Material:

Say the following words individually at first; then precede each word with the words *the, but, of,* as follows: *the slit, but slit, of slit,* and so forth.

sleeve	slack	slave	scream	scrub	skein
slit	slop	slight	skin	scuttle	scowl
slick	slaw	slide	schedule	scope	skewer
slender	slam	slough	scan	scone	squill

Read the following phrases without lisping:

1. Sewing the sleeve.

2. Freeing the slave.

3. Running on schedule.

4. Taking up the slack.

5. Scowling at the tangled skein.

6. Eating a Scotch scone and sipping tea.

7. Sloughing off the skin.

8. Seeing the snow slide.

9. Slamming the screen door.

10. Dieting to keep slim and slender.

Read the following sentences without lisping:

1. The young girl stood by the side of the stone wall.
2. The sailor snatched a bite to eat before going on duty.
3. Did you see the Stop sign at the corner?
4. We had to stand in line for an hour before we could be served.
5. Tom stole the stick that belonged to Sam.
6. The snapdragon bloomed at the south side of the garden.
7. The tired student stifled a yawn.
8. The severe snow storm made travel difficult.
9. Dinner will be served at seven o'clock.
10. The farmer started to build a stone wall at the beginning of the summer.

Test:

1. Can you read the words given in the Practice Material in the manner suggested, without lisping?

2. Can you read the words given in the exercises for *st* [st] (page 115) individually, and then with the words *the, but, of* before each one?

3. Can you read, without lisping, the phrases and sentences given in the Practice Material?

4. Can you read the sentences given for initial *st* [st] (page 115) without lisping?

CONTRACT 5

Objective:

Initial *s* [s], *z* [z], *st* [st], *sn* [sn], *sl* [sl], and *sk* [sk] in sentences.
Initial *sp* [sp], *sm* [sm], and *sw* [sw] in syllables, words, and phrases.

Procedure:

Make the sound *s* [s] correctly; then press the lips together gently, and separate them suddenly by the force of the breath, thus forming the sound *p* [p].

Do the following exercise five times:

sss—p	sss—p	sss—p	sp
s—pā	s—pā	s—pā	spā [speɪ]
s—pē	s—pē	s—pē	spē [spi:]
s—pah	s—pah	s—pah	spah [spɑ:]
s—pōō	s—pōō	s—pōō	spōō [spu:]
s—pē	s—pah	s—pōō	spē spah spōō [spi: spɑ: spu:]

Make the sound *s* [s]; now close the lips gently, lower the soft palate, and let the voiced sound *m* [m] flow out through the nose.   Put the sounds together as with *sp* [sp].

Make the sound *s* [s]; round the lips and thrust them forward, thus forming the voiced sound *w* [w].   Put the sounds together as above.

Do the following exercises:

s—mī	s—mī	s—mī	smī [smaɪ]
s—mō	s—mō	s—mō	smō [smoᴛʊ]
s—mē	s—mē	s—mē	smē [smiː]
s—mah	s—mah	s—mah	smah [smɑː]
s—mo͞o	s—mo͞o	s—mo͞o	smo͞o [smuː]
s—mē	s—mah	s—mo͞o	smē smah smo͞o [smiː smɑː smuː]
s—wē	s—wē	s—wē	swē [swiː]
s—wah	s—wah	s—wah	swah [swɑː]
s—wo͞o	s—wo͞o	s—wo͞o	swo͞o [swuː]
s—wē	s—wah	s—wo͞o	swē swah swo͞o [swiː swɑː swuː]

Caution:

Be sure that the tongue is held high (behind the top of the *upper* teeth) when making the sound *s* [s].

Practice Material:

Continue the exercises suggested in the Procedure, placing *sp* [sp], *sm* [sm] and *sw* [sw] before all vowels and diphthongs.

Say the following words individually at first; then place the words *the*, *but*, *of*, and *with* before each one.

spin	spurn	swim	swirl	smear	small
spend	spun	swear	swung	smooth	smart
span	spoon	swam	swoon	smote	smile

Read the following phrases, pronouncing all sounds correctly:

1. Swimming in the swimming pool.
2. Spending the afternoon by the sea.
3. Swinging and singing in the garden.
4. Learning to spin and weave.
5. Swearing to tell the whole truth.
6. Smiling at the small boy.
7. Smelling a sweet odor.
8. Smearing paint on the sofa in the sitting-room.

Read the following sentences without lisping:

1. The girl skated silently around the lake.
2. Mary slept soundly through the thunder storm.
3. The old lady slipped on the cellar floor and strained her knee.
4. Sam threw a stone into the stream.
5. The thermometer stood at zero for an entire week.
6. The sea still ran high although the wind had died down.
7. The traveler drove through Sleepy Hollow in a sleet storm.
8. The snow made it difficult to steer the stalwart steed.
9. The steer snorted in fear, and ran up the mountain.
10. "Truth forever on the scaffold,
    Wrong forever on the throne."

Test:

1. Can you say the words given in the Practice Material in the manner suggested, without lisping?

2. Can you read the phrases and sentences given in the Practice Material without lisping?

3. Can you prepare ten more sentences and read them without lisping?

4. Are you careful to pronounce s [s] correctly in your conversation?

CONTRACT 5A

Objective:

See Contract 5.

Procedure:

See Contract 5.

Caution:

Be sure that the tip and front of the tongue are free when making the sound s [s].

Practice Material:

Say the following words individually at first; then place the words *and, of,* and *a* before each one:

spill	spoil	swindle	swine	smitten	smudge
spurt	spear	swan	swain	smack	smoke
spunk	spare	swore	swollen	smother	smite

Read the following phrases without lisping:

1. Crying over spilt milk.
2. Swindling the public.
3. Sparing the rod and spoiling the child.
4. Going for a ride in a swan-boat.
5. Smothering the fire.
6. Seeing a cloud of smoke.
7. Feeding the swine.
8. Getting a spurt of speed.
9. Carrying a heavy spear.
10. Scolding the spunky little girl.

Read the following sentences without lisping:

1. Stanley climbed to the top of the steeple on Sunday.
2. The student made a definite statement in regard to the attitude of the student body.
3. The guard carried a stout stick made of red cedar.
4. The steward stood at the door of the stateroom.
5. The cook made the stuffing of stale bread.
6. Sarah strode angrily out of the room and slammed the door.
7. The people of the little mountain community feared a snow-slide.
8. I think I can buy a stamp at the drug store on the corner.
9. Stanley studied a sleight-of-hand trick.
10. The old man walked slowly but steadily up the steep hill.

Test:

1. Can you say the words given in the Practice Material in the manner suggested, without lisping?
2. Can you read the phrases and sentences given in the Practice Material without lisping?
3. Can you read the sentences given for *sn* [sn] (page 113) without lisping?

CONTRACT 6

Objective:

All initial sibilant combinations in sentences.
The sounds *sh* [ʃ], *zh* [ʒ], *ch* [tʃ], and *j* [dʒ] correctly pronounced.

Procedure:

See page 37 for the correct production of the sounds *sh* [ʃ], *zh* [ʒ], *ch* [tʃ], and *j* [dʒ].

Caution:

Remember that *ch* [tʃ] and *j* [dʒ] are digraphs—made up of two sounds.

Remember that each begins with the tip of tongue pointed on the middle of the upper gum.

Remember that *zh* [ʒ] never occurs at the beginning of a word.

Practice Material:

Pronounce the following words correctly:

sheen	pleasure	church	agitate
share	measure	smirch	judge
shatter	garage	birch	jump
sure	treasure	lurch	gorge
shine	seizure	wretches	edge

Read the following phrases, pronouncing all sounds correctly:

1. Showing good judgment.
2. Sharing a pleasure.
3. Measuring the sugar.
4. Shining only one shoe.
5. Putting the car in the garage.
6. Going to church "rain or shine."
7. Shattering the treasured object.
8. Jumping over the edge of the gorge.
9. Enjoying the white birch tree.
10. Agitating the jury.

Read the following sentences, pronouncing all sounds correctly:

1. The slender girl swung swiftly around the track.
2. The snail moved slowly down the middle of the street.
3. The strict teacher had a stimulating effect upon the student.
4. The Scandinavian student stood high in every study.
5. The snake stared at the singing bird.
6. Carl Sandburg wrote a book of poetry called *Smoke and Steel.*
7. The gift of sugar gave much pleasure to the child.

8. The sun shone today; tomorrow the rain may dash down.

9. The sick child will certainly recover at the seashore.

10. The children enjoyed watching the snow storm.

Test:

1. Can you pronounce correctly the words given in the Practice Material?

2. Can you read the phrases and sentences given in the Practice Material, pronouncing all sounds correctly?

3. Can you read the sentences given in the exercises for *sw* [sw] (page 111) without lisping?

4. Can you read the words given in the exercises for *sh* [ʃ], *zh* [ʒ], *ch* [tʃ], and *j* [dʒ] (pages 119–120), pronouncing each word correctly?

CONTRACT 6A

Objective:

See Contract 6.

Procedure:

See Contract 6.

Caution:

See Contract 6.

Practice Material:

Read the following phrases, pronouncing all sounds correctly:

1. Spending the afternoon at the Dog Show.

2. Seeing an ancient art treasure at the picture gallery.

3. Singing a Negro Spiritual.

4. Pouring water from the Spode pitcher.

5. Clinching the argument with a strong statement.

6. Putting the colt in the stable and the car in the garage.

7. Seeking shelter from the heat in the cool church.

8. Attending Summer School at Richmond.

9. Planning to meet Virginia in the Sweet Shop.

10. Sending a Jumping Jack to the sick child.

Read the following sentences pronouncing all sounds correctly:

1. Mary wore a smart new smock.

2. Sarah ironed the skirt smoothly.

3. He spent the summer in South America.

4. The sleep-walker stopped at the edge of the gorge.

5. The sweet child got a silver spoon for her birthday.

6. The bully struck the small boy and stood sneering at him.

7. She slapped her small son spitefully and severely.

8. The maid polished the silver sugar bowl until it shone brightly.

9. The judge and jury were agreed that the poor wretch had committed the crime.

10. When the clock struck twelve, Cinderella ran for her pumpkin coach.

Test:

1. Can you read, without lisping, the phrases and sentences given in the Practice Material?

2. Can you read the sentences given for *sh* [ʃ], *zh* [ʒ], *ch* [tʃ], and *j* [dʒ] (pages 120–121), pronouncing all sounds correctly?

3. Are you careful to pronounce your sibilant sounds correctly in conversation?

CONTRACT 7

Objective:

The correct pronunciation of final *s* [s] and *z* [z] in syllables, words, phrases, and short sentences.

Procedure:

Make the sound *z* [z] correctly (see page 36).
Do the following exercise:

zā zā zā [zeɪɪ]

Now place the sound *a* before *z* and say:

ā—z ā—z ā—z āz [eɪɪz]

Make the sound *s* [s] correctly.
Do the following exercise:

sā sā sā [seɪɪ]

Now place the sound *a* before *s* and say:

ā—s ā—s ā—s ās [eɪɪs]

Do the following exercises five times each:

ē—z	ē—z	ē—z	ease ['iːz]
ē—s	ē—s	ē—s	lease ['li·s]
ā—z	ā—z	ā—z	haze ['heɪz]
ā—s	ā—s	ā—s	ace ['eɪs]
ī—z	ī—z	ī—z	eyes ['aɪz]
ī—s	ī—s	ī—s	ice ['aɪs]
ō—z	ō—z	ō—z	goes ['goʊz]
ō—s	ō—s	ō—s	dose ['doʊs]
ōō—z	ōō—z	ōō—z	lose ['luːz]
ōō—s	ōō—s	ōō—s	loose ['lu·s]
ŭ—z	ŭ—z	ŭ—z	buzz ['bʌz]
ŭ—s	ŭ—s	ŭ—s	us ['ʌs]

Proceed in this manner, placing all vowels and diphthongs before *s* [s] and *z* [z].

Caution:

Remember that *s* [s] and *z* [z], when they occur as final sounds, are made exactly the same as when they occur as initial sounds.

Practice Material:

Read the following double columns of words horizontally:

graze	grass	peas	peace	sins	since
grows	gross	pries	price	crows	cross
lose	loose	pens	pence	laws	loss

Say the following phrases without lisping:

1. Seeing peas and beans in the garden.
2. Seeking for a trace of some chemical.
3. Finding everything mixed up.
4. Hearing the bees buzz.
5. Skimming over the lake on skates.
6. Hanging the dress in Mary's room.
7. Sitting at ease.
8. Making all kinds of lace.
9. Baking cakes and pies.
10. Standing in line for tickets.

Read the following sentences without lisping:

1. I am going to buy some skates.
2. This is a lovely afternoon.

3. See my beautiful rose bushes.

4. The honeybees are in the apple blossoms.

5. Will you please put the cookies in the cake box?

6. That boy has common sense.

Test:

1. Can you say the words in the Practice Material without lisping?

2. Can you read, without lisping, the phrases and sentences given in the Practice Material?

3. Can you prepare ten additional phrases and sentences, and read them without lisping?

CONTRACT 7A

Objective:

See Contract 7.

Procedure:

See Contract 7.

Caution:

Take time to place your tongue correctly when making your final sibilants.

Practice Material:

Say the following words without lisping:

please	suppose	police	loose
blaze	seize	place	cease
close	raise	pass	mace
daze	phase	race	dose

Read the following phrases without lisping:

1. Striving to please the public.

2. Making sure such was the case.

3. Stopping the embargo on lace.

4. Eating an ice-cream cone.

5. Sitting in judgment on the culprits.

6. Shutting the doors surreptitiously.

7. Teaching a class in mathematics.

8. Telling the girls to cease their noise.

9. Seeing the finish of the race.

10. Attempting to pass two cars.

Read the following sentences without lisping:

1. Will you please put the place-cards on the table?

2. I think Sarah's new dress is very pretty.

3. Do you know Mary's permanent address?

4. Please tell each member of the class to come forward.

5. Bob is cutting the grass in front of the house.

6. This new glass-cutter is very handy.

7. It is unwise to tease the fierce dog.

8. All the electric clocks stopped because of the storm.

Test:

1. Can you say the words given in the Practice Material without lisping?

2. Can you read the phrases and sentences given in the Practice Material without lisping?

3. Can you read the sentences given for *z* [z] (pages 109–110) without lisping?

CONTRACT 8

Objective:

Final *s* [s] and *z* [z] in longer sentences.
Final *st* [st] and *sk* [sk] in syllables, words, and phrases.

Procedure:

Say the sound *s* [s] correctly; raise the pointed tip of tongue to the middle of the upper gum, and say *t* [t]. (See page 35 for more detailed instruction in regard to *t* [t].) Do the following exercise:

s—t　　s—t　　s—t　　st

Say the sound *s* [s] correctly; raise the back of the tongue until it touches the soft palate, and say the sound *k* [k]. (See page 38 for production of *k* [k].)
Do the following exercise:

s—k　　s—k　　s—k　　sk

Do the following exercises:

ā—st	ā—st	ā—st	haste ['herĭst]
ĭ—st	ĭ—st	ĭ—st	list ['lɪst]
ē—st	ē—st	ē—st	beast ['bi·st]
ĕ—st	ĕ—st	ĕ—st	west ['werʈst]
ō—st	ō—st	ō—st	boast ['borŭst]

å—sk	å—sk	å—sk	ask	['ɑsk]
ĭ—sk	ĭ—sk	ĭ—sk	risk	['ɹɪsk]
ĕ—sk	ĕ—sk	ĕ—sk	desk	｜'deᴛsk]
ŭ—sk	ŭ—sk	ŭ—sk	husk	['hʌsk]

Proceed in like manner with all vowels and diphthongs, making a word at the end whenever possible.

Caution:

Try to carry the correct pronunciation of all sibilant sounds into your daily speech.

Practice Material:

Say the following words without lisping:

least	boost	hoist	risk	task
wrist	cost	boast	desk	dusk
best	lost	bisque	ask	husk
last	diced	disc	mask	tusk

Read the following phrases without lisping:

1. Sitting at the desk writing notes.
2. Feeding the beast at the zoo.
3. Seeing the obelisk in Central Park.
4. Asking the guest to stay for tea.
5. Telling a ghost story.
6. Wearing a wrist watch.
7. Making tomato bisque.
8. Taking a great risk.

Read the following sentences without lisping:

1. Hawthorne is the author of *Twice-Told Tales.*
2. Boys should not be tied to their mother's apron strings.
3. Sarah has a pass for the motion pictures on Saturday afternoons.
4. The cherry blossoms are one of the sights of Washington in the spring.
5. Mary is studying diligently to prepare for her test in mathematics.
6. Did you enjoy reading *Tom Brown's School Days?*
7. Lewis Carroll wrote *Alice's Adventures in Wonderland* and *Through the Looking Glass.*
8. This train is an express and makes very few stops.

9. Let's take the bus to Bronx Park and visit the zoo.

10. Did you hear a famous actress read *The White Cliffs of Dover?*

Test:

1. Can you say the words in the Practice Material without lisping?

2. Can you read the phrases and sentences in the Practice Material without lisping?

3. Can you read the sentences for *sk* [sk] on pages 113–114 without lisping?

CONTRACT 9

Objective:

Final *s* [s], *z* [z], *st* [st], and *sk* [sk] in sentences.

Final *sp* [sp], *sl* [sl], *zl* [zl], and *zm* [zm] in syllables, words, and phrases.

Procedure:

Make the sound *s* [s]; flatten the front of the tongue against the upper gum and make the sound *l* [l] (see page 36).

Make the sound *z* [z]; follow it with the sound *l* [l]. Do the following exercises:

$$
\begin{array}{ccc}
\text{s—l} & \text{s—l} & \text{s—l} \\
\text{z—l} & \text{z—l} & \text{z—l}
\end{array}
$$

Make the sound *s* [s]; press the lips together gently, then force them apart by means of the breath, thus forming the sound *p* [p] (see page 33). Do the following exercise:

$$
\text{s—p} \qquad \text{s—p} \qquad \text{s—p}
$$

Make the sound *z* [z]; close the lips, lower the soft palate and let the sound *m* [m] flow out through the nose (see page 33). Do the following exercise:

$$
\text{z—m} \qquad \text{z—m} \qquad \text{z—m}
$$

Do the following exercises:

å—sp	å—sp	å—sp	clasp ['klɑsp]
ĭ—sp	ĭ—sp	ĭ—sp	crisp ['kɹɪsp]
ĭ—sl	ĭ—sl	ĭ—sl	missile ['mɪsl̩]
ŭ—sl	ŭ—sl	ŭ—sl	hustle ['hʌsl̩]
å—sl	å—sl	å—sl	castle ['kɑsl̩]
ă—zm	ă—zm	ă—zm	chasm ['kæzm̩]
ĭ—zm	ĭ—zm	ĭ—zm	prism ['pɹɪzm̩]
ĭ—zl	ĭ—zl	ĭ—zl	drizzle ['dɹɪzl̩]
ă—zl	ă—zl	ă—zl	dazzle ['dæzl̩]
ŭ—zl	ŭ—zl	ŭ—zl	puzzle ['pʌzl̩]

Caution:

Go slowly; take time to pronounce the sibilant sounds correctly.
Say the following words without lisping:

clasp	castle	drizzle	chasm
gasp	wrestle	guzzle	spasm .
rasp	vessel	muzzle	schism
crisp	missile	puzzle	prism
lisp	hustle	sizzle	truism

Read the following phrases without lisping:

1. Going to the castle.
2. Putting a muzzle on the dog.
3. Serving lunch in the chasm.
4. Throwing a missile.
5. Taking a trip on a large vessel.
6. Breaking the clasp of the necklace.
7. Asking for a crisp piece of toast.
8. Solving a difficult puzzle.
9. Walking across the trestle.
10. Striving to overcome a lisp.

Read the following sentences without lisping:

1. The last travelers returned at dusk.
2. Mary continues to boast about her new wrist watch.
3. You will take a great risk if you leave those important papers on the desk.
4. Sarah's fox coat cost six hundred dollars.
5. Those students who have had the least opportunities sometimes do best.
6. John went west for his vacation last summer.
7. The saying "Haste makes waste" is particularly true when one attempts to overcome a lisp.
8. Mary seems to be the brightest child in the seventh grade.
9. John's mother told him to hustle with his lessons if he wished to see the guest.
10. The soap bubble danced gaily about the room, and then burst.

Test:

1. Can you read the words in the Practice Material without lisping?

2. Can you read the phrases in the Practice Material without lisping?

3. Can you read the sentences in the Practice Material without lisping?

4. Can you read ten of the sentences given for *s general* (pages 117–119) without lisping?

CONTRACT 10

Objective:

Final sibilants in sentences, paragraphs, and conversation.

Procedure:

See Contracts 5 and 6.

Caution:

Remember to make the sibilant sounds correctly *whenever* and *wherever* you speak.

Practice Material:

Read the following sentences without lisping:

1. *American Notes* shows Dickens' contempt for the American people.

2. Please pull down the shades in the sitting-room.

3. My mind is still running over some of the speeches I heard this afternoon.

4. The man is sane and honest and chivalrous.

5. The class gave a dance to raise money for the Old Soldiers' Home.

6. This is your last chance to stay in school.

7. The coarse pens are on the highest shelf.

8. I have lost the clasp of my silver chain.

9. Please ask Mrs. Cox for her daughter's dress pattern.

10. There is a very dangerous chasm near our house.

Read without lisping the following paragraph from Washington Irving's *The Legend of Sleepy Hollow:*

It was toward evening that Ichabod arrived at the castle of Heer Van Tassel, which he found thronged with the pride and flower of the country. Old farmers, a spare, leathern-faced race, in homespun coats and breeches, blue stockings, huge shoes, and pewter buckles. Their brisk, withered, little dames, in close crimped caps, long waisted gowns, homespun petticoats, with . . . gay calico pockets hanging on the outside. . . . The sons in short square-skirted coats, with rows of stupendous brass buttons, and their hair generally queued in the fashion of the times, especially if they could procure an eel-skin for the purpose, it being esteemed throughout the country, as a potent nourisher and strengthener of the hair.

Give a brief talk on a subject in which you are interested. The following suggested topics may serve as a guide:

Hobbies
The School Play
The Most Exciting School Game I Ever Saw
An Interesting Trip

Test:

1. Can you do the exercises in the Practice Material without lisping?

2. Can you make up ten more sentences and then read them without lisping?

3. Can you carry on a conversation without lisping?

CONTRACT 11

Objective:

Medial sibilants in syllables, words, phrases, and sentences.

Procedure:

Note that medial sibilants frequently occur at the beginning of a syllable; in such cases they should be treated as initial sibilants. If they end syllables, they should be treated as final sounds.

Do the following exercises five times each:

āsa	āsa	āsa [eᴛĭsə]
āza	āza	āza [eᴛĭzə]
ēza	ēza	ēza [i:zə]
ēsa	ēsa	ēsa [i·sə]
ahza	ahza	ahza [ɑ:zə]
ahsa	ahsa	ahsa [ɑ·sə]
ōōza	ōōza	ōōza [u:zə]
ōōsa	ōōsa	ōōsa [u·sə]
ēza	ahza	ōōza [i:zə ɑ:zə u:zə]

ēsa	ahsa	o͞osa [i·sə ɑ·sə u·sə]
åska	åska	åska [ɑskə]
ispa	ispa	ispa [ɪspə]
ăspa	ăspa	ăspa [æspə]

Caution:

Remember that *wherever* a sibilant occurs in a word, it is always pronounced in the *same* way.

Practice Material:

Say the following words without lisping:

history	beseem	beseech	busily	lazily
peaceful	casement	basement	buzzing	misery
tastefully	forsook	beside	dizzy	prosaic

Read the following phrases without lisping:

1. Living in solitude in a basement.

2. Standing beside a brook.

3. Opening the casement windows.

4. Lying lazily in the sun.

5. Studying the history assignment.

6. Teasing the cook for a morsel of food.

7. Seeking a peaceful retreat.

8. Asking for help in mathematics.

Read the following sentences without lisping:

1. It is hard for a lisper to say a sibilant sound.

2. The correct pronunciation of a sibilant sound is acquired through much persistent practicing.

3. The lisper must not expect to become perfect after the second lesson.

4. We must make haste slowly if we wish to be successful.

5. We left for the party at precisely seven o'clock Thursday evening.

6. As a result of the collision, our car was seriously damaged.

7. Bessie went to the hospital for an operation for appendicitis.

8. A car racing at breakneck speed crashed into us and caused a serious accident.

9. Some students read poetry in a most prosaic and uninteresting fashion.

10. The teacher asked the student to list the historical events of the last ten years in chronological order.

Test:

1. Can you do all the exercises in the Procedure and Practice Material without lisping?

2. Can you read fifteen sentences for *s general, st* [st], and *sk* [sk] (pages 117–119, 116–117, and 113–114) without lisping?

3. Can you carry on, without lisping, a conversation in the classroom? at home? with your friends?

CONTRACT 12

Objective:

Correct production of all sibilant sounds in sentences, paragraphs, and conversation.

Procedure:

See Contracts 1 to 7 for proper formation of sounds.

Caution:

Speak slowly; be sure the sibilant sounds are pronounced correctly in every situation.

Practice Material:

Read the following sentences without lisping:

1. Theater-goers always enjoy seeing *Alice in Wonderland*.

2. The sleeves in the coats and dresses are large this spring.

3. Psychology is one of the most interesting subjects studied in school.

4. Years ago the gallery gods hissed the actors they disliked and often threw things at them.

5. Classes will be dismissed in a few days.

6. Have you had the pleasure of visiting the castle?

7. The beads scattered all over the schoolroom when the clasp of the chain broke.

8. "The shattering trumpet shrilleth high."

9. The girls had just a smattering of French in school.

10. He swore on the Bible that what he said was true.

11. The sneak thief stole many costly jewels.

12. Are you sure you can pronounce the sibilant sounds correctly in all cases?

Read, without lisping, the following paragraph from Washington Irving's *Sketch Book:*

We had now come in full view of the old family mansion, partly thrown in deep shadow, and partly lit up by the cold moonshine. It was an irregular building of some magnitude, and seemed to be of the architecture of different periods. One wing was evidently very ancient, with heavy stone-shafted bow windows jutting out and overrun with ivy, from among the foliage of which the small diamond-shaped panes of glass glittered with the moonbeams. The rest of the house was in the French taste of Charles the Second's time, having been repaired and altered, as my friend told me, by one of his ancestors, who returned with that monarch at the Restoration. The grounds about the house were laid out in the old formal manner of artificial flower-beds, clipped shrubberies, raised terraces, and heavy stone balustrades, ornamented with urns, a leaden statue or two, and a jet of water. The old gentleman, I was told, was extremely careful to preserve this obsolete finery in all its original state. He admired this fashion in gardening; it had an air of magnificence, was courtly and noble, and befitting good old family style. The boasted imitation of nature in modern gardening had sprung up with modern republican notions, but did not suit a monarchical government; it smacked of the levelling system. I could not help smiling at this introduction of politics into gardening, though I expressed some apprehension that I should find the old gentleman rather intolerant in his creed. Frank assured me, however, that it was almost the only instance in which he had ever heard his father meddle with politics; and he believed that he had got this notion from a member of parliament who had once passed a few weeks with him. The Squire was glad of any argument to defend his clipped yew trees and formal terraces, which had been occasionally attacked by modern landscape-gardeners.

Test:

1. Can you read the sentences in the Practice Material without lisping?

2. Prepare ten more sentences and then read them without lisping.

3. Can you read the paragraph without lisping?

4. Can you converse freely without lisping?

CONTRACT 13

Objective:

Lists of words with difficult combinations of sibilant sounds.
Use of these words in sentences, paragraphs, and conversation.

Procedure:

Do the following exercises:

sfā	ksthā	sfā [sfeɪ	ksθeɪ	sfeɪ]
sfē	ksthē	sfē [sfi:	ksθi:	sfi:]
sfī	ksthī	sfī [sfaɪ	ksθaɪ	sfaɪ]
sfō	ksthō	sfō [sfoʊ	ksθoʊ	sfoʊ]

Proceed in a like manner with other vowels and diphthongs.

Caution:

Go slowly with the difficult combinations.

Practice Material:

Say the following words without lisping:

fists	chests	presents	grasps	sifts	statistics
thrusts	nests	strikes	lisps	strength	sisters
toasts	crusts	knocks	tulips	brands	churches
posts	boasts	casks	shafts	whistles	judges
tests	streets	stocks	rafts	resistance	switches
mists	tats	rasps	rifts	kisses	catches

Read the following sentences without lisping:

1. Tulips are my sister's favorite spring flower.

2. "My good blade carves the casques of men,
My tough lance thrusteth sure."

3. The lists of students show many of foreign extraction.

4. This summer has brought us a great many fogs and mists on the Atlantic coast.

5. Statistics show that seventy-six bad checks were returned this season.

6. The rifts in the clouds are a welcome sight these stormy days.

7. He toasts his fingers and toes at the fireside.

8. Opportunity knocks but once.

9. The cook whistles as she sifts the flour and pits the raisins for the plum pudding.

Read the following paragraph without lisping:

As the train whistles for the station, the soldier lifts his suitcase from the baggage-rack, collects his trunk checks, gathers up his various belongings, and says good-bye to his mates. As he descends from the train, he greets his friends who have gathered at the station to meet him. He gives his trunk checks to the porter and posts six letters in the post box at the station. Then he hails a taxi and rides through the familiar streets. He notices that the tulips and squills are in bloom. He takes deep breaths of the fragrant air and smiles as he boasts to himself that the station hacks and even the lamp posts seem like old friends.

Test:

1. Can you read the material in the Practice Material without lisping?

2. Can you read the sentences given for *s* [s], *z* [z], *st* [st], *sp* [sp], *sl* [sl], *sw* [sw], *sn* [sn], *sm* [sm] (pages 108–119) without lisping?

CONTRACT 14

Objective:

Correct pronunciation of all sibilant sounds in prepared paragraphs (chosen by student), sight reading, and conversation.

Procedure:

See Contract 12.

Caution:

Make it a habit to pronounce the sibilant sounds correctly at all times.

Practice Material:

To be provided by the student.
Selections for sight reading from the following suggested books:

Goldsmith, *The Vicar of Wakefield*
Scott, *Ivanhoe*
Stevenson, *Travels with a Donkey*
Dickens, *David Copperfield*
Aesop's Fables

Classroom conversation based on the following suggested topics:

The Baseball Team
Making a Garden

Planning a Luncheon
A School Picnic
The Lure of New York
A Favorite Sport

Test:

1. Can you read aloud, without lisping, the material that you have prepared? selections at sight?

2. Are you careful to pronounce the sibilant sounds correctly whenever you speak?

CONTRACT SHEET
Defective Phonation*

---

1. Lists of words and phrases read to discover defects in pronunciation.

---

2. Correct pronunciation of consonants *t* [t] and *k* [k].

Correct use of these sounds in words, phrases, and sentences.

---

3. Correct pronunciation of *t* [t] and *k* [k] in sentences, paragraph and conversation.

---

4. Correct pronunciation of the consonants *d* [d] and *g* [g].

Correct use of these sounds in words, phrases, and sentences.

---

5. Correct pronunciation of *d* [d] and *g* [g] in sentences and paragraphs.

---

6. Correct pronunciation of sounds *w* [w] and *r* [ɹ].

Correct use of these sounds in words, phrases, and sentences.

---

7. Correct pronunciation of *w* [w] and *r* [ɹ] in sentences, paragraphs, and conversation.

---

8. Correct pronunciation of *l* [l] as initial, middle, and final sound.

Correct pronunciation of *l* [l] in words, phrases, and sentences.

---

* At the beginning of every practice period, do Contract 1 of "Careless Speech."

9. Correct pronunciation of *l* [l] in sentences, paragraphs, and conversation.

10. Correct pronunciation of sibilant sounds.

11. Correct pronunciation of all sounds in sentences and conversation.

12. Correct pronunciation of all sounds in prepared paragraphs, sight reading, and conversation.

CONTRACT 1

Objective:

Discovery of sounds that are mispronounced.

Test:

1. Read the following words:

bee	last	shoe	cot	try	tour
did	fern	put	song	loiter	floor
very	church	oath	rather	Troy	pleasure
then	up	note	cake	wound	Tuesday
says	judge	go	take	round	hew
care	soon	all	kite	theater	tune
land	zoo	because	white	rare	duke

2. Read the following phrases:

a. Taking a cake to the fair.

b. Skating around the town on roller skates.

c. Wearing a red rose in the right lapel.

d. Thinking out a problem.

e. Lying around on the sand.

f. Winding the clock faithfully.

g. Rounding the bend.

h. Watering the plants.

i. Hearing the moaning of the wind.

j. Leaving the child with his father.

k. Taking a last look at the sand dunes.

l. Shoeing a spirited horse.

m. Taking the poor boy on a journey.

n. Measuring the young man for a suit of clothes.

o. Whining about everything.

p. Going to the lily pond.

> *Note to instructor:* In general you will find the sound *t* [t] substituted for *k* [k], *d* [d] for *g* [g], *w* [w] substituted for *r* [ɪ], and the sound *l* [l] and the sibilants mispronounced. These mispronunciations are pro-

255

vided for in the following contracts. If the student lisps, the contracts for lisping should be taken up immediately. The exercises for the various sounds in Part III will afford opportunity for practice of any other sounds that may be mispronounced.

CONTRACT 2

Objective:

Correct pronunciation of consonants *t* [t] and *k* [k].
Correct use of these sounds in words, phrases, and sentences.

Procedure:

Place the tip of the tongue on the upper gum and say:

t	t	t
tā	tā	tā [teɪɪ̆]
tī	tī	tī [taɪ̆]
tō	tō	tō [toɪŭ]

Proceed in the same way with other vowels and diphthongs.
Say the following:

ăt	ăt	ăt [æt]
ĕt	ĕt	ĕt [eɪt]
ĭt	ĭt	ĭt [ɪt]

Proceed in like manner with other vowels and diphthongs.
Place the back of the tongue against the soft palate, remove it quickly, and say:

kā	kā	kā [keɪɪ̆]
kī	kī	kī [kaɪ̆]
kō	kō	kō [koɪŭ]

Proceed in like manner with other vowels and diphthongs.
Do the following exercises:

ăk	ăk	ăk [æk]
ĭk	ĭk	ĭk [ɪk]
ĕk	ĕk	ĕk [eɪk]

Proceed in like manner with other vowels and diphthongs.

Caution:

Do not confuse the two sounds *t* [t] and *k* [k].

Practice Material:

Say the following words, exercising great care in the pronunciation of *k* [k]:

keep	colonel	cone	kale	cast
kitty	cup	call	cage	could
kettle	consider	car	cowl	cane
cattle	cool	kine	cow	coil

Read the following sets of words horizontally and vertically, being particularly careful about the pronunciation of the sounds *t* [t] and *k* [k]:

teem	keen	task	cast	took	cook
tick	kit	Turk	curt	toque	coat
ten	ken	tuck	cut	talk	caught
tack	cat	tool	cool	tock	cot
tart	cart	tike	kite	tear	care

Read the following phrases, exercising particular care with *t* [t] and *k* [k]:

1. Taking Kate to the party.
2. Tacking the carpet to the floor.
3. Keeping the test papers in the desk drawer.
4. Telling the tale of the fox and the crow.
5. Carrying a pitcher of water.
6. Keeping time to the music.
7. Going to a quilting party.
8. Covering the tulips with leaves.
9. Casting about for an idea.
10. Cooking for ten people.

Read the following, taking great care with the sounds *t* [t] and *k* [k]:

1. Carrie and Kate took Cousin Tom to see the tugboat race.
2. Kitty went coasting on her new sled Christmas day.
3. Crowds of children went skating today.
4. There was scarcely a drop of water in the pitcher.
5. The teacher scolded Cora for not telling the truth.
6. The class was scanning a line of poetry.
7. The hungry children ate crackers and crab-apple jelly.
8. Catherine had ice cream and cake at the Christmas party.
9. You will catch cold if you are not careful.
10. Tom caught a turkey for Thanksgiving dinner.

Test:

1. Can you do all the exercises in the Practice Material, pronouncing every *k* [k] and *t* [t] correctly?

2. Can you read all the sentences for *t* [t] (pages 98–99) and for *k* [k] (page 104), making these sounds correctly?

CONTRACT 3

Objective:

Correct pronunciation of *t* [t] and *k* [k] in sentences, paragraphs, and conversation.

Procedure:

See Contract 2.

Caution:

See Contract 2.

Practice Material:

Read the following sentences, exercising great care in the pronunciation of *t* [t] and *k* [k]:

1. The king had the courage of his convictions.

2. The farmer is carrying corn and cabbage to market.

3. Will you come to The Corner Cupboard for afternoon tea?

4. At what date does Congress convene?

5. Catherine makes herself a congenial companion.

6. Conrad had a comfortable trip to Connecticut.

7. Claudia took a black chocolate cake to the picnic.

8. Take your time in climbing up the embankment.

9. Tom was congratulated because he was such a fine conversationalist.

10. Can you tell the answer to this conundrum?

Read the following paragraph from Scott's *Ivanhoe*, exercising great care with the sounds *t* [t] and *k* [k]:

The consequences of the encounter were not instantly seen, for the dust raised by the tramping of so many steeds darkened the air, and it was a minute ere the anxious spectators could see the fate of the encounter. When the fight became visible, half the knights on each side were dismounted, some by the dexterity of their adversary's lance,—some by the superior weight and strength of opponents,—some lay stretched on the earth as if never more to rise,—some had already gained their feet, and were closing hand to hand with those of their antagonists who were in the same predicament,—and several on both sides, who had received wounds by which they were disabled, were stopping their blood with their scarfs, and endeavoring to extricate themselves from the tumult. The mounted knights, whose lances had been almost all broken by the fury of the encounter, were now closely engaged with their swords, shouting their war-cries, and exchanging buffets, as if honor and life depended on the issue of the combat.

Test:

1. Can you read the exercises given in the Practice Material, pronouncing correctly all words containing the sounds *t* [t] and *k* [k]?

2. Can you tell the story of the above encounter, using the sounds *t* [t] and *k* [k] correctly?

3. Can you make up ten more sentences containing these sounds and then read them correctly?

CONTRACT 4

Objective:

The correct pronunciation of the sounds *g* [g] and *d* [d].

The correct pronunciation of these sounds in words, phrases, and sentences.

Procedure:

Place the tip of the tongue on the upper gum and make the voiced sound *d* [d].

Note that *d* [d] is made exactly the same as *t* [t] except that *d* [d] is *voiced* and *t* [t] is *voiceless*. (For further instruction about the production of *d* [d], see page 35.)

Do the following exercises:

d	d	d
dā	dā	dā [deɪ]
dī	dī	dī [daɪ]
dō	dō	dō [doтŭ]

Proceed in the same manner with other vowels and diphthongs. Do the following exercises:

ăd	ăd	ăd [æd]
ĕd	ĕd	ĕd [eтd]
ĭd	ĭd	ĭd [ɪd]

Proceed in like manner, placing other vowels and diphthongs before *d* [d].

Place the back of the tongue against the soft palate and say the voiced sound *g* [g]. Note that *g* [g] is made in exactly the same manner as is *k* [k] except that *g* [g] is *voiced* and *k* [k] is *voiceless*. (For further instruction about the production of *g* [g], see page 38.)

Do the following exercises:

gā   gā   gā [geɪɪ]
gē   gē   gē [giː]
gō   gō   gō [goʊ]

Proceed in like manner with other vowels and diphthongs.
Do the following exercises:

ăg   ăg   ăg [æg]
ĭg   ĭg   ĭg [ɪg]
ŏg   ŏg   ŏg [ɒg]

Proceed in like manner, placing other vowels and diphthongs before *g* [g].

Caution:

Do not confuse the sounds *d* [d] and *g* [g].

Practice Material:

Say the following words, exercising great care about the production of *g* [g]:

geese	gasp	good	guard	gown
give	girl	going	gale	goiter
get	gun	Gaul	guide	gore
gallery	goose	got	gold	gear

Read the following sets of words horizontally and vertically, being particularly careful not to confuse the sounds *d* [d] and *g* [g]:

deal	geese	dawn	Gaul	dough	go
did	give	dot	got	doled	gold
debt	get	dart	guard	down	gown
done	gun	day	gay	doubt	gout

Read the following phrases, being careful not to confuse the sounds *d* [d] and *g* [g]:

1. Doing a good deal of work.

2. Going down town to shop.

3. Guiding a blind man to the door.

4. Getting a raw deal.

5. Gazing at the ducks and geese.

6. Giving a donation to the Red Cross.

7. Daring to go down the shaft.

8. Feeling gay all day.

9. Darting after the growling dog.

10. Gossiping at the door.

Read the following sentences, being careful not to confuse the sounds *d* [d] and *g* [g]:

1. The miser doled out the gold stingily.

2. What time do you plan to go down town?

3. Did you give Gertrude her book?

4. You will never get out of debt unless you save your money.

5. Mary got a dotted-swiss dress at the sale.

6. Did the girls buy new evening gowns when they were downtown today?

7. The player darted around the guard.

8. The Great Dane gained a good deal of weight.

9. Did you forget to close the gate?

10. The dish was garnished with greens.

Test:

1. Can you read the words in the Practice Material, pronouncing all sounds correctly?

2. Can you read the phrases and sentences in the Practice Material, pronouncing all sounds correctly?

3. Can you prepare ten more sentences containing the sounds *d* [d] and *g* [g], and read them without confusing those sounds?

CONTRACT 5

Objective:

The correct pronunciation of the sounds *d* [d] and *g* [g] in sentences and paragraphs.

Procedure:

See Contract 4.

Caution:

See Contract 4.

Practice Material:

Read the following sentences; be careful not to confuse the sounds *d* [d] and *g* [g]:

1. The banker did not deign to consider such a small gain.

2. Did you try to get Gertrude on the telephone again?

3. Dave gave Dora a book about rock-gardens.

4. We will gain an hour of daylight with Daylight Saving Time.

5. Delia was delighted to act as a guide at the Guild Exhibit.

6. Mary guessed that her gift would be a Governor Winthrop desk.

7. Gladys decided to vote against the amendment.

8. The rain is dashing against the window and the wind is blowing a gale.

9. Today's assignment is the first five chapters of *The House of the Seven Gables*.

10. Go get a gun from the gun-rack in the den if you wish to go hunting.

Read the following paragraph from Washington Irving's *Christmas Dinner*, paying careful attention to the pronunciation of the sounds *g* [g] and *d* [d]:

> From these and other anecdotes that followed, the crusader appeared to be the favorite hero of ghost stories throughout the vicinity. His picture which hung up in the hall, was thought by the servants to have something supernatural about it, for they remarked that, in whatever part of the hall you went, the eyes of the warrior were still fixed on you. The old porter's wife, too, at the lodge, who had been born and brought up in the family, and was a great gossip among the maid-servants, affirmed that in her young days she had often heard say, that on Midsummer Eve, when it is well known all kinds of ghosts, goblins, and fairies become visible and walk abroad, the crusader used to mount his horse, come down from his picture, ride about the house, down the avenue, and so to the church to visit the tomb; on which occasion the church door most civilly swung open by itself: not that he needed it; for he rode through closed gates and even stone walls, and had been seen by one of the dairymaids to pass between two bars of the great park gate, making himself as thin as a sheet of paper.
>
> All these superstitions I found had been very much countenanced by the Squire, who, though not superstitious himself, was very fond of seeing others so. He listened to

every goblin tale of the neighboring gossips with infinite
gravity, and held the porter's wife in high favor on account
of her talent for the marvellous.

Test:

1. Can you read the sentences in the Practice Material, pronouncing all sounds correctly?

2. Can you read the paragraphs in the Practice Material, pronouncing all sounds correctly?

3. Can you read the sentences given for *g* [g] in the exercise material
in Part III (page 104), pronouncing all sounds correctly?

CONTRACT 6

Objective:

Correct pronunciation of the sounds *w* [w] and *r* [ɹ].
Correct use of these sounds in words, phrases, and sentences.

Procedure:

Round the lips gently and make the sound *w* [w] (see page 34).
Do the following exercises:

wā	wā	wā [wetɪ]
wō	wō	wō [wotŭ]
wī	wī	wī [waɪ]
wē	wē	wē [wiː]

Proceed in like manner with other vowels and diphthongs.

Raise the front of the tongue toward the roof of the mouth;
curl it slightly back toward the soft palate and make the sound *r* [ɹ]
(see page 36). Do the following exercises:

rā	rā	rā [ɹetɪ]
rō	rō	rō [ɹotŭ]
rī	rī	rī [ɹaɪ]
rē	rē	rē [ɹiː]

Proceed in a like manner for other vowels and diphthongs.

Caution:

Do not confuse these two sounds.

Practice Material:

Say the following words, exercising great care in the pronunciation
of the sound *r* [ɹ]:

real	rather	very	cherry	dress
wrist	rice	bury	carry	grass
rust	rail	Kerry	barrier	crash
root	rear	Jerry	berry	thrash
roll	rare	married	ferry	press
raw	roar	merry	curry	trash

Read the following sets of words horizontally and vertically, exercising great care not to substitute *w* [w] for *r* [ɹ]:

weed	read	wear	rare	woe	row
wig	rig	won	run	wad	rod
wed	red	woo	rue	wight	right
wide	ride	wade	raid	we're	rear
wait	rate	wound	round	wooer	truer

Read the following phrases, exercising special care with the sounds *w* [w] and *r* [ɹ]:

1. Wearing a red dress.
2. Reading a ridiculous story.
3. Writing a very fine book.
4. Weeding the rose garden.
5. Running around town.
6. Reaching up to the high window.
7. Wondering what is the right thing to do.
8. Wrestling with a problem.

Read the following sentences, being careful not to confuse the sounds *w* [w] and *r* [ɹ]:

1. Mary was reading a red book.
2. These ready-made dresses are very practical.
3. Rita was worrying because she was afraid she would not be allowed to go to the boat races.
4. The teacher wondered what made the children so very restless.
5. Robert solved many problems in arithmetic.
6. Fred wished that he might study French.
7. We will have nice fresh strawberries for supper.
8. Mr. West recently took a trip to France.
9. Ralph rode the roan mare in the race.
10. The Rhine and the Rhone are beautiful rivers.

Test:

1. Can you do all the exercises in the Practice Material without confusing w [w] and r [ɹ]?

2. Can you read all the sentences on pages 102–103, pronouncing all the r [ɹ] sounds correctly?

CONTRACT 7

Objective:

Correct use of w [w] and r [ɹ] in sentences, paragraphs, and conversation.

Procedure:

See Contract 6.

Caution:

See Contract 6.

Practice Material:

Read the following sentences, exercising great care not to substitute w [w] for r [ɹ]:

1. Rose was cramming for an examination in algebra.

2. The reasonably priced dresses are on the street floor.

3. "There are tricks in all trades."

4. The dogs followed the rabbit's tracks in the snow.

5. Have you read the April number of *Scribners' Magazine?*

6. There are some very interesting new books in the Free Public Library.

7. There is neither rhyme nor reason in the preacher's rambling sermons.

8. I wonder if I could borrow Mary's recipe for Hot Cross Buns?

9. Richard scribbled a hasty note to say that he would leave for Rochester tomorrow.

10. "I love thy rocks and rills,
Thy woods and templed hills,
My heart with rapture thrills
Like that above."

Read the following paragraph from Scott's *Ivanhoe*, exercising great care in the pronunciation of r [ɹ]:

Beside the swineherd, for such was Gurth's occupation, was seated, upon one of the fallen Druidical monuments, a person about ten years younger in appearance, and whose dress, though resembling his companions in form, was of better materials, and of a more fantastic appearance. His jacket had been stained of a bright purple hue, upon which there had been some attempt to paint grotesque ornaments in different colors. To the jacket he added a short cloak which scarcely reached halfway down his thigh; it was of crimson cloth, though a good deal soiled, lined with bright yellow; and as he could transfer it from one shoulder to the other, or at his pleasure draw it all around him, its width contrasted with its want to longitude, formed a fantastic piece of drapery. He had thin silver bracelets upon his arms, and on his neck a collar of the same metal, bearing the inscription, "Wamba, the son of Witless, is the thrall of Cedric of Rotherwood."

Test:

1. Can you read the exercises given in the Practice Material, pronouncing all the *r* [ɹ] sounds correctly?

2. Can you find another paragraph and read it, pronouncing the sound *r* [ɹ] correctly?

3. Who was Cedric of Rotherwood?

4. Can you tell the story of the tournament in *Ivanhoe*, pronouncing the *r* [ɹ] sounds correctly?

CONTRACT 8

Objective:

Correct pronunciation of *l* [l] as an initial, middle, and final sound.
Correct pronunciation of *l* [l] in words, phrases, and sentences.

Procedure:

Spread the front of the tongue on the upper gum, and let the sound *l* [l] come off both sides of the tongue.
Do the following exercises:

lā	lā	lā [leɹɪ]
lī	lī	lī [laɪ]
lō	lō	lō [loɹŭ]
lē	lē	lē [li:]

Proceed in like manner with other vowels and diphthongs.
Do the following exercises:

ĭl	ĭl	ĭl [ɪl]
awl	awl	awl [ɔ:l]
ōl	ōl	ōl [oɹŭl]
ĕl	ĕl	ĕl [eɹl]

Proceed in like manner with other vowels and diphthongs.

Do the following exercise:

lily	lily	lily
lolly	lolly	lolly
lally	lally	lally

Caution:

Be sure that the tongue is flattened and held well front for this sound. Otherwise the sound will be the dialect form, the so-called "dark *l*."

Practice Material:

Say the following words, exercising great care in the pronunciation of *l* [l]:

learn	lot	leal	pull	lily	wholly
lug	lie	lilt	roll	jelly	calling
loon	lane	fell	all	rally	lalling
look	loud	earl	loll	early	ailing
lone	loiter	lull	Carl	dully	filing
law	leer	pool	lisle	fully	howling

Read the following phrases, using great care in the pronunciation of *l* [l]:

1. Leading a busy life.
2. Lending all he owned.
3. Attending a lively play.
4. Losing a lot of money.
5. Leaving for a long time.
6. Throwing out a life line.
7. Listening to a hailstorm.
8. Looking for landing lights.
9. Hanging clothes on the line.
10. Dilly-dallying in the hall.

Read the following sentences, exercising great care in the pronunciation of *l* [l]:

1. We shall serve lettuce and tomato salad for luncheon.
2. Lillian had a delightful time at the play last night.
3. "Elaine, the lily-maid of Astolat."
4. The lad may possess a great deal of latent talent.
5. Leander was cutting his lawn with a lawn mower.
6. The locust trees are in blossom in June.
7. The poem *Evangeline* was written by Henry Wadsworth Longfellow.
8. James Russell Lowell wrote *The Vision of Sir Launfal.*

9. Lucy lost her emerald necklace near the lilypond.

10. Will you please lend me a lead pencil?

Test:

1. Can you do all the exercises in the Practice Material, pronouncing the sound *l* [l] correctly?

2. Can you read all the sentences under the sound *l* [l] in the practice exercises (pages 101–102), pronouncing the sound correctly?

3. Can you tell the story of *The Vision of Sir Launfal*, pronouncing the sound *l* [l] correctly?

CONTRACT 9

Objective:

Correct pronunciation of *l* [l] in sentences, paragraphs, and conversation.

Procedure:

See Contract 8.

Caution:

If there is any difficulty in making the sound *l* [l] clearly, press the tongue very slightly against the upper gum.

Practice Material:

Read the following sentences, exercising great care in the pronunciation of *l* [l]:

1. "Whether we look, or whether we listen,
We hear life murmur or see it glisten."

2. "The little bird sits at his door in the sun,
Atilt like a blossom among the leaves,
And lets his illumined being o'errun
With the deluge of summer it receives."

3. It was such a clear night that William was sure he could see millions and trillions of stars.

4. Washington Irving wrote *The Legend of Sleepy Hollow*.

5. *The Lady of the Lake* is a long poem the action of which takes place in the highlands of Scotland.

6. Matilda's father lost a billion dollars in Wall Street.

7. Lucy is a filing clerk employed by Lovelace and Locke.

8. Have you read *The Deserted Village* by Oliver Goldsmith?

9. Step lightly, or else you may rouse the sleeping children.

10. "The evil that men do lives after them."

Read the following lines, being careful to pronounce the sound *l* [l] correctly:

> The little brook heard it and built a roof
> 'Neath which he could house him, winter-proof;
> All night by the white stars' frosty gleams
> He groined his arches and matched his beams;
> Slender and clear were his crystal spars
> As the lashes of light that trim the stars;
> He sculptured every summer delight
> In his halls and chambers out of sight;
> Sometimes his tinkling waters slipt
> Down through a frost-leaved forest crypt,
> Long, sparkling aisles of steel-stemmed trees
> Bending to counterfeit a breeze;
> Sometimes the roof no fretwork knew
> But silvery mosses that downward grew;
> Sometimes it was carved in sharp relief
> With quaint arabesques of ice-fern leaf;
> Sometimes it was simply smooth and clear
> For the gladness of Heaven to shine through, and here
> He had caught the nodding bulrush-tops
> And hung them thickly with diamond drops,
> That crystalled the beams of moon and sun
> And made a star of every one.

Test:

1. Can you read the sentences in the Practice Material, pronouncing the sound *l* [l] correctly?

2. Can you read the lines of poetry in the Practice Material, pronouncing the sound *l* [l] correctly?

3. Can you find a prose paragraph and then read it, pronouncing the sound *l* [l] correctly?

CONTRACT 10

Objective:

Correct pronunciation of sibilant sounds.

Procedure:

See the "Contracts for Lisping" (pages 219–251).

Caution:

See "Contracts for Lisping."

Practice Material:

See "Contracts for Lisping."

Test:

Can you pronounce the sibilant sounds correctly in all cases?

> *Note to instructor:* If the student mispronounces the sibilant sounds, he should take the "Contracts for Lisping."

CONTRACT 11

Objective:

Correct pronunciation of all sounds in sentences and conversation.

Procedure:

See Contracts 2, 4, 6, 8, and any others you need for review.

Caution:

Go slowly, and be careful about the pronunciation of difficult sounds.

Practice Material:

Read the following sentences:

1. Please turn on the electric light in the living room.

2. Rebecca turned around and stood looking out of the window.

3. Mrs. Reed is president of the Women's Relief Bureau.

4. Be sure to turn to the right when you come to the corner of Raritan Street and Ridgewood Road.

5. Have you ever read *Love's Labour's Lost?*

6. *Love's Labour's Lost* is one of the earlier plays of William Shakespeare.

7. Mrs. Lester sent her little daughter to Ladycliff Academy.

8. The automobile was laden with bright red apples.

9. Gilbert and Sullivan were well-known writers of light opera.

10. *A Christmas Carol* is a well-loved story by Charles Dickens.

11. The king lavished great riches upon his favorite courtiers.

12. Make a list of all the difficult sounds in these sentences.

13. Nearly everyone loves the spring time.

14. Laura left her automobile license in the bureau drawer.

15. If you are an early riser, you will not be late to school.

16. It will be a pleasure to go there.

17. The noise on the fifth floor was unbearable last night.

18. We danced for a while after the theater.

Answer the following questions in complete sentences:

1. Who said, "Give me liberty or give me death!"?
2. Which is your favorite season of the year? Why?
3. Where is the Statue of Liberty located?
4. In what book is Uriah Heep a well-known character?
5. Of what famous revolution was "Liberty, Equality, Fraternity" the slogan?
6. (a) What is your favorite game?
   (b) Explain the rules of this game clearly and carefully.
7. Describe a trip you have taken recently.
8. What is your favorite poem?
9. Who wrote "Snow Bound"?
10. What does eleven times eleven equal?
11. Who said, "The quality of mercy is not strained"?
12. From what poem are the following lines taken:

> "Cannon to right of them,
> Cannon to left of them,
> Cannon in front of them
> Volleyed and thundered."

13. Who wrote the above poem?
14. What is your favorite study? Why?
15. What does the following proverb mean: "It is a long lane that has no turning"?

Test:

1. Can you read the sentences in the Practice Material, pronouncing all sounds correctly?
2. Can you answer in complete sentences all the questions in the Practice Material, and pronounce all sounds correctly?
3. Can you carry on a conversation, pronouncing all sounds correctly?

CONTRACT 12

Objective:

Correct pronunciation of all sounds in prepared paragraphs, sight reading, and conversation.

Procedure:

See Contract 11.

Caution:

See Contract 11.

Practice Material:

Read the following paragraphs from Scott's *Ivanhoe*, pronouncing all sounds correctly:

> The door accordingly was opened; and the hermit, a large, strong-built man, in his sack-cloth gown and hood, girt with a rope of rushes, stood before the knight. He had in one hand a lighted torch, or link, and in the other a baton of crabtree, so thick and heavy, that it might well be termed a club. Two large shaggy dogs, half greyhound, half mastiff, stood ready to rush upon the traveller as soon as the door should be opened. But when the torch glanced upon the lofty crest and golden spurs of the knight, who stood without, the hermit, altering probably his original intentions, repressed the rage of his auxiliaries, and, changing his tone to a sort of churlish courtesy, invited the knight to enter his hut, making excuse for his unwillingness to open his lodge after sunset, by alleging the multitude of robbers and outlaws who were abroad, and who gave no honor to Our Lady or St. Dunstan, nor to those holy men who spend life in their service.
>
> "The poverty of your cell, good father," said the knight, looking around him, and seeing nothing but a bed of leaves, a crucifix rudely carved in oak, a missal, with a rough hewn table and two stools, and one or two clumsy articles of furniture—"the poverty of your cell should seem a sufficient defense against any risk of thieves, not to mention the aid of two trusty dogs, large and strong enough, I think, to pull down a stag, and of course, a match for most men."
>
> "The good keeper of the forest," said the hermit, "hath allowed me the use of these animals, to protect my solitude until the times shall mend."
>
> Having said this, he fixed his torch in a twisted branch of iron which served for a candlestick; and placing the oaken trivet before the embers of the fire, which he refreshed with some dry wood, he placed a stool upon one side of the table, and beckoned the knight to do the same upon the other.

Classroom conversation based on the following suggested topics:

Robin Hood and His Merry Men

The Identity of the Black Knight (referred to in the passage from *Ivanhoe*)

How the Black Knight and the Hermit Spent the Evening
The Most Interesting Character in the Story of *Ivanhoe*
My Favorite Book

Selections for sight reading from the following suggested books:

Scott, *Ivanhoe*
———*Redgauntlet*
Stevenson, *Treasure Island*
————*Travels with a Donkey*
Salten, *Bambi*
Dickens, *Christmas Stories*

Test:

1. Can you read the paragraphs given in the Practice Material, pronouncing all sounds correctly?

2. Can you read at sight, pronouncing all sounds correctly?

3. Are you careful to pronounce all sounds correctly when you are talking to your family and friends?

CONTRACT SHEET
Stammering*

1. The sounds *ō* [oтʊ] as in *go*, *l* [l], and *n* [n] said smoothly and freely.

Syllables and words containing these sounds pronounced smoothly and freely.

Phrases containing these sounds read smoothly and freely.

---

2. The sounds *ô* [ɔ:] as in *all*, *m* [m], *ng* [ŋ], and *th voiced* [ð] said smoothly and freely.

Syllables and words containing these sounds said smoothly and freely.

Phrases and sentences containing these sounds read smoothly and freely.

---

3. The sounds *ä* [ɑ:] as in *father*, *ŏ* [ɒ] as in *hot*, *ā* [eтɪ] as in *play*, *d* [d], *t* [t], and *h* [h] said smoothly and freely.

Syllables and words containing these sounds said smoothly and freely.

Phrases and sentences containing these sounds read smoothly and freely.

---

4. The sounds *ē* [i:] as in *see*, *ī* [aɪ] as in *ice*, *s* [s], *z* [z], and *w* [w] said smoothly and freely.

Words, phrases, and sentences containing these sounds read smoothly and freely.

---

5. The sounds *ă* [æ] as in *at*, *g* [g], *k* [k], *p* [p], *b* [b], and *wh* [ʍ] said smoothly and freely. Words, sentences, and paragraph containing sounds studied since contract one read smoothly and freely.

---

* Every lesson should start with the relaxation exercises given on page 67. The student should also practice these night and morning, and at intervals during the day.

6. The sounds ĭ [ɪ] as in *it,* ōō [uː] as in *soon, sh* [ʃ], *zh* [ʒ], *j* [dʒ], and *r* [ɹ] said smoothly and freely.

Words, sentences, and a paragraph containing these sounds read smoothly and freely.

7. The sounds ŭ [ʌ] as in *up, ow* [aʊ] as on *now, oi* [ɔɪ] as in *boy, v* [v], *f* [f], and *th voiceless* [θ] said smoothly and freely.

Words, sentences, and a few stanzas of poetry containing these sounds read smoothly and freely.

8. The sounds ŏŏ [ʊ] as in *book,* ŏŏr [ʊɚ] as in *poor,* ōr [ɔɚ] as in *floor,* à [ɑ] as in *ask,* ĕ [eɪ] as in *let,* and *ch* [tʃ] said smoothly and freely.

Words containing these sounds said smoothly and freely.

A paragraph read smoothly and freely.

Questions based on this paragraph answered in complete sentences.

9. The sounds û [ɜː] as in *bird,* à [ə] as in *about,* ę [ɪɚ] as in *here,* â [ɛɚ] as in *care,* ū [juː] as in *tune,* and *y* [j] said smoothly and freely.

Words, sentences, and a paragraph containing these sounds read smoothly and freely.

10. Paragraphs containing all sounds read smoothly and freely.

Questions based on these paragraphs answered smoothly and freely in complete sentences.

11. A trip described in a few sentences which flow smoothly and freely.

12. A short story read smoothly and freely.

13. A joke, a short story, or some interesting incident told smoothly and freely.

---

14. A selection read at sight smoothly and freely.

---

15. Several telephone conversations carried on smoothly and freely.

Note to the teacher: In several of the later contracts, suggestions have been made in the section marked *Test* that enable the student to perform various speaking activities outside the classroom. These are merely suggestions; the student may not be ready to do anything as difficult as some of these tasks, or he may be able to do things that are more difficult. Some of the things suggested may not be possible to arrange. The teacher will have to be the guide, and will surely be able to think of other activities that will be feasible in her situation and that of the children with whom she is working.

CONTRACT 1

Objective:

The sounds ō [oʀʊ] as in *go*, *l* [l], *n* [n], said smoothly and freely.
Syllables and words containing these sounds said smoothly and freely.
Phrases containing these sounds read smoothly and freely.

Procedure:

Say the following smoothly and freely:

oh	oh	oh	[oʀʊ]
no	no	no	[noʀʊ]
lo	lo	lo	[loʀʊ]
oh no	oh no	oh no	[oʀʊ noʀʊ]

Caution:

Go slowly. There is no hurry.

Practice Material:

Say the following words smoothly and freely:

low	know	only	oh	own
lone	known	knoll	no	lonely

Say the following phrases smoothly and freely:

1. Oh no, oh no, oh no.
2. Low knoll.
3. Lonely knoll.
4. Low and lonely.
5. Only a lonely knoll.
6. Alone and lonely.

Test:

Can you do all the exercises in the Practice Material smoothly and freely?

Note: If you are in doubt as to how these sounds are made, see pages 30, 35–36.

CONTRACT 2

Objective:

The sounds ô [ɔ:] as in *all*, *m* [m], *ng* [ŋ], *th voiced* [ð] said smoothly and freely.

Syllables and words containing these sounds said smoothly and freely.

Phrases and sentences containing these sounds read smoothly and freely.

Procedure:

Do the following exercises smoothly and freely:

law	law	law [lɔ:]
maw	maw	maw [mɔ:]
naw	naw	naw [nɔ:]

Caution:

Remember to speak slowly.

Practice Material:

Say the following words smoothly and freely:

all	Maude	owe
law	maul	moan
loam	gnaw	gnome

Read the following phrases and sentences smoothly and freely:

1. Knowing all.
2. Lonely mole.
3. A low moan.
4. Mow the lawn.
5. Know the law.
6. The law is known to all.

Test:

Can you do all the exercises given in the Practice Material smoothly and freely?

Note: If you are in doubt as to how any of these sounds is made, see pages 27, 33–35, and 39.

CONTRACT 2A

Objective:

See Contract 2.

Procedure:

Do the exercises given in Contracts 1 and 2.

Caution:

Read slowly.

Practice Material:

Read the following phrases and sentences smoothly and freely:

1. Mowing the lawn.
2. "Alone, alone, all, all alone."
3. Loaning the lawn mower.
4. The gnome is all alone.
5. The mole knows no law.
6. The gnome knows all the laws.

Test:

1. Can you read the phrases and sentences in the Practice Material smoothly and freely?

2. Ask your teacher to allow you to open the window, or to do some other helpful task in the classroom. (Remember to speak slowly.)

CONTRACT 3

Objective:

The sounds *ä* [ɑ:] as in *father*, *ŏ* [ɒ] as in *hot*, *ā* [eɪ] as in *play*, *d* [d], *t* [t], and *h* [h] said smoothly and freely.

Syllables and words containing these sounds said smoothly and freely.

Phrases and sentences containing these sounds read smoothly and freely.

Procedure:

Say the following slogan three times smoothly and freely, holding the sound *o* [oʊ]:

I know that I can speak smoothly.

Do the following exercises smoothly and freely:

lah	lah	lah [lɑ:]	dā	dā	dā [deɪ]
lā	lā	lā [leɪ]	tah	tah	tah [tɑ:]
dah	dah	dah [dɑ:]	tā	tā	tā [teɪ]

Caution:

Remember to go slowly.

Practice Material:

Say the following words smoothly and freely:

lane	art	mar	tardy	home	hot
dame	name	tar	tart	hate	odd

Read the following phrases and sentences smoothly and freely:

1. Lonely toad.

2. Doleful mole.

3. Toting a load.

4. Tote the load to the lawn.

5. The toad knows the mole.

6. They laid the tar on the lane.

Test:

1. Can you do all the exercises in the Practice Material smoothly and freely?

2. Tell your teacher in a few words about something interesting that happened to you today.

Note: If you are in doubt about how any of these sounds is made, see pages 27, 28, 35, 40.

CONTRACT 3A

Objective:

See Contract 3.

Procedure:

Review the exercises in Contracts 1, 2, and 3.

Caution:

Remember that there is no hurry.

Practice Material:

Read the following phrases and sentences smoothly and freely:

1. Late mail.

2. The lonely gnome.

3. Dawdling along in the morning.

4. Name the lane.

5. All dawdled along dolefully.

Test:

1. Can you read the phrases and sentences in the Practice Material smoothly and freely?

2. Can you tell your teacher and a few members of the class about a school game you attended recently? Can you do this speaking smoothly and freely?

CONTRACT 4

Objective:

The sounds *e* [iː] as in *see*, *ī* [aɪ] as in *ice*, *s* [s], *z* [z], and *w* [w] said smoothly and freely.

Words, phrases, and sentences containing these sounds said smoothly and freely.

Procedure:

Say the following slogan three times smoothly and slowly, prolonging the sound *ō* [oʊ]:

I know that I can speak smoothly.

Caution:

Speak slowly and be sure of what you are going to say before you start.

Practice Material:

Say the following words smoothly and freely:

eyes	mice	slice	ease	see	we
ice	my	slight	lea	seize	wine
lies	sigh	size	lease	tease	wail

Read the following phrases and sentences smoothly and freely:

1. Sighing for ease.
2. Seeing the ice.
3. Easing the eyes.
4. It is time to dine.
5. See the stars.
6. The tide is low at nine.

Test:

1. Can you do all the exercises in the Practice Material smoothly and freely?

2. Can you write five more phrases and five more sentences containing the words given in the Practice Material and then read them smoothly and freely?

Note: If you are in doubt about how any of these sounds is made, see pages 20, 29, 34, 36.

CONTRACT 4A

Objective:

See Contract 4.

Procedure:

Review the exercises given in previous contracts.

Caution:

Remember that there is no reason for haste.

Practice Material:

Read the following phrases and sentences smoothly and freely:

1. Sowing the seed.
2. Dining at ease.
3. Seeding the lawn.
4. Leila lay on the lea.
5. They sailed on the sea.
6. The sailor went to sea.
7. The farmers sowed the seed.
8. It is easy to sew a seam.

Test:

1. Can you read all the phrases and sentences in the Practice Material smoothly and freely?

2. Tell the teacher and the class about one of the tricks your pet dog or cat can do. (Know what you are going to say before you start, and speak slowly.)

CONTRACT 5

Objective:

The sounds ă [æ] as in *at*, *g* [g], *k* [k], *p* [p], *b* [b], and *wh* [ʍ] said smoothly and freely.

Words, sentences, and a paragraph containing sounds studied since Contract 1 read smoothly and freely.

Procedure:

Say the following slogan three times slowly and smoothly:

I know that I can speak freely.

Caution:

Speak slowly. Read slowly.

Practice Material:

Say the following words smoothly and freely:

back	ban	bag	bind	why
pack	can	gap	guile	while
cab	pan	babble	kind	whale
cap	plan	gabble	pine	whine

Read the following sentences smoothly and freely:

1. The sailboat seemed to be going back.

2. Sam buys nine pies.

3. Pack the boxes and bags.

4. The gardener sold beans and peas.

5. The lamb gambols on the lea.

6. They whiled away the time.

Read the following paragraph smoothly and freely:

Sam and Bill like to go skating. Sometimes they skate all day. When the snow is deep, they go skiing and coasting. Skating and coasting and skiing are their main sports.

Test:

1. Can you read all the sentences in the Practice Material smoothly and freely?

2. Can you read the paragraph in the Practice Material smoothly and freely?

3. Tell the class in a few words about one of your experiences in winter sports.

Note: If you are in doubt about how any of these
sounds is made, see pages 22, 33, 34, 38.

CONTRACT 5A

Objective:

See Contract 5.

Procedure:

Review the exercises given in previous contracts.

Caution:

Speak slowly and smoothly.

Practice Material:

Read the following sentences slowly and smoothly:

1. I told the tale of the lonely mole.

2. "Lower the boats!" called the captain.

3. I planted seeds in the garden.

4. Leila bought peas and beans.

5. I like to go coasting in the deep snow.

6. Although I am alone, I am not lonely.

Read the following paragraph slowly and smoothly:

Long, long ago, a king named Saul led an army into battle. The battle lasted all night long. Saul died at the close of the battle, and all the people sang songs of mourning for the kind old king.

Test:

1. Can you read the sentences in the Practice Material smoothly and freely?

2. Can you read the paragraph in the Practice Material smoothly and freely?

3. Ask your mother to let you go the grocery store and order a short list of groceries—one or two articles. Make a list and consult it if necessary. (Before you go to the store, practice what you are going to say. Keep in mind always that you are going to speak smoothly and freely.)

CONTRACT 6

Objective:

The sounds ĭ [ɪ] as in *it*, ōō [u:] as in *soon*, *sh* [ʃ], *zh* [ʒ], *j* [dʒ], and *r* [ɪ] said smoothly and freely.

Words, sentences, and a paragraph containing these sounds read smoothly and freely.

Procedure:

Say the following slogan three times smoothly and freely:

I feel that I can speak better each day.

Do the exercises given in all preceding contracts.

Caution:

Be sure of what you are going to say before you start to speak; then speak slowly.

Practice Material:

Say the following words smoothly and freely:

boon	jig	sheet	root	decision
loon	gypsy	shine	right	derision
soothe	midget	shoe	rode	measure
spoon	ridge	show	raw	pleasure

Read the following sentences smoothly and freely:

1. The gypsies camped on the ridge.
2. Will you have toast and tea with ginger and jam?
3. The measurements of the room are nine by sixteen.
4. The jackrabbit ran gingerly over the ridge.
5. The jays squawked at the farmers who garnered the wheat.
6. It is a pleasure to ride on the ridge in the spring.
7. They were doing the spring cleaning at the mansion on the hill.
8. They painted the room cream trimmed with green.

Read the following paragraph smoothly and freely:

Bob and Paul were playing baseball on the highway. An automobile came by, and Paul was slightly injured. Bob called the policeman on the corner, and he carried Paul to the hospital. Paul had abrasions on his arms and legs, but no bones were broken. He went home gaily the next day, and will not play ball on the highway again.

Test:

1. Can you do the exercises in the Practice Material smoothly and freely?

2. Ask your father to allow you to go to the newsstand and get the evening paper for him. (Practice asking the newsdealer for the paper before you go, and remember that you are going to speak smoothly.)

Note: If you are in doubt about how any of these sounds is made, see pages 21, 25, 36, 37.

CONTRACT 7

Objective:

The sounds *ŭ* [ʌ] as in *up, ow* [aʊ] as in *now, oi* [ɔɪ] as in *boy, v* [v], *f* [f], and *th* voiceless [θ] said smoothly and freely.

Words, sentences, and a few stanzas of poetry read smoothly and freely.

Procedure:

Say the following slogan five times:

I will speak slowly and well.

Caution:

Do not try to hurry. Remember, "Haste makes waste."

Practice Material:

Say the following words smoothly and freely:

up	boil	town	think	vain	fine
come	doily	loud	thrift	vine	fail
fun	join	found	throw	villa	fade
hum	loiter	vow	thought	vibrate	fancy

Read the following sentences smoothly and freely:

1. The boys joined the Athletic Association.

2. The father of the family vowed that he would take plenty of life insurance.

3. "Make hay while the sun shines."

4. "It is always darkest just before dawn."

5. Can you find the fellow who fired the pistol?

6. The paper hangers were papering the northeast bedroom.

7. Singing is a sign of happiness.

8. The ivy vine grows over the front of the building.

9. "A place for everything, and everything in its place" is a good motto.

10. Christmas and Easter are family feast days.

Read the following stanzas from *The Bridge* by Longfellow smoothly and freely:

> I saw her bright reflection
> In the waters under me,
> Like a golden goblet falling
> And sinking into the sea.
>
> How often, O how often,
> In the days that had gone by,
> I had stood on that bridge at midnight
> And gazed on that wave and sky.

Test:

1. Can you read the words and sentences given in the Practice Material smoothly and freely?

2. Can you read the stanzas given above smoothly and freely?

3. Ask your teacher to allow you to go to another teacher with a written message. *Tell* the teacher to whom the note is written that you have brought the note from your teacher and will wait for an answer. (Remember to practice what you are going to say before you go; be assured that you will do the errand successfully.)

> *Note:* If you are in doubt about how any of these
> sounds is made, see pages 24, 29, 30, 34.

CONTRACT 8

Objective:

The sounds *ŏŏ* [ʊ] as in *book*, *ŏŏr* [ʊɝ] as in *poor*, *ōr* [ɔɝ] as in *floor*, *à* [ɐ] as in *ask*, *ĕ* [eᴛ] as in *let*, and *ch* [tʃ] said smoothly and freely.
Words containing these sounds said smoothly and freely.
A paragraph read smoothly and freely.
Questions based on this paragraph answered in complete sentences.

Procedure:

Repeat aloud several times the slogans you have been given thus far.

Caution:

Go slowly.

Practice Material:

Say the following words smoothly and freely:

ask	butcher	best	boor	core
class	foot	check	moor	door
last	look	chest	poor	floor
past	pull	wretch	sure	shore

Read smoothly and freely the following adaptation from Washington Irving's *Rip Van Winkle:*

> In that same village, and in one of those very houses, (which, to tell the precise truth, was sadly time-worn and weather-beaten) there lived . . . while the country was yet a province of Great Britain, a simple, good-natured fellow, of the name of Rip Van Winkle. He was a descendant of the Van Winkles who figured so gallantly in the chivalrous days of Peter Stuyvesant, and accompanied him to the siege of Fort Christina. He inherited, however, little of the martial character of his ancestors. I have noted that he was a simple, good-natured man; he was, moreover, a kind neighbor, and an obedient and hen-pecked husband.

Answer the following questions in complete sentences:

1. In what kind of house did Rip Van Winkle live?

2. What kind of person was Rip Van Winkle?

3. Was he like his ancestors?

4. What did his ancestors do?

5. What sort of woman was Dame Van Winkle?

Test:

1. Can you read the words and the paragraph in the Practice Material smoothly and freely?

2. Can you read to the class smoothly and freely another short paragraph from *Rip Van Winkle?*

3. Can you answer the questions in the Practice Material smoothly and freely?

Note: If you are in doubt about how any of these sounds is made, see pages 22, 23, 26, 31, 37.

CONTRACT 9

Objective:

The sounds *û* [ɜ:] as in *bird*, *ȧ* [ə] as in *about*, *ẹ* [ɪə] as in *here*, *â* [ɛə] as in *care*, *ū* [ju:] as in *tune*, and *y* [j] said smoothly and freely.

Words, sentences, and a paragraph containing these sounds read smoothly and freely.

Procedure:

Say the following slogan slowly and smoothly five times:

I know that I can speak smoothly; therefore I will always try to do so.

Caution:

Speak slowly and rhythmically.

Practice Material:

Read the following words smoothly and freely:

bird	fearless	care	dew	about	yes
earth	cheer	where	news	around	yellow
curtain	appear	there	tune	attach	year
third	clear	hair	Tuesday	aloud	yearn

Read the following sentences smoothly and freely:

1. Winter is beginning early this year.
2. The man will be thirty-three years old tomorrow.
3. The musical comedy had few new songs.
4. The sand dunes are high on Cape Cod.
5. Were you walking around the house about five o'clock?
6. They met at the corner of Thirty-first Street and Fifth Avenue.
7. Have you been to the theatre recently?
8. The newspaper told about the fire Tuesday.
9. This product violates the Pure Food laws.
10. On the third morning, the sky was blue, the earth was green, and I heard the birds singing.

Read the following paragraph from Irving's *The Legend of Sleepy Hollow* smoothly and freely:

All was now bustle and hubbub in the late quiet schoolroom. The scholars were hurried through their lessons without stopping at trifles, those who were nimble skipped over half with impunity, and those who were tardy, had a smart application, now and then, in the rear, to quicken their speed, or help them over a tall word. Books were flung aside without being put away on the shelves, inkstands were overturned, benches thrown down, and the whole school was turned loose an hour before the usual time, bursting forth like a legion of young imps, yelping and racketing about the green, in joy of their early emancipation.

Answer the following questions smoothly and freely, and in complete sentences:

1. How did the students do their lessons on the afternoon in question?

2. What was done with the books?

3. What happened to the ink-stands?

4. What was done with the benches?

5. Were the students glad to get out early?

6. How did they show this?

Test:

1. Can you read the sentences in the Practice Material smoothly and freely?

2. Can you read the paragraph given above smoothly and freely?

3. Can you find another paragraph from the *Legend of Sleepy Hollow* and read that smoothly and freely?

4. Can you answer the questions listed above smoothly and freely?

5. Go to a soda fountain and order a glass of milk and a sandwich or whatever you wish. Can you do this in a poised manner and with free, smooth speech?

> *Note:* If you are in doubt about how any of these
> sounds is made, see pages 23, 24, 25, 30, 31, 38.

CONTRACT 10

Objective:

Paragraphs containing all sounds read smoothly and freely.
Questions based on these paragraphs answered smoothly and freely in complete sentences.

Procedure:

Say the following slogan slowly and with conviction:

I have proved that I can say all the sounds of the English language smoothly and freely; therefore I know that I can always do so.

Caution:

Remember that you will have greater poise if you speak and move slowly.

Practice Material:

Read the following paragraphs from Irving's *Legend of Sleepy Hollow* smoothly and freely:

The gallant Ichabod now spent at least an extra half hour at his toilet, brushing and furbishing up his best, and indeed only suit of rusty black, and arranging his looks by a bit of broken looking glass, that hung up in the schoolhouse. That he might make his appearance before his mistress in the true style of a cavalier, he borrowed a horse from . . . Hans Van Ripper, and thus gallantly mounted, issued forth, like a knight-errant in search of adventures. . . . The animal he bestrode was a broken down ploughhorse, that had outlived almost everything but his viciousness. He was gaunt and shagged, with a ewe neck and a head like a hammer. His rusty mane and tail were tangled and knotted with burrs. One eye had lost a pupil and was glaring and spectral, but the other had the gleam of a genuine devil in it. Still he must have had fire and mettle in his day, if we can judge from the name he bore of "Gunpowder."

Ichabod was a suitable figure for such a steed. He rode with short stirrups which brought his knees nearly up to the pummel of the saddle. His sharp elbows stood out like grasshoppers'. He carried his whip perpendicularly in his hand like a sceptre, and as his horse jogged on, the motion of his arms was not unlike the flapping of a pair of wings. A small wool hat rested on the top of his nose, for so his scanty strip of forehead might be called; and the tails of his black coat fluttered out almost to the horse's tail. Such was the appearance of Ichabod and his steed, as they shambled out of the gate of Hans Van Ripper, and it was altogether such an apparition as is seldom to be met with in broad daylight.

Answer the following questions smoothly and freely in complete sentences:

1. What color was Ichabod's best suit?
2. Did he have any other suit?
3. To whom did the horse belong?
4. What was the name of the horse?
5. Was the horse gentle?
6. Was the horse young or old?
7. Describe the horse's eyes.
8. Describe the general appearance of the horse.

Test:

1. Can you read the paragraph above smoothly and freely?

2. Can you answer the questions smoothly and freely?

3. Describe an amusing character from another story.

4. Ask your mother to let you go to the library, and ask the librarian for a certain book. Ask your mother to give you the names of two or more books so that if one is not available, you may ask for another.

CONTRACT 11

Objective:

A trip described in a few sentences which flow smoothly and freely.

Procedure:

Say the following slogan many times a day:

I know that I can appear poised in a small social gathering as well as in a classroom.

Caution:

Remember that you have proved that you can say all the sounds of the language smoothly and freely. Hence, if you go slowly, you will speak well.

Practice Material:

Furnished by the student.

Test:

1. Can you tell in a few sentences about some trip you have taken?

2. Can you speak smoothly and freely when doing this?

3. Whenever your family has one or two guests, assume some social responsibility, talk with the guests, and try to make them feel at home. (Remember to concentrate on making the guest comfortable; think about the other person instead of yourself, and there is no doubt that you will be poised.)

CONTRACT 12

Objective:

A short story read smoothly and freely.

Procedure:

Review the slogans that have proved to be the most helpful; say them both aloud and silently many times a day.

Caution:

Read slowly and you will read smoothly. (Practice reading the story aloud at home before presenting it before the class.)

Practice Material:

The Town Mouse and the Country Mouse

Now you must know that a Town Mouse once upon a time went on a visit to his cousin in the country. He was rough and ready, this cousin, but he loved his town friend and made him heartily welcome. Beans and bacon, cheese and bread were all he had to offer, but he offered them freely. The Town Mouse rather turned up his long nose at this country fare, and said, "I cannot understand, Cousin, how you can put up with such poor food as this, but, of course, you cannot expect anything better in the country; come you with me and I will show you how to live. When you have been in town a week you will wonder how you could ever have stood a country life." No sooner said than done. The two mice set off for the town and arrived at the Town Mouse's residence late that night. "You will want some refreshments after our journey," said the polite Town Mouse, and took his friend into the grand dining room. There they found the remains of a fine feast, and soon the two mice were eating up jellies and cakes and all that was nice. Suddenly they heard growling and barking. "What is that?" said the Country Mouse. "It is only the dogs of the house," answered the other. "Only!" said the Country Mouse. "I do not like that music at my dinner." Just at that moment, the door flew open, and in came two mastiffs, and the two mice had to scamper down and run off. "Good-bye, Cousin," said the Country Mouse. "What! going so soon?" said the other. "Yes," he replied:

"*Better beans and bacon in peace than cakes and ale in fear.*"

Test:

1. Can you read the above fable smoothly and freely?

2. Can you tell the story in your own words smoothly and freely?

3. Go to a policeman and ask him for directions to a certain place. (Remember that you should be sure of what you are going to say before you address the policeman; if you will feel more sure of yourself by so doing, rehearse what you are going to say.)

CONTRACT 13

Objective:

A joke, a short story, or some interesting incident told smoothly and freely.

Procedure:

Say the following slogan:

I know that I can tell this story well as long as I remember to go slowly.

Caution:

Think the story through carefully before you begin speaking; be sure you know exactly what you are going to say before you start. (This does not mean that you are to memorize the story.)

Practice Material:

To be furnished by the student.

Test:

1. Can you tell a joke, a short story, or an incident, speaking smoothly and freely?

2. When you go to a party, try to find someone who is ill at ease and shy. Talk to that person and try to draw him into the conversation. Think about the other person's comfort, and you yourself will be poised and free.

CONTRACT 14

Objective:

A selection read at sight smoothly and freely.

Procedure:

Repeat the following slogan several times before starting to read:

I know that I shall feel comfortable and at ease; therefore I shall enjoy reading this story.

Caution:

You have proved that you can read smoothly and freely material that you have practiced. If you take time and try to understand the author's thought, you will read well at sight.

Practice Material:

Read the following smoothly and freely at sight:

The Fox and the Stork

At one time the Fox and the Stork were on visiting terms, and seemed very good friends. So the Fox invited the Stork to dinner. For a joke he put nothing before her but some soup in a very shallow dish. This the Fox could easily lap up, but the Stork could only wet the end of her long bill in it, and left the meal as hungry as when she began.

"I am sorry," said the Fox, "that the soup is not to your liking."

"Pray do not apologize," said the Stork. "I hope you will return this visit, and come and dine with me soon."

So a day was appointed when the Fox should visit the Stork, but when they were seated at table, all that was for their dinner was contained in a very narrow, long-necked jar with a narrow mouth. The Fox could not insert his snout in this, so all he could manage to do was to lick the outside of the jar.

"I will not apologize for the dinner," said the Stork: "*One bad turn deserves another.*"

Test:

1. Can you read the above selection at sight smoothly and freely?

2. Can you tell the story smoothly and freely in your own words?

3. Can you find another selection and read it at sight smoothly and freely?

4. Go to a large department store; ask the person at the Information Desk to tell you where to find three different articles. Take a list with you, and consult it if necessary.

CONTRACT 15

Objective:

Several telephone conversations carried on smoothly and freely.

Procedure:

Say the following slogan many times:

I have proved that I can speak freely in many situations.
I believe that I shall always do so in all situations in the future.

Caution:

Be sure that you know exactly what you are going to say before you pick up the receiver.

Practice Material:

1. Call up your best friend and invite him to come to see you.

2. Call up the Western Union and ask for the correct time.

3. Call up the Information Bureau of some railroad and ask what time there is a train leaving for a certain city.

Test:

1. Can you carry on a short telephone conversation, speaking smoothly and freely?

2. Take every opportunity to answer the telephone and to make telephone calls.

CONTRACT SHEET
Breathiness*

---

1. Controlled breathing.

---

2. Clear tone on the following sounds: *ä* [ɑ:], *ā* [eɪ], *ē* [i:], *ô* [ɔ:], *ō* [oʊ], *o͞o* [u:].

Clear tone in syllables, words, and phrases that contain these sounds.

---

3. Clear tone on the following sounds: *ī* [aɪ], *ă* [æ], *û* [ɜ:], *ŭ* [ʌ], *oi* [ɔɪ], *ow* [aʊ], *o͝o* [ʊ].

Clear tone in syllables, words, and phrases that contain these sounds.

---

4. Clear tone on the following sounds: *ĕ* [eʈ], *à* [ɑ], *ŏ* [ɒ], *ĭ* [ɪ], *ę* [ɪɚ], *â* [ɛɚ], *o͝or* [ʊɚ], *ōr* [ɔɚ], and *ū* [ju:].

Clear tone in syllables, words, and phrases containing these sounds.

---

5. Clear tone in sentences requiring energy.

---

6. Clear tone in a selection requiring volume and energy.

---

7. Clear, energized tone in selection that does not require a great deal of volume.

---

* Start every practice period with the relaxation exercises given in Part III (page 67).

8. Clear, energized tone in sight reading.

9. Clear, energized tone in conversation.

CONTRACT 1

Objective:

Controlled breathing.

Procedure:

Stand erect, firmly on both feet; feel that your whole body is energized; place one hand on the abdominal muscles and the other on the waistline. Inhale and expand the lungs, particularly the lower part; exhale, pushing firmly with the abdominal muscles. (If you have difficulty with this, lie flat on your back, relax completely, inhale and exhale naturally a few times, and proceed as above.)

For the explanation of the breathing process, see page 5.

Caution:

Be certain that you have enough breath; to make sure, inhale audibly during the practice period.

Be sure that you push the breath out firmly with the abdominal muscles.

Practice Material:

Page 6, Exercises 1–6.

Test:

1. Can you take a breath and push it out firmly with the abdominal muscles?

2. Can you count from 1 to 5, using a single inhalation and exhalation for each number?

3. Can you count from 1 to 5 in this fashion?

    Inhale—exhale, saying: 1
       "   "   "   1–2
       "   "   "   1–2–3
       "   "   "   1–2–3–4
       "   "   "   1–2–3–4–5

4. In the above exercises, is the throat relaxed? Is there a good firm push with the abdominal muscles? Did you have enough breath, not too much nor too little?

CONTRACT 2

Objective:

Clear tone on the following sounds: *ä* [ɑ:] as in *father*, *ā* [eɪɪ] as in *ate*, *ē* [i:] as in *see*, *ô* [ɔ:] as in *all*, *ō* [oʊ] as in *go*, and *ōō* [u:] as in *soon*.

Clear tone in syllables, words, and phrases containing those sounds.

Procedure:

See pages 20–30 for the proper position of the organs of articulation for the above sounds.

Inhale and vocalize the sound *ō* [oʊ], prolonging it as long as you can comfortably; repeat with the other sounds given above.

After vocalizing the sounds, say them in a clear tone, first with rising, then with falling, and finally with straight inflection.

Caution:

Be sure the lips are rounded for the round sounds.

Do not try to hold the breath too long. Avoid strain.

Practice Material:

Do the following exercise in a clear tone:

lah	lah	lah [lɑ:]	law	law	law [lɔ:]
lā	lā	lā [leɪɪ]	lō	lō	lō [loʊ]
lē	lē	lē [li:]	lōō	lōō	lōō [lu:]

Place other consonant sounds before the above vowels and diphthongs, and proceed in a like manner.

Do the following exercise, using one breath for each line:

```
ah  [ɑ:]
ah  ā      [ɑ:  eɪɪ]
ah  ā  ē   [ɑ:  eɪɪ  i:]
ah  ā  ē  aw   [ɑ:  eɪɪ  i:   ɔ:]
ah  ā  ē  aw  ō   [ɑ:  eɪɪ  i:   ɔ:  oʊ]
ah  ā  ē  aw  ō  ōō   [ɑ:  eɪɪ  i:  ɔ:   oʊ  u:]
```

Place various consonants before the sounds given above, and proceed in a like manner.

Say the following words in a clear tone:

barn	cane	bean	all	blow	blue
car	fame	keen	caught	dome	cool
cart	mail	leap	hall	no	loot
farm	rate	leave	law	roam	pool

Say the following phrases in a clear tone:

1. Hold the goal.
2. True blue.
3. Blowing snow.
4. Saving the game.
5. Sweet dreams.
6. Rolling stone.
7. Blue moon.
8. Toeing the mark.
9. Baying the moon.
10. Calling Maude.

Test:

1. Can you read the words in the Practice Material in a clear tone?

2. Can you read the phrases given in the Practice Material in a clear tone?

CONTRACT 2A

Objective:

See Contract 2

Procedure:

See Contract 2.

Caution:

Try to increase your breath span *gradually.* *Use* all your breath; do not waste it; avoid strain.

Practice Material:

Repeat the following exercises in a clear tone:

hä	hä	hä	hard	['hɑːd]
hō	hō	hō	home	['horʊm]
hōō	hōō	hōō	whom	['huːm]
haw	haw	haw	hall	['hɔːl]
mō	mō	mō	moan	['morʊn]
nō	nō	nō	gnome	['norʊm]
fō	fō	fō	foam	['forʊm]
paw	paw	paw	Paul	['pɔːl]
tōō	tōō	tōō	tool	['tuːl]
lā	lā	lā	lame	['leɾɪm]
mē	mē	mē	mean	['miːn]

Say the following words in a clear tone:

go	hard	who	same	seem	law
slow	part	loon	train	feet	taught
told	heart	boot	cane	lean	fall
drone	mart	boon	late	dream	drawn

Say the following phrases in a clear tone:

1. Oh, you.	**6.** Moaning and groaning.
2. Hard hearts.	**7.** Rating the papers.
3. "Oh, you hard hearts."	**8.** Saving the plane.
4. Go slowly.	**9.** Peas and beans.
5. Gnawing a bone.	**10.** "Sweet and low."

Test:

1. Can you do all the exercises given in the Practice Material in a clear tone?

2. Can you prepare lists of words and phrases containing the above sounds, and then read them in a clear tone?

CONTRACT 3

Objective:

Clear tone on the sounds *ī* [aɪ] as in *ice*, *ă* [æ] as in *at*, *û* [ɝ:] as in *bird*, *ŭ* [ʌ] as in *up*, *oi* [ɔɪ] as in *choice*, *ow* [aʊ] as in *now*, and *ŏŏ* [ʊ] as in *look*. Clear tone on syllables, words, and phrases containing these sounds.

Procedure:

See pages 22–30 for the proper position of the organs of articulation for the production of the above sounds.

Inhale and vocalize the sounds given in Contract 2.

Inhale and vocalize the sound *ow* [aʊ], prolonging it as long as you can comfortably; proceed in like manner with the other sounds given above.

After vocalizing the sounds, say them in a clear tone, first with rising, then with falling, and finally, with a straight, inflection.

Do the following exercise to increase your breath span:

```
ī [aɪ]
ī   ă   [aɪ  æ]
ī   ă   oi  [aɪ  æ   ɔɪ]
ī   ă   oi  ŭ   [aɪ  æ   ɔɪ  ʌ]
ī   ă   oi  ŭ   ŏŏ   [aɪ  æ   ɔɪ  ʌ   ʊ]
ī   ă   oi  ŭ   ŏŏ  ow  [aɪ  æ   ɔɪ  ʌ   ʊ   aʊ]
```

Do the above exercise placing the consonants *m* [m], *n* [n], and *l* [l] before each sound.

Caution:

Be sure that your tone is clear when doing the above exercises. Try to carry the clear tone over into your conversation.

Practice Material:

Combine the sounds given above with consonants to make syllables and words, as follows:

now	now	now	noun ['naʊn]
lī	lī	lī	line ['laɪn]
mă	mă	mă	man ['mæn]
lû	lû	lû	learn ['lɜ:n]
fŏŏ	fŏŏ	fŏŏ	foot ['fʊt]
noi	noi	noi	noise ['nɔɪz]
bŭ	bŭ	bŭ	bun ['bʌn]

Say the following words in a clear tone:

bound	fine	ban	birth	cook	cup	boy
doubt	life	candy	earn	foot	gun	choice
grouch	might	fat	girl	look	nut	coin
pounce	pint	snatch	perch	put	one	oyster

Read the following phrases in a clear tone:

1. Throwing a life-line.
2. Banning the book.
3. Earning money.
4. Coining a word.
5. Sighing and crying.
6. Boiling oil.
7. Cutting a cake.
8. Having a fine time.
9. Going down town.
10. Cooking supper.

Test:

1. Can you do the exercises given in the Practice Material in a clear tone?

2. Can you prepare ten other phrases and read them in a clear tone?

3. Do you try to carry over a clear tone into your daily speech?

CONTRACT 3A

Objective:

See Contract 3.

Procedure:

See Contract 3.

Caution:

See Contract 3.

Practice Material:

Say the following words in a clear tone:

down	fight	bat	burn	could	cut	boil
gown	height	catch	earth	book	gull	doily
round	mind	fan	fern	took	none	oil

Read the following phrases in a clear tone:

1. Burning the doily.
2. Looking for a good book.
3. Pining for a sight of land.
4. Looking down at the earth from the clouds.
5. Running around down town.
6. Fanning the wood fire.
7. Fighting with might and main.
8. Training the animals to catch a ball.
9. Looking at all the books on the counter.
10. Going on a journey to the Holy Land.

Test:

1. Can you say the words in the Practice Material in a clear tone?

2. Can you read the phrases in the Practice Material in a clear tone?

3. Can you prepare ten more phrases and read them in a clear tone?

CONTRACT 4

Objective:

The following sounds given in a clear tone: ĕ [eт] as in *let*, ȧ [ɑ] as in *ask*, ŏ [ɒ] as in *coffee*, ĭ [ɪ] as in *it*, ę [ɪɔ̌] as in *here*, â [ɛɔ̌] as in *care*, ŏŏr [ʊɔ̌] as in *poor*, ōr [ɔɔ̌] as in *floor*, and ū [juː] as in *tune*.

Clear tone in syllables, words, and phrases containing these sounds.

Procedure:

See Part II, Chapter IV, Vowel and Diphthong sections for the correct production of the sounds given above.

Inhale and vocalize all the sounds studied thus far.

Inhale and vocalize the sound ĕ [eт], prolonging it for as long a period as you can do so comfortably; proceed in like manner with the other sounds given above.

After vocalizing the sounds, say them in a clear tone, first with rising inflection, then with falling inflection, and, finally, with straight inflection.

Caution:

Be sure that your throat does not become tense in the effort to produce a clear tone; if you notice any tenseness, stop and yawn.

Practice Material:

Combine the sounds given above with consonants to make syllables and words:

lĕ	lĕ	lĕ	lend	['leɾnd]
mȧ	mȧ	mȧ	mast	['mɑst]
kŏ	kŏ	kŏ	coffee	['kɒfɪɾ]
mĭ	mĭ	mĭ	mitten	['mɪtn̩]
hȩ	hȩ	hȩ	here	['hɪɚ]
kå	kå	kå	care	['kɛɚ]
po͝or	po͝or	po͝or	poor	['pʊɚ]
flōr	flōr	flōr	floor	['flɔɚ]
nū	nū	nū	new	['nju:]

Read the following words three times each in a clear tone:

bend	ask	office	bit	cheer
dent	class	coffee	city	clear
met	dance	chocolate	hinder	dear

bare	boor	door	beauty
chair	moor	floor	cute
hair	poor	pour	duty

Read the following phrases in a clear tone:

1. Cheering for the home team.
2. Having hot chocolate in the office.
3. Brushing and combing her hair.
4. Asking the class to hold a dance.
5. Going to the city for the winter.
6. Driving rapidly around the bend.
7. Buying a new pair of shoes.
8. Pouring water over the kitchen floor
9. Hearing an inspiring speech.
10. Taking a long walk on the moor.

Test:

1. Can you read the words in the Practice Material in a clear tone?
2. Can you read the phrases in the Practice Material in a clear tone?
3. Can you prepare ten more phrases and read them in a clear tone?

CONTRACT 4A

Objective:

See Contract 4.

Procedure:

See Contract 4.

Add the following exercise to the exercises given in Contracts 1, 2, and 3 for increasing the breath span:

> ĕ [eт]
> ĕ ĭ [eт ɪ]
> ĕ ĭ ŏ [eт ɪ ɒ]
> ĕ ĭ ŏ ȧ [eт ɪ ɒ ɑ]
> ĕ ĭ ŏ· ȧ ẹr [eт ɪ ɒ ɑ ɪ̆ŏ]
> ĕ ĭ ŏ ȧ ẹr ōor [eт ɪ ɒ ɑ ɪ̆ŏ ʊ̆ŏ]

Do the above exercise preceding each sound with *m* [m], *n* [n], and *l* [l].

Caution:

Try to take just enough breath each time; be sure that you have enough breath for the last syllables; do not waste breath. If you have breath left over after saying the last syllable, take a deep, cleansing breath, exhale it, and start over again, using the breath with greater care.

Practice Material:

Read the following phrases in a clear tone:

1. Serving Christmas dinner to the poor.
2. Locking all the doors in the house.
3. Paying the rent for March and April.
4. Visiting the city in winter.
5. Going to a beauty parlor on Tuesday.
6. Fearing to ask for news.
7. Wearing a pair of silver slippers.
8. Giving a dinner party for the office force.
9. Lending aid to the poor and needy.
10. Paying careful attention to the teacher's instructions.
11. Yawning and relaxing the throat.
12. Pouring coffee for the many guests.

13. Having a harsh, unpleasant voice.

14. Skiing swiftly down the mountain side.

15. Appearing at the dance in sport clothes.

Test:

1. Can you do the exercise given in the Procedure, having enough breath to say the last syllable in a clear tone?

2. Can you read the phrases in the Practice Material in a clear tone?

3. Do you try to use a clear tone in your everyday speech?

CONTRACT 5

Objective:

Clear tone in phrases and sentences requiring energy.

Procedure:

Vocalize all vowels and diphthongs.

Take a breath and explode the sound ō [oʊ] (let all breath come out at once). Do the same with other vowels and diphthongs, but work on open and round sounds first to avoid strain.

Caution:

Be sure you use a firm abdominal push for each sound.
Be careful to have plenty of breath for each phrase.
Be sure your body is energized throughout.
If your throat becomes tired, stop and yawn.

Practice Material:

Say the following words explosively:

halt	jump	police	don't	stop	sold
run	fire	leap	go	gone	whoa
shoot	shout	ready	hark	beware	down

Say the following phrases explosively:

1. Ready, set, go.
2. On your mark.
3. Company halt.
4. Right face.
5. Down, sir.
6. Going, going, gone.
7. Run for your life.
8. On your mark, get set, go.

Read the following sentences explosively, using one breath for each phrase:

1. "Once more, unto the breach, dear friends, once more,
   Or close the wall up with our English dead!"

2. "Follow your spirit, and upon this charge cry, 'God for Harry, England, and Saint George!'"

3. "Down, sir," said the master, as the dog leaped upon the man.

4. "On your mark! Get set! Go!" shouted the starter.

5. The auctioneer said, "Going, going, gone!"

6. "Right face!" said the commander.

7. "Company halt!" said the captain.

8. "Yield, ye youths, ye yeomen, yield your yell!"

9. "'Good speed!' cried the watch as the gate-bolts undrew."

10. "'Speed!' echoed the wall to us galloping through."

Test:

1. Can you do all the exercises in the Practice Material in a clear tone?

2. Can you prepare other exercises that require energy and then read them in a clear tone?

3. Can you read in a clear tone one of "Exercises for Volume and Energy of Tone" given in Part III?

CONTRACT 5A

Objective:

See Contract 5.

Procedure:

See Contract 5.

Caution:

Be sure that you breathe correctly in your daily conversation as well as when you read aloud.

Practice Material:

Read the following expressions explosively:

1. Hip! Hip! Hurrah!

2. Watch your step!

3. Step lively!

4. Company halt!

5. All aboard!

6. Going! Going! Gone!

7. All ashore!

8. On your mark!

9. Order, please!

10. Keep in line!

Read the following sentences in an explosive quality of tone:

1. "Play ball," shouted the umpire.
2. "A horse! A horse! My kingdom for a horse!"
3. "Rah! Rah! Rah!" shouted the cheer leader.
4. "Team! Team! Team!" yelled the excited throng.
5. "Victory! Victory! Victory!" called the players.
6. "Whoa!" shouted the driver to the spirited horse.
7. "Fie, fie, Gratiano! Where are all the rest?"
8. "I'll have my bond; speak not against my bond: I have sworn an oath that I will have my bond."
9. "How now! What news with you?"
10. "My daughter! O my ducats! O my daughter! Fled with a Christian!"

Test:

1. Can you read the expressions given above in a clear, explosive tone?

2. Can you read the sentences given above in a clear, explosive tone?

3. Can you read one of the "Exercises for Volume and Energy" (Part III) in a clear, explosive tone?

CONTRACT 6

Objective:

Clear tone in a selection requiring volume and energy.

Procedure:

See Contract 5.

Caution:

If your throat becomes tense, stop and yawn.

Practice Material:

Read Shakespeare's *Julius Caesar*, Act I, Sc. 1, ll. 36–60. (See Part III, selection under "Exercises for Volume and Energy of Tone," beginning "Wherefore rejoice?")

Read Tennyson's *The Charge of the Light Brigade*.

Test:

1. Can you read in a clear, energized tone the selections suggested in the Practice Material?

2. Can you find another selection and read it in a clear, energized tone?

CONTRACT 6A

Objective:

See Contract 5.

Procedure:

See Contract 5.

Caution:

See Contract 5.

Practice Material:

See Contract 5.

Read "Marching Along" and "Boot! Saddle! To Horse! and Away!" from Browning's *Cavalier Tunes*. (See Part III.)

Read the speech of the French Herald from Shakespeare's *King John*. (See Part III.)

Test:

1. Can you read in a clear tone the poems from Browning's *Cavalier Tunes* suggested in the Practice Material?

2. Can you read in a clear tone the passage from *King John* suggested in the Practice Material?

CONTRACT 7

Objective:

Clear, energized tone in a selection that does not require a great deal of volume.

Procedure:

See Contract 5.

Caution:

Be sure that the entire body is energized, and that the breathing is correct.

Practice Material:

Read in a clear, energized tone the following selection from *American Notes* by Dickens. Read it first in a large room and then in a small room, using enough (but not too much) voice in each case:

The city is a beautiful one, and cannot fail, I should imagine, to impress all strangers very favorably. The private dwelling houses are, for the most part, large and elegant; the shops extremely good; and the public buildings handsome. The State House is built upon the summit of a hill, which rises gradually at first, and afterwards by a steep ascent, almost from the water's edge. In front is a green enclosure, called the Common. The site is beautiful: and from the top there is a charming panoramic view of the whole town and neighborhood. In addition to a variety of commodious offices, it contains two handsome chambers; in one the House of Representatives of the State hold their meetings: in the other, the Senate. Such proceedings as I saw here, were conducted with perfect gravity and decorum; and were certainly calculated to inspire attention and respect.

There is no doubt that much of the intellectual refinement and superiority of Boston is referable to the quiet influence of the University of Cambridge, which is within three or four miles of the city. The resident professors at that university are gentlemen of learning and varied attainments; and are, without one exception that I can call to mind, men who would have shed a grace upon, and do honor to, any society in the civilized world. Many of the resident gentry in Boston and its neighborhood, and I think I am not mistaken in adding, a large majority of those who are attached to the liberal professions there, have been educated at this same school. Whatever the defects of American universities may be, they disseminate no prejudices; rear no bigots; dig up the buried ashes of no old superstitions; never interpose between the people and their improvement; exclude no man because of his religious opinions; above all, in their whole course of study and instruction, recognize a world, and a broad one too, lying beyond the college walls.

Test:

1. Can you read the selection given in the Practice Material in a clear, energized tone?

2. Can you find another selection and read it in a clear, energized tone?

3. Do you remember to use a clear tone in your everyday speech?

CONTRACT 8

Objective:

Clear, energized tone in sight reading.

Procedure:

See Contract 5.

Caution:

Energize the body from the toes up.

Practice Material:

See Contract 5.
Selections for sight reading from the following suggested books, or from any others of your own choice:

Dickens, *A Tale of Two Cities*
————*David Copperfield*
Stevenson, *Travels with a Donkey*
Morley, *Mince Pie*

Test:

Can you read at sight in a clear, free tone?

CONTRACT 9

Objective:

Clear, energized tone in conversation.

Procedure:

See Contract 7.

Caution:

See Contract 7.

Practice Material:

See Contract 5.
Classroom conversation based on the following suggested subjects:
A Railroad Accident
A Pleasant Journey
A Project to Raise Money for a School Team
A Class Election
The Lure of Travel

Test:

1. Can you use a clear, energized tone in everyday conversation when talking to your family? when talking to your friends?

2. Do you remember to use a clear, energized tone all the time?

CONTRACT SHEET
Hoarse Voice and Throatiness*

---

1. Controlled breathing.

---

2. Clear, free tone on the following sounds: *ō* [oᴛŭ], *ô* [ɔ:], *ow* [aŭ], *ōō* [u:], *ŏŏ* [ʊ], *ä* [ɑ:], *ŏ* [ɒ], and *oi* [ɔɪ].

Clear, free tone on syllables and words containing these sounds.

Clear, free tone on short phrases containing these sounds.

---

3. Clear, free tone for all other vowels and diphthongs.

Clear, free tone in words and syllables containing these sounds.

Clear, free tone in short phrases containing these sounds.

---

4. Round, full tone, forward in the mouth, on sounds given in Contract 2.

Round, full tone in words, phrases, and sentences containing round and open sounds.

---

5. Round, full tone, forward in the mouth, on sounds given in Contract 3.

Round, full tone, forward in the mouth, in words, phrases, and sentences.

---

6. Clear, explosive tone on all sounds given in Contract 2.

Clear, explosive tone on syllables, words, and phrases containing these sounds.

---

7. Clear, explosive tone on all sounds given in Contract 3.

Clear, explosive tone in syllables, words, and short phrases.

---

* Start each practice period with the relaxation exercises given on page 67.

8. Clear, free, energized (not explosive) tone in sentences containing many round sounds.

9. Clear, free, energized tone in paragraph and verse containing many round sounds.

10. Clear, free, energized tone in a paragraph containing all sounds.

11. Clear, free, energized tone in paragraphs containing all sounds.

12. Clear, free, energized tone in conversation.

CONTRACT 1

Objective:

Controlled breathing.

Procedure:

Stand erect, firmly on both feet; feel that your whole body is energized from the toes up; place the hands on the abdominal muscles. Inhale and expand the lungs, especially the lower part; exhale, pushing firmly with the abdominal muscles. (If you have difficulty with this, lie flat on your back in a relaxed position, inhale and exhale naturally a few times, and then proceed as above.)

For the explanation of the breathing process, see page 5.

Caution:

Be certain that you have enough breath; to make sure, inhale audibly during the practice period.

Be careful to push the breath out firmly with the abdominal muscles.

Practice Material:

Page 6, Exercises 1, 2, 3, and 6.

Test:

1. Can you take a breath and push it out firmly with the abdominal muscles?

2. Can you count from 1 to 5, using a single inhalation and exhalation for each number?

3. Can you count from 1 to 5 in this fashion:

```
Inhale—exhale, saying: 1
   "       "       "      1—2
   "       "       "      1—2—3
   "       "       "      1—2—3—4
   "       "       "      1—2—3—4—5
```

4. In the above exercises is the throat relaxed? Is there a good firm push with the abdominal muscles? Did you have enough breath—neither too much nor too little?

315

CONTRACT 2

Objective:

Clear, free tone on the following sounds: *o* [oʀŭ] as in *go*, *ô* [ɔ:] as in *all*, *ow* [aŭ] as in *now*, *ōō* [u:] as in *soon*, *ŏŏ* [ʊ] as in *good*, *ä* [ɑ:] as in *ah*, *ŏ* [ɒ] as in *coffee*, and *oi* [ɔɪ] as in *oil*.

Clear, free tone in syllables and words containing these sounds.

Clear, free tone in short phrases containing these sounds.

Procedure:

Inhale, round the lips carefully (use a mirror), and exhale saying *ō* [oʀŭ] as in *go*. If tone sounds tight, relax muscles of the neck and throat by rotating the head several times, saying *easy—ah, lazy—ah*, dropping the jaw on *ah* [ɑ:]. Try the sound *ō* [oʀŭ] again; listen to it carefully, and try to make it sound smooth and free. Proceed in the same manner with *aw* [ɔ:], *ow* [aŭ], *ōō* [u:], *ä* [ɑ:], and *oi* [ɔɪ]. (See pages 25–29.)

Caution:

Do not continue if your throat feels tired. Whenever this happens, stop and yawn. (It is well to start every practice period with a yawning exercise.) Remember *several five-minute periods* of practice *daily* are better than one or two *longer* periods.

Practice Material:

Open your mouth wide (comfortably, without straining), draw in breath, and yawn.

Inhale and exhale on the sounds *ō* [oʀŭ], *ow* [aŭ], *ô* [ɔ:], *ōō* [u:], *ä* [ɑ:], and *oi* [ɔɪ], *intoning* the sound and holding it as long as you can comfortably. (Five times each.)

Inhale and say *ō* [oʀŭ], *ô* [ɔ:], *ow* [aŭ], *ōō* [u:], *ä* [ɑ:], *oi* [ɔɪ]. (Five times each.)

Increase your breath span by doing the following exercise:

ō [oʀŭ]					
ō	*ah* [oʀŭ ɑ:]				
ō	*ah*	*aw* [oʀŭ ɑ: ɔ:]			
ō	*ah*	*aw*	*ow* [oʀŭ ɑ: ɔ: aŭ]		
ō	*ah*	*aw*	*ow*	*oi* [oʀŭ ɑ: ɔ: aŭ ɔɪ]	
ō	*ah*	*aw*	*ow*	*oi*	*ōō* [oʀŭ ɑ: ɔ: aŭ ɔɪ u:]

Do the preceding exercise, placing *l* [l], *m* [m], and *n* [n] before each sound.

Warning: Do not strain; if you cannot do all six sounds comfortably on one breath, do as many sounds as you can comfortably, and increase the breath span *gradually*.

Say the following words in a clear, free tone:

hope	noon	now	coffee	could
stone	spoon	toll	chocolate	good
clothes	farm	paw	office	wool
choice	sound	blow	dog	put

Say the following phrases in a clear, free tone:

1. Oh no.
2. Blue moon.
3. True blue.
4. Blow hard.
5. Low tone.
6. Brown cow.
7. Law and order.
8. Noisy boy.
9. Down town.
10. So-so.

Test:

1. Can you vocalize (intone) the sounds given above so that each tone is clear as long as it is held?

2. Can you say with a prolonged rising inflection and clear tone the sounds given above?

3. Can you say the above with a falling inflection and clear, free tone?

4. Can you do all the exercises in the Practice Material in a clear, free tone?

5. Can you make a list of ten more phrases containing these sounds and say them with a clear, free tone?

CONTRACT 2A

Objective:

Same as Contract 2.

Procedure:

Same as Contract 2.

Caution:

Be sure that the throat is relaxed.

Practice Material:

Close the mouth, open the back of the throat, keeping the mouth closed, and try to suppress a yawn; finally open the mouth and yawn widely. Do this several times.

Inhale-yawn.

Inhale and say *ah* [ɑ:].

Inhale-yawn.
Inhale and say ō [oтʊ̆].
Inhale-yawn.
Inhale and say ōō [u:].
Inhale-yawn.
Inhale and say ô [ɔ:].
Inhale-yawn.
Inhale and say ow [aʊ̆].

If the tone sounds tight and if the throat feels tense, yawn before each sound.

Intone the sounds as in Contract 2.

Say each of the following words in a clear, free tone on one breath; now try to say each word three times on one breath:

bone	pool	wrote	choose	tone
low	pose	know	calm	post
close	comb	tool	noose	soil
pound	fold	roof	soon	group

Say the following phrases in a clear, free tone on one breath:

1. Hold the goal.
2. Row the boat.
3. Mow the lawn.
4. Going home.
5. Ha, ha, ha.
6. Boil the water.
7. Ho, ho, ho.
8. Pausing at the door.
9. Before and after.
10. Hoeing a row.

Test:

1. Can you vocalize the sounds given above so that the tone is clear as long as it is held?

2. Can you say the above sounds in a clear, free tone with a rising inflection?

3. Can you say the sounds in a clear, free tone with a falling inflection?

4. Can you do all the exercises in the Practice Material in a clear, free tone?

5. Can you make a list of ten more words and phrases and then read them in a clear, free tone?

CONTRACT 3

Objective:

Clear, free tone for all other vowels and diphthongs: ē [i:] as in *see*, ĭ [ɪ] as in *it*, ĕ [eт] as in *let*, ă [æ] as in *at*, à [ɑ] as in *ask*, û [ɜ:] as in *fur*, *ŭ* [ʌ] as in *hut*, *ā* [eɪ̆] as in *ate*, *ī* [aɪ̆] as in *ice*, *ę* [ɪɚ̆] as in *fear*, *â* [ɛɚ̆] as in *there*, *ŏŏr* [ʊɚ̆] as in *poor*, *ōr* [ɔɚ̆] as in *floor*, and the digraph *ū* [ju:] as in *tune*.

Clear, free tone in words and syllables containing these sounds.
Clear, free tone in short phrases containing these sounds.

Procedure:

See pages 20–31 for instructions about making these sounds.

Use a mirror to *see* that the organs of articulation are in the correct position; *listen* to the sound made by the instructor, compare your sound with this, and try to imitate it; *feel* the organs of articulation in the correct position.

Caution:

Do not continue if the throat becomes tired.   Stop and yawn.

Practice Material:

Vocalize the vowel sounds in the following words, prolonging the sounds as long as you can comfortably:

see [i:]	there [ɛɚ̆]	hut [ʌ]	ice [aɪ̆]
it [ɪ]	at [æ]	ask [ɑ]	ate [eɪ̆]
let [eт]	fur [ɜ:]	floor [ɔɚ̆]	fear [ɪɚ̆]

Say the sounds in the above words: (a) with a prolonged rising inflection; (b) with a falling inflection.

Do the exercise below three time, first using one breath for each sound and then using one breath for the entire line:

ē ah o̅o̅ [i: ɑ: u:]
ē ah o̅o̅ ow oi [i: ɑ: u: aʊ̆ ɔɪ̆]

Do the following exercise:

m—ah	m—ah	m—ah	mah [mɑ:]
m—ē	m—ē	m—ē	mē [mi:]
m—ir	m—ir	m—ir	mir [mɜ:]
mē	mah	mo̅o̅ [mi: mɑ: mu:]	
nē	nah	no̅o̅ [ni: nɑ: nu:]	
mē	mah	mo̅o̅	mow moi [mi: mɑ: mu: maʊ̆ mɔɪ̆]
nē	nah	no̅o̅	now noi [ni: nɑ: nu: naʊ̆ nɔɪ̆]

Say the following words—first once on a breath, then two and three times on a breath; remember to use a clear, free tone:

frame	put	mat	word	try
hat	ice	slice	poor	cape
seem	up	cup	weird	hit
hence	hit	try	floor	word

Say the following phrases in a clear, free tone on one breath:

1. Lame duck.
2. Fat man.
3. Peas and beans.
4. Black and white.
5. Pies and cakes.
6. Putting the shot.
7. Footing the bill.
8. Wordy message.
9. Hopping up.
10. Skipping rope.

Test:

1. Can you vocalize in a clear, free tone the sounds given in the Practice Material?

2. Can you say those sounds clearly?

3. Can you do all the exercises in the Practice Material in a clear, free tone?

4. Can you make up ten other words and phrases, and then read them in a clear, free tone?

CONTRACT 3A

Objective:

Same as Contract 3.

Procedure:

Same as Contract 3.

Caution:

Be sure to keep the throat relaxed and the rest of the body energized.

Practice Material:

Vocalize and say the vowel sounds as in Contract 3.

Say the following in a round, full tone, using one breath for each line:

```
    ah [ɑ:]
    ah    ā [ɑ: eɪɪ]
    ah    ā    ē [ɑ: eɪɪ i:]
    ah    ā    ē    aw [ɑ: eɪɪ i: ɔ:]
    ah    ā    ē    aw    ō [ɑ: eɪɪ i: ɔ: oʊ]
    ah    ā    ē    aw    ō    ōō [ɑ: eɪɪ i: ɔ: oʊ u:]
mah [mɑ:]
mah   mā [mɑ: meɪɪ]
mah   mā   mē [mɑ: meɪɪ mi:]
mah   mā   mē   maw [mɑ: meɪɪ mi: mɔ:]
mah   mā   mē   maw   mō [mɑ: meɪɪ mi: mɔ: moʊ]
mah   mā   mē   maw   mō   mōō [mɑ: meɪɪ mi: mɔ: moʊ mu:]
```

Proceed in a like manner, placing other consonants before the sounds *ah* [ɑː], *ah* [ɑː]—*ā* [eʳɪ], and so forth.

Say the following words in a clear, free tone; first say each word on a breath, then say each word two and three times on a single breath:

card	cook	sake	fair	slow
shark	fall	draw	past	coffee
cheer	father	freeze	above	mind
eye	noise	trick	shoe	made

Read the following phrases in a clear, free tone on a single breath:

1. Pale moon.
2. Low stone.
3. Stony brook.
4. Once more.
5. Many a time.
6. Wherefore rejoice?
7. Once upon a time.
8. Happy ending.
9. Here and there.
10. Up and down.
11. Rich and poor.
12. Cellar door.

Test:

1. Can you say in a clear, free tone all the exercises given in the Practice Material?

2. Can you prepare ten other words and phrases and then read them in a clear, free tone?

CONTRACT 4

Objective:

Round, full tone, forward in the mouth, on the sounds given in Contract 2.

Round, full tone, forward in the mouth, in words, phrases, and sentences containing round and open sounds.

Procedure:

Vocalize all vowels and diphthongs, as in Contracts 2 and 3.

Say the sound *ō* [oʳŭ]; round the lips and feel that the mouth is full of tone. Do the same with the sounds *ô* [ɔː], *ow* [aŭ], *ōō* [uː], *ŏŏ* [ʊ], *ŏ* [ɒ], and *oi* [ɔɪ]. Open the mouth comfortably wide for *ä* [ɑː], but do not round the lips.

Do the following exercise, prolonging the vowels and diphthongs, and attempting to have the mouth full of tone:

lō [loʳŭ]
lō   lah [loʳŭ lɑː]
lō   lah   law [loʳŭ lɑː lɔː]
lō   lah   law   low [loʳŭ lɑː lɔː laŭ]
lō   lah   law   low   loi [loʳŭ lɑː lɔː laŭ lɔɪ]
lō   lah   law   low   loi   lōō [loʳŭ lɑː lɔː laŭ lɔɪ luː]

Caution:

Be sure that the lower jaw drops sufficiently for each sound, and that the lips are rounded.

Practice Material:

Read the following words, prolonging the vowels and diphthongs:

go	boo	barn	cowl	boy	ball	bull
low	do	card	down	coin	corn	could
no	rude	farm	found	noise	gnaw	full
tone	too	harm	prowl	toil	tall	wool

Read the following phrases, prolonging the round and open sounds:

1. Going to the barn.
2. Knowing what to do.
3. Opening the road.
4. Going to bowl.
5. Carding the wool.
6. Gnawing a bone.
7. *Much Ado About Nothing.*
8. Showing how.
9. Swinging low.
10. Growing tall.

Read the following quotations giving special attention to the round and open sounds:

1. "The ploughman homeward plods his weary way."
2. "All the air a solemn stillness holds."
3. "Drowsy tinklings lull the distant folds."
4. "No more the landscape holds its wealth apart."
5. "The red-oak, softer grained, yields all for lost."
6. "The horseman . . . rides through clouds of gold away."

Test:

1. Can you read the words in the Practice Material in a round, full tone?

2. Can you read the phrases in the Practice Material in a round, full tone?

3. Can you read the quotations in the Practice Material in a round, full tone?

CONTRACT 5

Objective:

Round, full tone, forward in the mouth, on the sounds given in Contract 3.

Round, full tone, forward in the mouth, in words, phrases, and sentences.

Procedure:

Vocalize all vowels and diphthongs as in Contract 3.

Say the sound ō [oᴛŭ], feeling that the mouth is full of tone.

Say ō [oᴛŭ] ē [i:]; *push* hard with the abdominal muscles, *pull* firmly with the lips, and feel the sound ē [i:] well in front of the mouth.

Say o͞o [u:], feeling that the mouth is full of tone.

Say o͞o [u:] ĕ [eᴛ], and feel ĕ [eᴛ] well forward in the mouth.

Say aw [ɔ:], feeling that the mouth is full of tone.

Say aw [ɔ:] ĭ [ɪ], and feel ĭ [ɪ] well forward in the mouth.

Proceed in like manner, placing ō [oᴛŭ], o͞o [u:] and aw [ɔ:] before other vowels and diphthongs, especially before those which tend to slip back into the throat—namely, ē [i:], ĭ [ɪ], ĕ [eᴛ], and ă [æ].

Do the following exercise:

lō	lō	lē [loᴛŭ loᴛŭ li:]
lō	lō	lĭ [loᴛŭ loᴛŭ lɪ]
lō	lō	lĕ [loᴛŭ loᴛŭ leᴛ]
lō	lō	lă [loᴛŭ loᴛŭ læ]
lo͞o	lo͞o	lē [lu: lu: li:]
lo͞o	lo͞o	lĭ [lu: lu: lɪ]
lo͞o	lo͞o	lĕ [lu: lu: leᴛ]
law	law	lă [lɔ: lɔ: læ]
law	law	lē [lɔ: lɔ: li:]

Caution:

If you wish to bring your tone forward in the mouth, *push* with the abdominal muscles, *pull* with the lips, *open the mouth* for the open sounds. Remember that a set jaw will not permit the sound to come forward in the mouth.

Practice Material:

Read the following sets of words horizontally and vertically:

loan—lean	ball—bean
load—lid	born—bin
loam—lend	bought—bet
noon—neat	maul—mean
noose—knit	morn—mend

Read the following phrases in a round full tone, prolonging the long vowels and diphthongs:

1. Loading a gun.
2. Intoning a psalm.
3. Combing hair.
4. Making a motion.
5. Lying at ease.

6. Playing ball.
7. Loafing in the sun.
8. Cooking beans.
9. Doing a lesson.
10. Moving a piano.

Read the following sentences in a round, full tone, forward in the mouth:

1. The boys were playing ball in the meadow.
2. Tom went to Oxford to see John Brown.
3. The exhibition is open to the public.
4. The farmer is sowing seed in the field.
5. The football team won ten games.
6. Joan brought the lame duck into the house.
7. The boys followed the clown around the town.
8. Mary bought a loaf of bread at the grocery store.

> *Note:* The phrases and sentences given above would naturally be read in a conversational tone; reading them in a round, full tone is merely an exercise to help in bringing the tone into the mouth.

Test:

1. Can you read the words given in the Practice Material with the tone well forward in the mouth?

2. Can you read the phrases and sentences in the Practice Material with the tone forward in the mouth?

3. Do you try to breathe properly, to use your lips, and to open your mouth in your conversation?

CONTRACT 6

Objective:

Clear, explosive tone on all sounds given in Contract 2.

Clear, explosive tone in syllables and words containing those sounds.

Clear, explosive tone in short phrases containing those sounds.

Procedure:

Vocalize vowel sounds as in Contracts 2 and 3. Say sounds as in Contracts 2 and 3.

Take a good breath and send it out in one sudden exhalation (explosion).

Inhale and with a sudden exhalation make the sound ō [oᴛŭ] (five times).

Proceed in a like manner with ô [ɔ:], ow [aŭ], ōō [u:] ä [ɑ:], and oi [ɔĭ].

Caution:

Be sure that the throat is relaxed and that the rest of the body is energized.

Be certain that you have enough breath.

Be sure that the organs of articulation are in the correct position for the sounds.

Practice Material:

Explode the following sounds, first on separate breaths and then on one breath:

oh	oh	oh	go	['goʊ]
nō	nō	nō	no	['noʊ]
hō	hō	hō	hold	['hoʊld]
hah	hah	hah	hard	['hɑ:d]
ow	ow	ow	now	['naʊ]
haw	haw	haw	halt	['hɔ:lt]

Say each of the following expressions explosively on one breath:

1. Oh no.	**6.** Yo ho ho.	**11.** How now.
2. Don't go.	**7.** Come down.	**12.** Blocks and stones.
3. You blocks.	**8.** You stones.	**13.** Now now.
4. Halt.	**9.** Forward march.	**14.** Go.
5. Charge.	**10.** Hurrah.	**15.** Blow, bugle, blow.

Test:

1. Can you say in a clear, explosive tone all the exercises given in the Procedure and Practice Material?

2. Can you make up six other expressions and then read them in a clear, explosive tone?

CONTRACT 7

Objective:

Clear, explosive tone for all sounds given in Contract 3.

Clear, explosive tone in syllables and words containing those sounds.

Clear, explosive tone in short phrases containing those sounds.

Procedure:

Vocalize vowel sounds and diphthongs as in Contracts 2 and 3.

Say the vowel sounds and diphthongs as in Contracts 2 and 3.

Explode the sounds as in Contract 4.

Explode the remaining vowel sounds and diphthongs (see Contract 3).

Caution:

See that the throat is relaxed. If it becomes tired, stop and yawn. It is a good plan to yawn many times during the exercises even if the throat does not seem tired.

Practice Material:

Explode the following, first on separate breaths and then on one breath:

hah	hah	hah [hɑ:]	rā	rā	rā [ɹeɪ̆]
hē	hē	hē [hi:]	hī	hī	hī [haɪ̆]
hĕ	hĕ	hĕ [heᴛ]	hō	hō	hō [hoᴛŏ]
hĭ	hĭ	hĭ [hɪ]	lī	lī	lī [laɪ̆]

Say each of the following words explosively on one breath, then three times on one breath:

awake	halt	run
come	fire	up
down	strike	wait
go	stop	whoa
forward	play	zounds

Say the following expressions explosively on one breath:

1. Who comes?
2. Hard hearts.
3. Hold hard.
4. What is it?
5. What's that noise?
6. Once more.
7. Going! Going! Gone!
8. Fly, brother fly!
9. Hip, hip, hurrah!
10. Loud and long.

Read the following explosively, pausing for breath at the vertical marks:

1. "'Forward | the Light Brigade! | Charge | for the guns!' | he said. | "

2. "Once more | unto the breach | dear friends | once more. | "

3. "Wherefore rejoice | what conquest | brings he | home? | "

4. "Awake! | Awake! | Ring | the alarum bell! | "

Test:

1. Can you do in a clear, explosive tone all the exercises in the Procedure and Practice Material?

2. Can you prepare five other exercises and read them in a clear, explosive tone?

CONTRACT 8

Objective:

Clear, free, energized (not explosive) tone in sentences containing many round sounds.

Procedure:

Proceed as in Contracts 2, 3, 4, and 7.

Caution:

An energized tone is not necessarily explosive. A tone may be round and full, or very quiet and conversational yet it must have energy. You have learned to acquire energy through using an explosive quality, but you must always aim for energy of tone whether or not the material is explosive.

Practice Material:

Read the following sentences first in a round, full, energized tone, and then in a conversational tone:

1. The boys are coasting down the road that goes to Goshen.
2. The bell buoy tolled and tolled to warn of the shoal.
3. The old crone groaned and moaned in the gloaming.
4. The countess was drowned on the voyage down the Rhone.
5. The lonely road was long and hot.
6. He told me he sold his boat for forty dollars.
7. The old nobleman was cold and lonely.
8. He told the story of *Ivanhoe* on the long voyage.
9. "The lowing herd winds slowly o'er the lea."
10. "How now, fool, whither wander you?"
11. "He sold his horses, sold his hawks and hounds."
12. "Down she came and found a boat
    Beneath a willow left afloat,
    And round about the prow she wrote
    The Lady of Shalott."

Test:

1. Can you do all the sentences in the Practice Material in a round, full, energized tone, and then in a clear, conversational tone?

2. Can you prepare ten other sentences and read them in the manner required for the sentences in the Practice Material?

3. Can you read in the same manner the sentences given under ō [oᴛŭ] in Part III?

CONTRACT 9

Objective:

Clear, energized tone in a paragraph containing many round sounds.

Procedure:

Same as Contract 8.

Caution:

Be sure that the throat is relaxed.

Practice Material:

Read the following paragraph first in a round, full, energized tone and then in a conversational tone:

> The old, broken man sat by the stove and brooded.
> It was a stormy afternoon. The low moaning of the wind
> echoed the low moaning of the ocean. It was dark and cold.
> All morning the storm clouds had glowered and gloomed,
> and at noon the snow began to fall, slowly at first, but with
> more and more force as the afternoon wore slowly on. As
> the day drew to a close, the tolling of a bell announced a boat
> in trouble offshore. The boys tunneled through the snow to
> go to man the lifeboats, but the old, broken man sat by the
> stove and brooded.

Read the following lines from Shakespeare's *King Henry IV, Part II*, in a round, full tone:

> The tide of blood in me
> Hath proudly flowed in vanity till now:
> Now doth it turn and ebb back to the sea,
> Where it shall mingle with the state of floods,
> And flow henceforth in formal majesty.
> Now call we our high court of Parliament:
> And let us choose such limbs of noble counsel,
> That the great body of our state may go
> In equal rank with the best governed nation;
> That war, or peace, or both at once, may be
> As things acquainted or familiar to us;
> In which you, father, shall have foremost hand.
> Our coronation done, we will accite,
> As I before remembered, all our state:
> And, God consigning to my good intents,
> Nor prince, nor peer shall have just cause to say,
> God shorten Harry's happy life one day.

Test:

1. Can you read the prose selection presented in the Practice Material in a round, full tone, and in a conversational tone?

2. Can you read the above selection from Shakespeare in a round, full tone?

3. Choose another selection requiring a round, full tone (see Part III), and read that with the tone well forward in the mouth.

CONTRACT 10

Objective:

Clear, free energized tone in a paragraph containing all sounds.

Procedure:

Proceed as in Contracts 8 and 9.

Caution:

Be sure that the throat is relaxed and that the rest of the body is energized.

Practice Material:

Read the following paragraph from Dickens' *The Seven Poor Travellers* in the manner suggested in Contracts 8 and 9:

I went back to my inn to give the necessary directions for the turkey and roast beef, and, during the remainder of the day, could settle to nothing for thinking of the Poor Travellers.   When the wind blew noisily against the windows, —it was a cold day, with dark gusts of sleet alternating with periods of wild brightness, as if the year were dying fitfully,—I pictured them advancing towards their resting-place along various cold roads, and felt delighted to think how little they foresaw the supper that awaited them.   I painted their portraits in my mind, and indulged in little heightening touches.   I made them footsore; I made them weary; I made them carry packs and bundles; I made them stop by finger-posts and milestones, leaning on their bent sticks, and looking wistfully at what was written there; I made them lose their way; and filled their five wits with apprehensions of lying out all night, and being frozen to death. I took up my hat, went out, climbed to the top of the old Castle, and looked over the windy hills that slope down to the Medway, almost believing that I could descry some of my Travellers in the distance.   After it fell dark, and the Cathedral bell was heard in the invisible steeple—quite a bower of frosty rime when I had last seen it—striking five, six, seven,

I became so full of my Travellers that I could eat no dinner, and felt constrained to watch them in the red coals of my fire. They were all arrived by this time, I thought, had got their tickets, and were gone in.—There my pleasure was dashed by the reflection that probably some Travellers had come too late and were shut out.

Test:

Can you read the above paragraph in a clear, energized tone?

CONTRACT 11

Objective:

Clear, free, energized tone in paragraphs containing all sounds.

Procedure:

Read the paragraphs first in a large room and then in a small room. Regulate the volume to fit each room.

Caution:

Be sure that the throat is relaxed.

Practice Material:

Read in the manner suggested above the following paragraphs from Washington Irving's *The Legend of Sleepy Hollow:*

He was, in fact, an odd mixture of small shrewdness and simple credulity. His appetite for the marvelous, and his powers of digesting it, were equally extraordinary; and both had been increased by his residence in this spellbound region. No tale was too gross or monstrous for his capacious swallow. It was often his delight, after school was dismissed in the afternoon, to stretch himself on the rich bed of clover, bordering the little brook that whimpered by the school-house, and there con over old Mather's direful tales, until the gathering dusk of the evening made the printed page a mere mist before his eyes. Then, as he wended his way by swamp, and stream and awful woodland, to the farmhouse where he happened to be quartered, every sound of nature at that witching hour, fluttered his excited imagination: the voice of the whippoorwill, that harbinger of storm; the dreary hooting of the screech-owl, or the sudden rustling in the thicket of birds frightened from their roost. The fireflies, too, which sparkled most vividly in the darkest places now and then startled him, as one of uncommon brightness would stream across his path, and if, by chance, a huge blockhead of a beetle came winging his blundering flight against him, the poor varlet was ready to give up the ghost, with the idea that he was struck with a witch's token.   His only resource on such occasions, either to drown thought, or drive away evil spirits, was to sing psalm tunes;—and the good people of Sleepy Hollow, as they sat by their doors of an evening, were often filled with awe, at hearing his nasal melody, "in linked sweetness long drawn out," floating from the distant hill or along the dusky road.

Another of his sources of fearful pleasure was to pass long winter evenings with the old Dutch wives as they sat spinning by the fire, with a row of apples roasting and spluttering along the hearth, and listen to their marvellous tales of ghosts and goblins, and haunted fields, and haunted brooks, and haunted bridges, and particularly of the headless horseman, or Galloping Hessian of the Hollow, as they sometimes called him.   He would delight them equally by his anecdotes of witchcraft . . . and with the alarming fact that the world did absolutely turn around, and that they were half the time topsy-turvy.

Test:

Can you read in both types of rooms the selection given above, using a clear, energized tone without throat strain?

CONTRACT 12

Objective:

Clear, free, energized tone in conversation.

Procedure:

See Contracts 1–7.

Caution:

Be sure the throat is kept relaxed.

Practice Material:

See Contracts 2, 3, 4, and 5.
Classroom conversation based on the following suggested topics:

A Good Trip to Take Some Day
A Worth-While Book
An Enjoyable Play
The Fascination of a City
See America First

Test:

Can you use a clear, energized tone in everyday conversation when talking to your friends? when talking to your family?

CONTRACT SHEET
Nasality

---

1. Controlled breathing.

---

2. Control of soft palate.

---

3. Free tone on *ä* [ɑː], *ō* [oтʊ], *ow* [aʊ], *ô* [ɔː], *oi* [ɔɪ], *ōō* [uː].
Free tone in syllables and words containing these sounds.
Free tone in short phrases containing these sounds.

---

4. Free tone on all other vowels and diphthongs.
Free tone in syllables and words containing these sounds.
Free tone in short phrases containing these sounds.

---

5. Free tone in phrases containing all sounds.

---

6. Free tone in sentences.

---

7. Free tone in selections requiring energy.

---

8. Free tone in selections requiring conversational tone.

---

9. Free tone in sight reading.

---

10. Free tone in conversation.

Note to instructor: It frequently happens that a nasal voice is also tense and throaty; in such a case the soft palate, instead of being lowered through uncontrolled relaxation, is held in a lowered position through tension; this is called *a tense nasality*, or, more technically, *nasopharyngeal resonance*. If such a condition exists, have the student take the contracts for Throatiness as well as for Nasality.

CONTRACT 1

Objective:

Controlled breathing.

Procedure:

Stand erect, firmly on both feet; feel that your whole body is energized; place your hands on the abdominal muscles. Inhale and expand the lungs, especially the lower part; exhale, pushing firmly with the abdominal muscles. (If you have difficulty with this, lie flat on your back, in a relaxed position; inhale and exhale naturally a few times, and continue as above.)

For an explanation of the breathing process, see page 5.

Caution:

Be certain that you have enough breath; to make sure, inhale audibly during the practice period.

Be careful to push the breath out firmly with the abdominal muscles.

Practice Material:

Page 6, Exercises 1, 2, 3, and 6.

Test:

1. Can you take a breath and push it out firmly with the abdominal muscles?

2. Can you count from 1 to 5, using a single inhalation and exhalation for each number?

3. Can you count from 1 to 5 in this fashion?

Inhale—exhale, saying: 1
    "   "   "   1—2
    "   "   "   1—2—3
    "   "   "   1—2—3—4
    "   "   "   1—2—3—4—5

4. In the above exercise, is the throat relaxed? Is there a firm push with the abdominal muscles? Did you have enough breath—neither too much nor too little?

CONTRACT 2

Objective:

Control of soft palate.

Procedure:

Place the tip of the tongue against the back of the upper front teeth; move it upwards over the gum until it reaches a hard surface, the hard palate. If you continue moving the tongue upwards and back, it will reach a soft surface, known as the soft palate. Take a mirror, and open the mouth wide. (The tongue should be kept out of the way by placing its tip against the back of the lower front teeth.) Look at the throat. The crocus-shaped muscular tissue that hangs down in the center of the back of the mouth is the uvula, the end of the soft palate. With the mouth well opened, say *ah* [ɑ:]. Watch the uvula rise, and *feel* it rise; feel the throat expand. When the uvula is raised, the soft palate is spread like a curtain before the entrance to the nasal passage. Now make the sound with the uvula lowered; notice how this sound differs from the one made when the uvula was raised. For *ah* [ɑ:], the soft palate and the uvula should be held high. All sounds in English should be made with the soft palate held well up, except *m* [m], *n* [n], and *ng* [ŋ]; these are nasal sounds and require that the soft palate be lowered.

Caution:

If the throat becomes tense at any time, stop and yawn.

Practice Material:

Yawn and feel how the whole throat opens.

Pant like a dog; feel the air in the back of the throat. Notice that the soft palate rises a bit when you inhale, and that it lowers when you exhale. Now try raising and lowering the soft palate without breathing.

Say *m* [m] (with the soft palate down), and then *ah* [ɑ:] (with the soft palate up). Repeat this exercise several times:

m—ah m—ah m—ah [m—ɑ:]

Do the same with *n* [n] and *ng* [ŋ].

Test:

1. Can you raise and lower the soft palate when panting like a dog?

2. Can you raise and lower the soft palate at will?

3. Do you know when a sound is nasal and when it has a proper resonance? Can you recognize nasality in the voices of others? in your own voice?

CONTRACT 3

Objective:

Free tone on ä [ɑː] as in *father*, ō [oᴛŭ] as in *go*, ô [ɔː] as in *all*, *ow* [aŭ] as in *now*, *oi* [ɔɪ] as in *boy*, ōō [uː] as in *choose*.

Free tone in syllables, words, and short phrases containing the sounds given above.

Procedure:

See the chapter on vowels and diphthongs for the correct production of the sounds given above.

Stand firmly on both feet; energize the whole body from the toes up, but keep the throat relaxed. Inhale and push the breath out firmly on the sound *ah* [ɑː], prolonging the sound in a singing tone. Proceed in the same manner with the other sounds.

Inhale and send all the breath out at once in an explosive tone. Proceed in the same manner with other sounds.

Caution:

Be sure the throat remains relaxed on explosive sounds; if it becomes tense, stop and yawn.

Be sure the whole body is energized.

Practice Material:

Inhale, exhale, prolonging the sounds of all the vowels and diphthongs given above. (Five times.) Explode the sounds (five times); say them (five times).

Say the following exercise three times:

> lah   lah   lah [lɑː]
> lō   lō   lō [loᴛŭ]

Combine all the sounds given in this contract with all possible consonant sounds.

Say the following words in a free tone:

barn	dough	ball	bound	boy	boo
card	go	fawn	doubt	coil	do
dart	hoe	horn	lounge	moist	rude
farm	slow	wall	pout	poise	true

Say the above words in an explosive tone.

Read the following phrases in a free tone:

1. Mark the court.
2. Half a pound.
3. Round and round.
4. O thou.
5. Lo and behold!

6. House and home.
7. Around the town.
8. Rolling stone.
9. Mow the lawn.
10. Half an hour.

Test:

1. Can you do all the exercises in the Practice Material without sounding nasal?

2. Can you detect when you are nasal?

CONTRACT 3A

Objective:

Same as Contract 3.

Procedure:

Same as Contract 3.

Caution:

Be sure that the soft palate is under control.
Be sure the whole body is energized.

Practice Material:

Repeat the following sounds three times:

ah   ah-hah [ɑ:] [ɑ:—hɑ:] (Stress first *ah* and *hah*.)
ah   ah   ah   hah [ɑ:] [hɑ:] (Stress *hah*.)
hah   hah   hah [hɑ:] (Explode each one, first on separate breaths and then the three on one breath.)

Proceed in a like manner with the other sounds given in Contract 3.

Say the following words in an explosive quality of tone:

dark	boat	call	bout	boil	boon
darn	tone	dawn	clown	coin	doom
heart	home	hall	mound	joint	plume
part	moat	worn	stout	soil	tomb

Read the following phrases in a free tone:

1. Boiling water.
2. Booing the clown.
3. Calling down the hall.

4. Slow down.
5. Boom town.
6. Going home.

7. Throwing the ball.   **9.** How now?

8. Darning the hole.   **10.** "Hark, hark, the lark."

Test:

1. Can you say the words given in the Practice Material in an explosive quality of tone?

2. Can you read the phrases in a free tone without nasality?

3. Can you tell when your voice is free from nasality?

CONTRACT 4

Objective:

Free tone on all other vowels and diphthongs: ē [i:] as in *see*, ĭ [ɪ] as in *it*, ĕ [eт] as in *let*, ă [æ] as in *at*, à [ɑ] as in *ask*, û [ɜ:] as in *bird*, ŭ [ʌ] as in *up*, ŏ [ɒ] as in *hot*, ŏŏ [ʊ] as in *book*, â [ɛɤ] as in *care*, ę [ɪɤ] as in *here*, ŏŏr [ʊɤ] as in *poor*, ōr [ɔɤ] as in *floor*.

Free tone in words and syllables containing those sounds.

Free tone in short phrases containing those sounds.

Procedure:

See chapter on vowels and diphthongs for the correct production of the above sounds.

Proceed as in Contract 3.

Caution:

Be sure the entire body is energized.

Be certain that the throat is relaxed; yawn if it becomes tense.

Practice Material:

Practice exhaling on all the above vowels and diphthongs (1) in a prolonged tone, (2) in an explosive tone. Do this exercise about five times every practice period, and say all the sounds in a conversational tone five times.

Repeat the following exercises three times in an explosive tone:

	ī	ī	ī [aɪ]
	mī	mī	mī [maɪ]
	mē	mē	mē [mi:]
	I	my	me [aɪ maɪ mi:]
fē	fah	fō	fum [fi: fɑ: foтŭ fʌm]

Say the following words explosively:

bee	red	fast	suds	not	bite	there	moor
bit	mad	burn	look	pay	here	pour	tube
lid	spat	turn	put	safe	fear	poor	tune

Say the following phrases explosively three times each:

1. Right time.
2. Fat man.
3. Rats and mice.
4. Thirty-third.
5. Wailing wind.
6. Many a time.
7. High tide.
8. When and where.
9. Many a man.
10. Kites fly high.
11. Curds and whey.
12. Tucks and seams.
13. Spends and gains.
14. Purple skirt.
15. Dreams and dreams.
16. Pouring water.

Test:

1. Can you say, without sounding nasal, everything suggested in the Practice Material?

2. Can you prepare five more phrases, and read those without sounding nasal?

CONTRACT 4A

Objective:

Same as Contract 4.

Procedure:

Same as Contract 4.

Caution:

Be sure the entire body is energized.
Be sure the soft palate is held well up.

Practice Material:

Vocalize and explode the sounds as in Contract 4.
Say the following sounds three times with a rising inflection: ĭ [aɪ], ē [i:], ă [æ].
Say the same sounds three times with a falling inflection.
Do the following exercise explosively:

ī	ī	ī [aɪ]
nī	nī	nī [naɪ]
mī	mī	mī [maɪ]
nē	nē	nē [ni:]
mē	mē	mē [mi:]
lĕ	lĕ	lĕ [leɪ]
lă	lă	lă [læ]

Do the above exercise with other sounds in Contract 4, emphasizing those that give trouble.

Say the following expressions three times each:

1. Fine time.	9. Right time.
2. Right mind.	10. Fight the good fight.
3. Five miles.	11. Scratch the match.
4. Way station.	12. Peas and beans.
5. Fat black cat.	13. Rains and rains.
6. Thirty-three.	14. Higher and higher.
7. Needles and pins.	15. Might and main.
8. Ninety-nine.	16. Sign of the times.

Test:

1. Can you do all the exercises in the Practice Material without sounding nasal?

2. Do you try to converse daily without sounding nasal?

CONTRACT 5

Objective:

Free tone in phrases containing all sounds.

Procedure:

See Contracts 3 and 4.

Caution:

Be sure that all sounds are correctly made.

Practice Material:

See Contracts 3 and 4.

Say the following phrases three times each:

1. The lion and the lamb.	11. Last chance.
2. Meeting place.	12. Up and out.
3. Five fifty-five Fifth Avenue.	13. Soon, too soon.
4. Purple velvet hat.	14. Length and strength.
5. Mannish clothes.	15. Chocolate pudding.
6. Black and tan terrier.	16. Law and order.
7. Time and place and action.	17. Father and mother.
8. Singing and swinging.	18. Sixty-five.
9. "Speak the speech."	19. Mighty fine.
10. Where and when.	20. Diamonds and rubies.

21. Hue and cry.
22. Just and unjust.
23. Here and there.
24. Rich and poor.
25. From top to bottom.
26. From ceiling to floor.
27. Boys and girls.
28. Seemingly slow.
29. Barking dogs.
30. Around and around.

31. Prunes and prisms.
32. Having a fine time.
33. Judge and jury.
34. Long and short.
35. Speaking plainly.
36. Training animals.
37. Signs and wonders.
38. Autumnal season.
39. Lines and squares.
40. Tunes and airs.

Test:

1. Can you say all the phrases in the Practice Material without sounding nasal?

2. Can you write several other phrases containing sounds that are particularly difficult for you, and read those without sounding nasal?

CONTRACT 6

Objective:

Free tone in sentences.

Procedure:

See Contracts 3 and 4.

Caution:

Be sure the sounds are correctly made; be sure that the soft palate is held well up.

Practice Material:

See Contracts 3 and 4.
Read the following sentences:

1. The boys and girls had a fine time at the party.

2. He said that he felt "fit as a fiddle" and "right as rain."

3. Richard the Lion-Hearted went on a crusade to the Holy Land.

4. The sound of many voices came echoing up the stairs.

5. The handsome man came from the south of England.

6. The train came laboring up the long, lonely mountain side.

7. It will be high tide at five o'clock today.

8. "Piper, pipe that song again."

9. The victorious army made a triumphal march through the city.

10. "Time and tide wait for no man."

Answer the following questions in complete sentences:

1. In what year was America discovered?

2. What is your favorite sport?

3. Who said, "Give me liberty or give me death"?

4. Who wrote *Ivanhoe?*

5. Name a well-known American poet.

Test:

1. Can you read the sentences and answer the questions in the Practice Material without sounding nasal?

2. Can you write ten more sentences and then read them without sounding nasal?

3. Can you read the sentences given for *ī* [aɪ] (pp. 85–86) and *ē* [iː] (page 75) without sounding nasal?

CONTRACT 7

Objective:

Free tone in selections requiring energy.

Procedure:

Prolong and explode vowels and diphthongs as suggested in Contracts 3 and 4.

Caution:

Stand firmly on both feet; exhale with a firm push of the abdominal muscles.

Practice Material:

See Contracts 3 and 4.

Read Shakespeare's *Julius Caesar*, Act I, Scene 1, lines 36–60.

Read *Macbeth*, Act II, Scene 3, lines 78–85. (Lines begin "Awake, awake!" See Part III.)

Test:

1. Can you read the suggested selection from *Julius Caesar* without sounding nasal?

2. Can you read the suggested selection from *Macbeth* without sounding nasal?

CONTRACT 7A

Objective:

Same as Contract 7.

Procedure:

Same as Contract 7.

Caution:

Be sure that the entire body is energized.

Practice Material:

Same as Contract 7.

Read Shakespeare's *King John*, Act II, Scene 1, lines 312–324. (Lines begin "Rejoice, you men of Angiers, ring your bells.")

Read "Marching Along" from Browning's *Cavalier Tunes*. (See Part III.)

Test:

1. Can you read without sounding nasal the selection from Shakespeare's *King John* suggested above?

2. Can you read without sounding nasal Browning's "Marching Along?"

CONTRACT 8

Objective:

Free tone in selections requiring a conversational tone.

Procedure:

Practice breathing exercises as suggested in Contracts 3 and 4.

Caution:

Be sure the entire body is energized; a good conversational tone requires energy.

Practice Material:

See Contracts 3 and 4.

Read the following selection from Washington Irving's *The Legend of Sleepy Hollow:*

> In this by-place of nature, there abode, in a remote period of American history, that is to say, some thirty years since, a worthy wight of the name of Ichabod Crane; who sojourned, or, as he expressed it, "tarried," in Sleepy Hollow, for the purpose of instructing the children of the

vicinity. He was a native of Connecticut; a state which supplies the Union with pioneers for the mind as well as for the forest, and sends forth yearly its legions of frontier woodsmen and country schoolmasters. The cognomen of Crane was not inapplicable to his person. He was tall, but exceedingly lank, with narrow shoulders, long arms and legs, hands that dangled a mile out of his sleeves, feet that might have served for shovels, and his whole frame most loosely hung together. His head was small, and flat at top, with huge ears, large green glassy eyes, and a long snipe nose, so that it looked like a weather-cock, perched upon his spindle neck, to tell which way the wind blew. To see him striding along the profile of a hill on a windy day, with his clothes bagging and fluttering about him, one might have mistaken him for the genius of famine descending upon the earth, or some scarecrow eloped from a corn field.

Test:

1. Can you read the selection in the Practice Material without sounding nasal?

2. Can you find another selection and read that without sounding nasal?

3. Can you carry on your everyday conversation without sounding nasal?

CONTRACT 9

Objective:

Free tone in sight reading.

Procedure:

See Contract 8.

Caution:

See Contract 8.

Practice Material:

See Contracts 3 and 4.
Selections for sight reading from the following suggested sources:

Thackeray, *Vanity Fair*
Dickens, *A Tale of Two Cities*
————*David Copperfield*
Stevenson, *Travels with a Donkey*
Magazine articles
Editorials from newspapers

Test:

Can you read at sight in a free tone?

CONTRACT 10

Objective:

Free tone in conversation.

Procedure:

See Contract 8.

Caution:

See Contract 8.

Practice Material:

See Contracts 3 and 4.
Classroom conversation based on the following suggested topics:

Hobbies
Travels with a Ford
Around the World in New York
Vacation Experiences
The School Newspaper

Test:

1. Can you use a free tone in everyday conversation?

2. Do you make a point of using a free tone in daily conversation?

CONTRACT SHEET
Denasalization

---

1. Controlled breathing.

---

2. Control of soft palate.

---

3. Sufficient nasal resonance on *m* [m].

Well-distributed resonance in syllables and words containing *m* [m].

---

4. Sufficient nasal resonance on *n* [n].

Well-distributed resonance in syllables and words containing *n* [n].

Well-distributed resonance in phrases containing *m* [m] and *n* [n].

---

5. Sufficient nasal resonance on *ng* [ŋ].

Well-distributed resonance in syllables and words containing *ng* [ŋ].

Well-distributed resonance in phrases containing *m* [m], *n* [n], *ng* [ŋ].

---

6. Well-distributed resonance in phrases containing all sounds.

---

7. Well-distributed resonance in sentences.

---

8. Well-distributed resonance in paragraphs.

---

9. Well-distributed resonance in the reading of poetry.

---

10. Well-distributed resonance in sight reading.

11. Well-distributed resonance in conversation.

CONTRACT 1

Objective:

Controlled breathing.

Procedure:

Stand erect, firmly on both feet; feel that your whole body is energized from the toes up; place the hands on the abdominal muscles. Inhale and expand the lungs, especially the lower part; exhale, pushing firmly with the abdominal muscles. (If you have difficulty with this, lie flat on your back in a relaxed position, inhale and exhale naturally a few times, and continue as above.)

For the explanation of the breathing process, see page 5.

Caution:

Be certain that you have enough breath; to make sure, inhale audibly during the practice period.

Be careful to push the breath out firmly with the abdominal muscles.

Practice Material:

Page 6, Exercises 1–6.

Test:

1. Can you take a breath and push it out firmly with the abdominal muscles?

2. Can you count from 1 to 5 using a single inhalation and exhalation for each number?

3. Can you count from 1 to 5 as indicated in the exercise below?

Inhale—exhale, saying: 1
” ” ” 1—2
” ” ” 1—2—3
” ” ” 1—2—3—4
” ” ” 1—2—3—4—5

4. In the above exercises is the throat relaxed? Is there a firm push with the abdominal muscles? Did you have enough breath—neither too much nor too little?

349

CONTRACT 2

Objective:

Control of the soft palate.

Procedure:

Place the tip of the tongue against the back of the upper front teeth; move it upwards over the gum until it reaches a hard surface, which is the hard palate. If you continue moving the tongue upwards and back, it will soon reach a soft surface, known as the soft palate. Take a mirror, and open the mouth wide. (The tongue should be kept out of the way by placing its tip against the back of the lower front teeth.) Look at the throat. The crocus-shaped muscular tissue that hangs down in the center of the back of the mouth is the uvula, the end of the soft palate. With the mouth well opened, say *ah* [ɑ:]. Watch the uvula rise, and *feel* it rise; feel the throat expand. When the uvula is raised, the soft palate is spread like a curtain before the entrance to the nasal passage. Now make the sound with the uvula lowered; notice how this sound differs from the one made when the uvula was raised. For *ah* [ɑ:] the soft palate and the uvula should be held high. All sounds in English should be made with the soft palate held well up, except *m* [m], *n* [n], and *ng* [ŋ]; these are nasal sounds and require the soft palate to be lowered.

Caution:

If the throat becomes tense, stop and yawn.

Practice Material:

Yawn; feel how the entire throat opens.

Pant like a dog; feel the air in the back of the throat. Notice how the soft palate rises a bit when you inhale and lowers when you exhale. Now try raising and lowering the soft palate without breathing.

Say the following exercises, remembering that for *m* [m] the soft palate is lowered, and for *ah* [ɑ:] it is held well up:

mmmmmmm   ah   mmmmmmm   ah   mmmmmmm   ah [m—ɑ:]
　　　'm—ah　　　　m—ah　　　　m—ah [m—ɑ:]

Do the above exercises with *n* [n] and *ng* [ŋ].

Test:

1. Can you raise and lower the soft palate when panting like a dog?

2. Can you raise and lower the soft palate at will?

3. Do you know when a sound lacks sufficient nasal resonance, and when it has a proper resonance? Can you recognize faulty resonance in the voices of others? in your own voice?

CONTRACT 3

Objective:

Sufficient nasal resonance on *m* [m].

Well-distributed resonance in words and syllables containing *m* [m].

Procedure:

Close the lips lightly, lower the soft palate, and let the sound *m* [m] come out through the nose. Hold your finger below the nostrils and feel the warm air emitted from the nose as the sound *m* [m] is produced.

Hold the soft palate down for *m* [m] and raise it for *ah* [ɑː] in this fashion:

m—ah	m—ah	m—ah [m—ɑ:]
m—ō	m—ō	m—ō [moʀʊ̆]
m—ā	m—ā	m—ā [meʀɪ]

Proceed in a like manner with other vowels and diphthongs.

Caution:

Be sure the soft palate is lowered for nasal sounds, and raised for other sounds.

Practice Material:

Hum softly the following exercises, prolonging the sounds *m* [m], *n* [n], and *ng* [ŋ]:

hum	hum	hum	humming	hum	[ˈhʌm]
drum	drum	drum	drumming	drum	[ˈdɹʌm]
come	come	come	coming	come	[ˈkʌm]
foam	foam	foam	foaming	foam	[ˈfoʀʊ̆m]
beam	beam	beam	beaming	beam	[ˈbiːm]
sum	sum	sum	summing	sum	[ˈsʌm]
mum	mum	mum	mumming	mum	[ˈmʌm]
numb	numb	numb	numbing	numb	[ˈnʌm]
chime	chime	chime	chiming	chime	[ˈtʃaɪm]
boom	boom	boom	booming	boom	[ˈbuːm]

Say the following words, prolonging the nasal sound:

home	plum	rhythm	from
come	comb	moonlight	foaming
blame	rumble	room	chime
time	tram	boom	cream

rhyme	crumble	ramble	beam
bomb	gamble	loam	gnome
dumb	name	clam	music
lamb	lime	gloaming	murmur
hammock	same	cram	mime

Test:

Can you do all the exercises in the Practice Material with well-distributed resonance?

CONTRACT 3A

Objective:

Same as Contract 3.

Procedure:

Same as Contract 3.

Caution:

Be sure to practice the exercises for the control of the soft palate, given in Contract 2.

Practice Material:

Hum the sound *m* [m], holding it as long as you can comfortably on a breath.   Do this exercise many times a day.

Hum the following, prolonging the nasal sounds:

dum	dum	dum	[ˈdʌm]
ahm	ahm	ahm	[ˈɑːm]
hum	hum	hum	[ˈhʌm]
am	am	am	[ˈæm]
seem	seem	seem	[ˈsiːm]
boom	boom	boom	[ˈbuːm]
plume	plume	plume	[ˈpluːm]
lamb	lamb	lamb	[ˈlæm]
mum	mum	mumming	mum [ˈmʌm]
dum	dum	dumming	dum [ˈdʌm]
hum	hum	humming	hum [ˈhʌm]

Say the following words, prolonging the nasal sound:

mimic	cram	seemingly
mamma	booming	stream
meeting	chum	murmuring
mumble	moral	rampart
bumblebee	mean	came
humble	mice	comely

hamlet	roaming	time
family	dreaming	timid
crumbling	bombing	smithy
some	thumb	smite

Test:

1. Can you do all the exercises in the Practice Material with proper resonance?

2. Can you prepare ten other words containing the sound *m* [m], and then read them with proper resonance?

CONTRACT 4

Objective:

Sufficient nasal resonance on *n* [n].

Well-distributed resonance in words and syllables containing *n* [n].

Well-distributed resonance in phrases containing *m* [m] and *n* [n].

Procedure:

Place the tip of the tongue on the gum above the upper front teeth, lower the soft palate, and let the sound *n* [n] come out through the nose. Place your finger below the nostrils, and feel the warm air emitted in making this sound.

Lower the soft palate for *n* [n] and raise it for *ah* [ɑ:] as you say:

n—ah	n—ah	n—ah [n—ɑ:]
n—ō	n—ō	n—ō [n—oᴛǔ]
n—ē	n—ē	n—ē [n—i:]

Reverse the process, saying:

ah—n	ah—n	ah—n [ɑ:—n]
ō—n	ō—n	ō—n [oᴛǔ—n]
ē—n	ē—n	ē—n [i:—n]

Do the same exercise with all vowels and diphthongs, prolonging the *n* [n].

Caution:

Be sure the soft palate is lowered for nasal sounds and raised for all other sounds.

Practice Material:

Hum the following as in Contract 3:

nine	nine	nine ['naɪn]	
bun	bun	bun ['bʌn]	
run	run	running	run ['ɪʌn]

sign	sign	signing	sign [ˈsaɪn]
gain	gain	gaining	gain [ˈgeɪɪn]
fan	fan	fanning	fan [ˈfæn]
pine	pine	pining	pine [ˈpaɪn]
train	train	training	train [ˈtɹeɪɪn]
zone	zone	zoning	zone [ˈzoʊn]
rain	rain	raining	rain [ˈɹeɪɪn]
plan	plan	planning	plan [ˈplæn]

Say the following words, prolonging the nasal sounds:

plain	tune	shining
fine	sand	preen
behind	ban	drone
pine	sin	drain
Jane	spin	divine
clean	clan	phone
sane	sign	feign
seen	bin	bean
sunny	cunning	sheen
swine	don	nineteen

Say the following phrases, prolonging the nasal sounds:

1. Fine time.
2. Same climate.
3. Trained animals.
4. Plain frame.
5. Fortune hunter.
6. Teeming rain.
7. Signing a contract.
8. Hands and knees.
9. Home-land.
10. Hunting knife.
11. Sandy land.
12. Ways and means.

Test:

1. Can you do all the exercises in the Practice Material with sufficient nasal resonance?

2. Can you prepare ten more phrases and read those with sufficient nasal resonance?

CONTRACT 4A

Objective:

See Contract 4.

Procedure:

See Contract 4.

Caution:

See Contract 4.

Practice Material:

Prolong the sound *n* [n] as long as your breath lasts; do this exercise several times a day.

Hum the following exercises, prolonging the nasal sounds:

nnnnnnnnnnnnnnnnnnnnn—ah [n—ɑ:]
nnnnnnnnnnnnnnnnnnnnn—ī [n—aɪ]
nnnnnnnnnnnnnnnnnnnnn—ē [n—i:]
mmmmmmmmmmmmmmm—ah [m—ɑ:]
mmmmmmmmmmmmmmm—ī [m—aɪ]
mmmmmmmmmmmmmmm—ē [m—i:]
nnnnnnn—ah—mmmmmmm [n—ɑ:—m]
nnnnnnn—ī —mmmmmmm [n—aɪ—m]
nnnnnnn—ē —mmmmmmm [n—i:—m]
mmmmmmm—ah—nnnnnnn [m—ɑ:—n]
mmmmmmm—ī —nnnnnnn [m—aɪ—n]
mmmmmmm—ē —nnnnnnn [m—i:—n]

name	name	naming	name ['neɪɪm]
crane	crane	craning	crane ['kɹeɪɪn]
tone	tone	toning	tone ['toɪʊn]
run	run	running	run ['ɹʌn]

Say the following words, prolonging the nasal sounds:

combine	sandwich	company	handsome
refine	temptation	panorama	pineapple
phantom	blinding	tannery	contrary
hunter	sunny	timorous	pantomime
somebody	phonetic	cranium	testament
constitution	principle	brain	winsome
panoply	timely	sandwich	young

Say the following phrases, prolonging the nasal sounds:

1. Many a time.
2. Same company.
3. Funny arrangement.
4. Candy and all kinds of confectionery.
5. Ham sandwiches.
6. Holding her own.
7. Kindly attention.
8. Frying pan.
9. Painting a fence.
10. Children's games.
11. Running for a train.
12. Seeing a fine panorama.

Test:

1. Can you do all the exercises in the Practice Material with proper resonance?

2. Can you prepare ten other phrases containing the sounds *m* [m] and *n* [n], and then read them with proper resonance?

CONTRACT 5

Objective:

Sufficient nasal resonance on *ng* [ŋ].

Well-distributed resonance in syllables and words containing *ng* [ŋ].

Well-distributed resonance in phrases containing all nasal sounds.

Procedure:

Place the back of the tongue firmly against the lowered soft palate and let the sound come out through the nose. Place your finger below the nostrils and feel the warm air emitted in making this sound.

Raise the soft palate for *ah* [ɑː] and lower it for *ng* [ŋ] as you say:

ah—ng　　　ah—ng　　　ah—ng [ɑː—ŋ]

Reverse the process as you say:

ng—ah　　　ng—ah　　　ng—ah [ŋ—ɑː]

Proceed in a like manner with the other vowels and diphthongs, prolonging the nasal sound.

Caution:

See Contract 4.

Practice Material:

Hum the following as in Contracts 3 and 4:

sing	song	sing	song ['sɪŋ 'sɒŋ]
ding	dong	ding	dong ['dɪŋ 'dɒŋ]
ring	ring	ringing	ring ['ɹɪŋ]
sing	sing	singing	sing ['sɪŋ]
twang	twang	twanging	twang ['twæŋ]
long	long	longing	long ['lɒŋ]
swing	swing	swinging	swing ['swɪŋ]
bring	bring	bringing	bring ['bɹɪŋ]

Say the following words, prolonging the nasal sounds:

making	taming	song	language
maiming	lining	ling	English
naming	scanning	spring	sanguine
timing	refining	twinkle	languish
thanking	planning	king	spangle
signing	cramming	sprinkle	triangle
grinding	ceiling	single	hunger

Say the following phrases, prolonging the nasal sound:

1. Young America.
2. Coming up.
3. Singing a song.
4. Playing a piano.
5. Gnawing a bone.
6. Riding the waves.
7. A long, long lane.
8. Twanging a musical instrument.
9. Planning the enemy's downfall.
10. Saving the nation's honor.
11. Sewing on a sewing machine.
12. Going a long distance.

Test:

1. Can you do all the exercises in the Practice Material with well-distributed resonance?

2. Can you compose ten other phrases and then read them with proper resonance?

CONTRACT 5A

Objective:

See Contract 5.

Procedure:

See Contract 5.

Caution:

See Contract 4.

Practice Material:

Prolong *ng* [ŋ] on a humming tone as long as you can comfortably with one breath.

In the following exercise, hold *ng* [ŋ] steadily until you come to a vowel:

ng—ng—ng—ng—ng—ng—ah [ŋ—ɑ:]
ng—ng—ng—ng—ng—ng—ē [ŋ—i:]
ng—ng—ng—ng—ng—ng—ī [ŋ—ɑɪ]
ng—ng—ng—ng—ng—ng—o͞o [ŋ—u:]

Hum the following, prolonging the nasal sound:

king	king	king ['kɪŋ]	
spring	spring	spring ['spɹɪŋ]	
ring	ring	ringing	ring ['ɹɪŋ]
cling	cling	clinging	cling ['klɪŋ]
clang	clang	clanging	clang ['klæŋ]

Say the following words, prolonging the nasal sounds:

raining	strong	linger	increasing
meaning	tingling	young	singing
stumbling	claiming	tongue	twinkling
cunning	banging	honoring	hiring
sewing	hammering	pleasing	playing
knitting	standing	clanging	sounding
belong	dangle	quivering	promising

Say the following phrases, prolonging the nasal sounds:

1. Sing a song.
2. Prancing along.
3. Trying a new dance step.
4. Clinging to old customs.
5. Preying on the mind.
6. Carrying a full program.
7. Bearing a banner.
8. Making a sweeping statement.
9. Lying in wait for the enemy.
10. Preening their feathers.
11. Swinging in the garden swing.
12. Keeping time to the music.

Test:

1. Can you do all the exercises in the Practice Material with a proper resonance?

2. Can you prepare ten more phrases and then read them with proper resonance?

CONTRACT 6

Objective:

Well-distributed resonance in phrases containing all sounds.

Procedure:

See Contracts 3, 4, and 5.

Caution:

See Contracts 3, 4, and 5.

Practice Material:

See Contracts 3, 4, and 5.
Read the following phrases:

1. Having a fine time.
2. Drawing a long face.
3. Preaching an endless sermon.
4. Cleaning the entire establishment.
5. Gaining nine pounds in a month.
6. Saying the same thing over and over again.
7. Planning a Washington's Birthday pageant.
8. Laying the blame on another.
9. Calling long distance.
10. Fencing with an opponent.
11. Sitting on the side lines watching the game.
12. Claiming high honors.
13. Framing an oil painting.
14. Opening a Christmas present.
15. Driving an automobile in the country.
16. Organizing classes in music.
17. Going here and there.
18. Putting a poor man to work.
19. Tuning a new piano.
20. Living on a lower floor.
21. Wheedling her father for a new dress.
22. Seeking new pleasures.
23. Losing a game of tennis.
24. Raising a hue and cry.
25. Looking back over yesterday's work.

Test:

1. Can you read with proper resonance all the phrases given in the Practice Material?

2. Can you prepare ten other phrases and then read them with proper resonance?

CONTRACT 7

Objective:

Well-distributed resonance in sentences.

Procedure:

See Contracts 3, 4, and 5.

Caution:

See Contracts 3, 4, and 5.

Practice Material:

See Contracts 3, 4, and 5.
Read the following sentences:

1. The dentist had an exclusive clientele.

2. It was a trying situation in many ways.

3. The tennis season begins in the spring.

4. Skating and skiing and tobogganing are winter sports in Switzerland.

5. The reforestation commission put many men to work.

6. The marines were marching to martial music.

7. The summer air came softly in through the open window.

8. It is only fifteen minutes to train time.

9. "Time and tide wait for no man" is a well-known saying.

10. A good conversationalist is an interesting person.

11. The dashing of the rain and the howling of the wind and the grumbling of the thunder made those nights things of terror.

12. "Necessity is the mother of invention."

13. The wrens and the robins were building nests in the elm tree near Mary's home.

14. Children enjoy swimming and paddling in the ocean.

15. English and German and Russian are difficult languages to learn.

Answer the following questions in complete sentences:

1. Did you take a trip during your summer vacation?

2. Where did you go on your trip?

3. What was the most interesting thing that you saw?

4. Which do you prefer, summer or winter sports?

5. Who wrote *Evangeline?*

6. What other well-known American poet lived in Cambridge, Massachusetts?

Test:

1. Can you read the sentences in the Practice Material with proper resonance?

2. Can you prepare ten more sentences and then read them with proper resonance?

3. Can you answer the questions in the Practice Material with proper resonance?

4. Can you read with proper resonance the sentences given for *m* [m], *n* [n], and *ng* [ŋ] in Part III?

CONTRACT 8

Objective:

Well-distributed resonance in paragraphs.

Procedure:

See Contracts 3, 4, and 5.

Caution:

See Contracts 3, 4, and 5.

Practice Material:

See Contracts 3, 4, and 5.

Read the following paragraph from Washington Irving's *Rip Van Winkle:*

Rip Van Winkle, however, was one of those happy mortals, of foolish, well-oiled dispositions, who take the world easy, eat white bread or brown, whichever can be got with the least thought or trouble, and would rather starve on a penny than work for a pound.   If left to himself, he would have whistled life away in perfect contentment; but his wife kept continually dinning in his ears about his idleness, his carelessness, and the ruin he was bringing on his family. Morning, noon and night, her tongue was incessantly going, and everything he said or did was sure to produce a torrent of household eloquence.   Rip had but one way of replying to all lectures of the kind, and that, by frequent use, had grown into a habit.   He shrugged his shoulders, shook his head, and cast up his eyes, but said nothing.   This, however, always provoked a fresh volley from his wife; so that he was fain to draw off his forces, and take to the outside of the house—the only side which, in truth, belongs to the hen-pecked husband.

Test:

1. Can you read with proper resonance the paragraph in the Practice Material?

2. Can you find another short paragraph which contains many nasal sounds, and read it with well-distributed resonance?

CONTRACT 9

Objective:

Well-distributed resonance in the reading of poetry.

Procedure:

See Contracts 3, 4, and 5.

Caution:

Try to use a well-distributed resonance in your conversation.

Practice Material:

Read the following stanzas from *The Shepherd of King Admetus* by James Russell Lowell:

> There came a youth upon the earth,
>   Some thousand years ago,
> Whose slender hands were nothing worth,
>   Whether to plow, or reap, or sow.
>
> Upon an empty tortoise-shell
>   He stretched some chords, and drew
> Music that made men's bosoms swell
>   Fearless, or brimmed their eyes with dew.
>
> Then King Admetus, one who had
>   Pure taste by right divine,
> Decreed his singing not too bad.
>   To hear between the cups of wine.
>
> And so, well pleased with being soothed
>   Into a sweet half-sleep,
> Three times his kingly beard he smoothed,
>   And made him viceroy o'er his sheep.
>
> His words were simple words enough,
>   And yet he used them so
> That what in other mouths was rough,
>   In his seemed musical and low.
>
>   .   .   .
>
> Men granted that his speech was wise,
>   But, when a glance they caught
> Of his slim grace and woman's eyes,
>   They laughed, and called him good-for-naught.

Yet after he was dead and gone,
  And e'en his memory dim,
Earth seemed more sweet to live upon,
  More full of love, because of him.

Test:

1. Can you read the lines of poetry given above with a well-distributed resonance?

2. Can you find a few more lines of poetry and read them with a well-distributed resonance?

CONTRACT 10

Objective:

Well-distributed resonance in sight reading.

Procedure:

See Contracts 3, 4, and 5.

Caution:

See Contracts 3, 4, and 5.

Practice Material:

See Contracts 3, 4, and 5.
Selections for sight reading from the following suggested books:

Aesop's Fables
Irving, *Sketch Book*
Dickens, *A Christmas Carol*

Test:

Can you read at sight, using a properly distributed resonance?

CONTRACT 11

Objective:

Well-distributed resonance in conversation.

Procedure:

See Contracts 3, 4, and 5.

Caution:

See Contracts 3, 4, and 5.

Practice Material:

See Contracts 3, 4, and 5.

Conversation based on the following suggested topics:

An Automobile Trip
A Party
A Luncheon Menu
A Basketball Game
A Motion Picture

Test:

Can you use a well-distributed resonance in everyday conversation?

APPENDIX

PRONUNCIATION LIST

PRONUNCIATION KEY

BIBLIOGRAPHY

Pronunciation List

A

abdomen
absolutely
absorb
absurd
accelerator
acclimate
across
activity
address
adjoin
adjourn
admirable
adult
advertisement
aerial
aeroplane
after
alias
allege
allies
alumni
amateur
amenable
American
amicable
apparatus
applicable
apricot
apron
architecture
Arctic
aristocrat
artists
aspirant
athlete
athletic
attacked
audacious
aviation
awful
ay *or* aye (*yes*)
ay *or* aye (*forever*)

B

battle
beautiful
because
being
bestial
book
bravado
breadths
Broadway
burst

C

Calliope
calm
candy
can't
catch
cello
cement
cerebrum
champion
chaos
chasm
chastisement
chimney
chiropodist
chocolate
city
clangor
clique
clothes
coadjutor
coffee
college
combatant
comely
comfortable
comma
commandant
company
comparable
compass
condolence
constitution
construe
consummate
contemplate
contractor
contrary
costume
couldn't
coupon
courteous
courtier
creek
cruel
culinary
curtsy

D

dance
data
daughter
deaf
defects
deficit
depths
despicable
detail (*n., v.*)
diamond
dictionary
didn't
diphtheria
diphthong
dirigible
disaster
discretion
drama
drawing
drought
drowned
duke
duty

E

economic
eighths
eleven
elm
endure
engine
England
English
entire
escape
exemplary
exigency
exquisite
extant
extraordinary

F

failure
fairy
family
faucet
February
fellow
fifths
film
finally
finance
finger
first
five
forehead
formidable
fought
fragrance
frequent (*adj.*, *v.*)

G

garage
garrulous
genealogy
general
gentleman
genuine
geometry
gesture
giant
gibbet
gifts
girl
God
gondola
government
gratis
grievous
grimace
grovel
guests

H

half
hangar
hanger
harass
hearth
height
helm
history
honorable
hospitable
howl
huge
human
humble

I

ignominy
impious
implacable
inclement
incomparable
indisputable
inexplicable
infamous
infantile
influence
inquiry
insane
interesting
irrelevant
irrevocable
isolate
Italian

J

judge
just

K

kept
kettle
kiln

L

lamentable
language
lantern
Latin
laugh
learn
length
lenient

library
lineament
linger
literature
little
livelong
longer
longevity
lyceum

M

magazine
mausoleum
mauve
memorable
might
military
million
minutely
mischievous
mountain
municipal
museum

N

nature
necessary
new
now
nuisance

O

oaths
obesity
obligatory
office
often
ogre
oil

only
open
orchestra
orgy
our

P

parent
particularly
party
past
pathos
peculiarly
penalize
perilous
personality
piano
picture
poem
point
police
poor
positively
precedence
precedent
precocious
prestige
primarily
prison
probably
program
psalm
ptomaine
pumpkin

Q

quay
quiet

R

radiator
rather
really
recess
recognize
remonstrate
reputable
requisite
research
resource
respiratory
respite
ribald
ridiculous
rinse
robust
romance
roof
root
rout
route

S

sacrilegious
salutary
sandwich
satiety
Saturday
scenic
schism
science
scourge
secondary
secretary
senile
sentences
simultaneous

since
sinecure
singer
single
slough (*n., v.*)
solace
soon
sound
sovereign
spectator
squalor
started
statistics
status
strength
stronger
strongest
subtle
such
suggest
superfluous
swept

T

taught
tedious
telephone
temperature
tepee
that
theater
thirty
this
three
tomato
toward
tremendous
truths
tube

Tuesday
tune
twenty

U

umbrella
umpire
untoward

V

vagary
various
vaudeville
vehement
version
voluminous

W

wanted
wasp
water
what
whip
widths
William
window
with
wont
won't

Y

yellow
yesterday
younger
youngest
youths

Z

zealous
zoölogy

Pronunciation Key*

Key Word	Diacritical Marking†	International Phonetic Script	
		PRINTED FORM	WRITTEN FORM
Vowels			
see......................	ē	i:	*i:*
it........................	ĭ	ɪ	*ɪ*
let.......................	ĕ	eᴛ	*eᴛ*
there....................	â	ɛ:	*ɛ:*
at.......................	ă	æ	*æ*
ask......................	ȧ	ɐ	*ɐ*
bird.....................	û	ɜ:	*ɜ:*
about....................	ȧ	ə	*ə*
up.......................	ŭ	ʌ	*ʌ*
moon....................	o͞o	u:	*u:*
foot.....................	o͝o	ʊ	*ʊ*
obey.....................	ŏ	oᴛ	*oᴛ*
all......................	ô	ɔ:	*ɔ:*
coffee...................	ŏ	ɒ	*ɒ*
farther..................	ä	ɑ:	*ɑ:*
Diphthongs			
ate......................	ā	eᴛɪ	*eᴛɪ*
ice......................	ī	aɪ	*aɪ*
old......................	ō	oᴛʊ̆	*oᴛʊ̆*
how.....................	ow	aʊ̆	*aʊ̆*
choice...................	oi	ɔɪ̆	*ɔɪ̆*
here.....................	ç	ɪə̆	*ɪə̆*
there....................	â	ɛə̆	*ɛə̆*
poor.....................	o͞or	ʊə̆	*ʊə̆*
floor....................	ōr	ɔə̆	*ɔə̆*

* Adapted with permission from *Teaching Speech in Secondary Schools*, by Letitia Raubicheck, published by Prentice-Hall, Inc.

† Adapted from diacritical markings in *Webster's New International Dictionary*.

Pronunciation Key (Continued)

Key Word	Diacritical Marking	International Phonetic Script	
		PRINTED FORM	WRITTEN FORM
Consonants			
pipe............................	p	p	
bit..............................	b	b	
man............................	m	m	
wet.............................	w	w	
which..........................	wh	ʍ	
fife..............................	f	f	
very............................	v	v	
think...........................	th	θ	
that.............................	~~th~~	ð	
tight............................	t	t	
did..............................	d	d	
none............................	n	n	
lull..............................	l	l	
ran..............................	r	ɹ	
sister...........................	s	s	
zero............................	z	z	
sure............................	sh	ʃ	
pleasure........................	zh	ʒ	
church..........................	ch	tʃ	
judge...........................	j	dʒ	
young...........................	y	j	
kick............................	k	k	
gig..............................	g	g	
song............................	ng	ŋ	
hunt............................	h	h	

Bibliography

Aikin, William A., *The Voice*, Longmans, Green & Company, 1910.

Anderson, Lewis O., *Stuttering and Allied Disorders*, The Williams & Wilkins Company, 1923.

Appelt, Alfred, *Real Cause of Stammering and Its Permanent Cure*, Methuen & Company, Ltd., 1929.

Bell, Alexander G., *Mechanism of Speech*, Funk & Wagnalls Company.

Birmingham, Anna I., and Krapp, George P., *First Lessons in Speech Improvement*, Charles Scribner's Sons, 1922.

Bluemel, Charles S., *Mental Aspects of Stammering*, The Williams & Wilkins Company, 1930.

———————————*Stammering and Cognate Defects of Speech*, C. E. Stechert & Company, 1913.

Borden, Richard C., and Busse, Alvin C., *Speech Correction*, F. S. Crofts & Company, 1925.

Fillebrown, Thomas, *Resonance in Singing and Speaking*, Oliver Ditson Company, Inc., 1911.

Fletcher, John M., *The Problem of Stuttering*, Longmans, Green & Company, 1928.

Fogerty, Elsie, *Stammering*, E. P. Dutton & Company, Inc., 1930.

Fröschels, Emil, *Speech Therapy*, Expression Company, 1933.

Gifford, Mabel Farrington, *Correcting Nervous Speech Disorders*, Prentice-Hall, Inc., 1939.

———————————*How to Overcome Stammering*, Prentice-Hall, Inc., 1940.

Gould, George M., *Medical Dictionary*, P. Blakiston's Son & Company, 1926.

Gray, Henry, *Anatomy of the Human Body*, Lea & Febiger, 1924.

Greene, James S., *Cause and Cure of Speech Disorders*, The Macmillan Company, 1927.

Head, Henry, *Aphasia and Kindred Disorders of Speech*, The Macmillan Company, 1926.

Johnson, Wendell, *Because I Stutter*, D. Appleton & Company, 1930.

———————————*The Influence of Stuttering on the Personality*, University of Iowa Press, 1930.

Jones, Daniel, *An English Pronouncing Dictionary*, Fourth Edition, E. P. Dutton & Company, Inc., 1937.

Kelson, W. H., *Diseases of the Throat, Nose, and Ear*, Oxford University Press, 1916.

Laurens, George, *Oto-Rhino-Laryngology*, William Wood & Company, 1922.

McCullough, Grace A., and Birmingham, Agnes V., *Correcting Speech Defects and Foreign Accent*, Charles Scribner's Sons, 1925.

McLean, Margaret P., *Good American Speech*, E. P. Dutton & Company, Revised Edition, 1942.

Manser, Ruth B., and Mulgrave, Dorothy I., *Conversations in Phonetic Transcription*, E. P. Dutton & Co., Inc., 1941.

Mills, Wesley, *Voice Production in Singing and Speaking*, J. B. Lippincott Company, 1913.

Mulgrave, Dorothy I., *Speech for the Classroom Teacher*, Prentice-Hall, Inc., 1936.

Negus, Victor E., *Mechanism of the Larynx*, The C. V. Mosby Company, 1929.

Nitchie, Edward B., *Lip-Reading Principles and Practise*, Frederick A. Stokes Company, 1919.

Parson, Beaufort S., *Lefthandedness, A New Interpretation*, The Macmillan Company, 1924.

Peppard, Helen M., *Correction of Speech Defects*, The Macmillan Company, 1925.

Raubicheck, Letitia, *Teaching Speech in Secondary Schools*, Prentice-Hall, Inc., 1935.

Raubicheck, Letitia, *How to Teach Good Speech in the Elementary Schools*, Noble & Noble, Publishers, Inc., 1937.

Raubicheck, Davis, and Carll, *Voice and Speech Problems*, Prentice-Hall, Inc., Revised Edition, 1939.

Scripture, Edward W., *Stuttering, Lisping and Correction of the Speech of the Deaf*, The Macmillan Company, 1923.

Stinchfield, Sara M., *Psychology of Speech*, Expression Co., 1928.

——————————*Speech Disorders*, Harcourt, Brace & Company, Inc., 1933.

——————————*Speech Pathology*, Expression Company, 1928.

Travis, Lee E., *Speech Pathology*, D. Appleton & Company, 1931.

Twitmyer, Edwin B., and Nathanson, Yale S., *Correction of Defective Speech*, P. Blakiston's Son & Company, 1932.

Voorhees, Irving W., *Hygiene of the Voice*, The Macmillan Company, 1923.

Waggett, Ernest B., *Diseases of Nose and Throat*, Oxford University Press, 1907.

Ward, Ida C., *Defects of Speech*, E. P. Dutton & Company, Inc., 1923.

Young, Edna H., *Overcoming Cleft Palate Speech*, Hill-Young School, Minneapolis, Minnesota, 1928.

INDEX

Index